CATALYTIC REACTOR DESIGN

M. Orhan Tarhan

CATALYTIC REACTOR DESIGN

McGraw-Hill Book Company

New York St. Louis San Francisco Auckland Bogotá Hamburg Johannesburg London Madrid Mexico Montreal New Delhi Panama Paris São Paulo Singapore Sydney Tokyo Toronto

NOTICE

The information presented in this book has been compiled from sources considered to be dependable and is accurate and reliable to the best of the author's knowledge and belief, but is not guaranteed to be so. The author assumes no responsibility whatsoever with respect to any use which may be made of any of the data or methods described in this book or any results obtained by such use. Nothing in this book is to be construed as a recommendation of any practice in violation of any patent, law, or regulation.

Library of Congress Cataloging in Publication Data

Tarhan, M. Orhan.
Catalytic reactor design.

Includes bibliographies and index.
1. Chemical reactors—Design and construction.
2. Catalysis. I. Title.
TP157.T35 1983 660.2′995 82-18015
ISBN 0-07-062871-8

1234567890 KGP/KGP 89876543

ISBN 0-07-062871-8

The editors for this book were Diane Heiberg and Geraldine Fahey, the designer was Elliot Epstein, and the production supervisor was Sally Fliess. It was set in Baskerville by Techna Type.

Printed and bound by The Kingsport Press.

CONTENTS

PREFACE

The purpose of this book is to teach the design of catalytic reactors. The book evolved from notes of summer short courses given between 1969 and 1973 at Lehigh University, Bethlehem, Pennsylvania, in Pocono Manor, Pennsylvania, and in Istanbul, Turkey. The material has been subsequently considerably expanded, updated, and of course, completely reorganized.

Although the title, *Catalytic Reactor Design*, covers all kinds of catalytic reactors, the book is limited to heterogeneous catalytic reactors, since their design presents the greatest challenge today. A particular kind of heterogeneous catalytic reactor, the fluidized-bed reactor, has been omitted, because an excellent and detailed book by Kunii and Levenspiel (*Fluidization Engineering,* John Wiley, New York, 1969) exists on these reactors.

Today the reactor designer must be an extremely sophisticated chemical engineer, who is well versed in catalysis, reaction kinetics, transport phenomena, mechanical engineering, and computer programming. It would obviously be undesirable to attempt to present adequate information in all these fields in a book of this size. Instead, this book concentrates on the process engineering aspect of reactor design, including computer solutions of design problems, in great detail and presents only a limited amount of information on catalysis, reaction kinetics, mechanical engineering, and general principles related to computer programming. This limitation is partially compensated by ample references to important and informative studies.

Separate chapters are devoted to the design of laboratory and pilot reactors and to the mechanical design of full-scale plant reactors. The vitally important question of reactor stability and safety is covered in an overview chapter. This subject was considered too important to be left out, yet too broad for a thorough coverage.

This book is primarily intended for seniors and graduate students in chemical engineering and for chemical engineers in the industry. The question as to who needs catalytic reactor design is answered in detail in Sec. 1.6 of this book.

Here the question arises: How knowledgeable and sophisticated must a chemical engineer be, in order to read and understand this book? An engineer will be able to read and understand it even with a modest background in catalysis, reaction kinetics, transport phenomena, and pressure vessel design. Familiarity with Fortran IV programming is also necessary, although it is not necessary to be a computer analyst.

While these limited backgrounds are adequate for reading and understanding this book, this does not necessarily mean that they are also adequate for carrying out a real reactor design assignment. After all, a person who has just learned to play simple exercises on the piano or the violin cannot immediately be expected to perform a Beethoven concerto.

This book teaches a great deal of what there is to teach today. However, designers would have to improve on their backgrounds and capabilities by reading some of the references, and, what is most important of all, by practicing what they have learned and using their own intuition and ingenuity. In this respect reactor design is still very much of an art and always will be.

The greatest difficulty in writing this book has been in finding published or publishable sets of experimental data on the kinetics of catalytic processes. Some published data have turned out to be inaccurate by as much as an order of magnitude. Others are incomplete sets (e.g., activation energy values without the corresponding frequency factors) and are useless. Some complete sets give obviously wrong reactor sizes. Thus, most reactor design examples in this book are based on assumed data that produce results within a reasonable range. The reader is strongly warned not to use these data in any design, but to procure credible experimental data before even starting any design work. Approximate results in a book that basically intends to teach general methods and strategies of reactor design are understandable and even admissible. However, using anything but accurate and reliable sets of experimental data in a temperature-sensitive NINAF reactor design would yield completely valueless results.

All the computer programs presented in Chap. 2, as well as in design examples, have been run on a computer and have been fully debugged. However, with certain highly nonlinear kinetic data, some programs might become unstable. In such cases, the designer must judiciously manipulate the parameters and input data to avoid such instability. Also, selection of excessively large step sizes (in numerical integration) might cause program instability, just as selection of excessively small step sizes might generate erroneous results. The reactor designer must watch for such pitfalls.

There are a number of books on catalytic reactor design on the market. Most of them were written by highly respected university professors, who have done an admirable job of analyzing the problems of catalytic reactor process design and setting up the required design differential equations. However, after that, readers are left largely to their own devices. There is, of course, a lot more to reactor design than setting up the design equations, and the present book is attempting to cover these other factors. Some of these are: a deep concern for the adequacy of the data that will be used in the design; an explanation of how things are really done in practice; the numerical solution of the design equations; the incorporation of the reactor design into the overall process design of the plant; mechanical design considerations; operating concerns; and, of course, the safety and stability of the reactor. Because of this orientation, this book is probably the first of its kind.

This book could not have been written without the patient tolerance of my dear wife Bürran, who for many years allowed me to utilize on this work the time that I would have otherwise spent with her. There are no words to express such gratitude.

I am particularly grateful to Prof. William E. Schiesser of Lehigh University, my partner in Catalytic Reactor Design Courses of 1971 to 1973, for valuable advice on, and review of, Chap. 2. Actually it was his lucid lectures during these courses that mostly inspired me to write Chap. 2. I am also grateful to Prof. Fazil Erdogan of Lehigh University for his review of Chap. 12, to Dr. Narendra J. Sheth of Bethlehem Steel Corporation for patient assistance in debugging computer programs, to Dr. Bernard S. Mikofsky for years of inspiring teaching and coaching on technical writing, and to Prof. Leonard A. Wenzel of Lehigh University and the research management of Bethlehem Steel Corporation for encouragement in the development of the summer courses that eventually led to this book.

M. Orhan Tarhan

CATALYTIC REACTOR DESIGN

Chapter 1 CLASSIFICATION OF REACTORS AND PHASES OF DESIGN

Catalytic reactors are vessels or containers in which catalytic chemical reactions take place. They may be made of a variety of materials, the choice of which depends on the temperature and pressure at which the reactions occur and the corrosion resistance qualities required. Catalytic reactors may also be of many types, depending on the types of catalyst used and the physical characteristics of the reactants and products.

1.1 CLASSIFICATION OF REACTORS

Catalytic reactors can be classified in a variety of ways. The classification that appears most logical is that based on the nature of the catalysis. Catalysis can be homogeneous or heterogeneous. If the catalyst does not constitute a separate phase from the reactants or the products, the catalysis is said to be *homogeneous*. In some cases the homogeneous catalyst is dissolved in a liquid and the reaction occurs in the liquid phase, even if some of the reactants or products are in the gas phase. An example of such a reaction is

$$2\ H_2S + SO_2 \rightarrow 3\ S + 2\ H_2O \tag{1.1}$$

which occurs in liquid water of pH 1 to 6 containing a certain amount of ions. The catalyst is the water. In other cases the catalyst and the reactants are in the gas phase, but the product may be in the gas, liquid, or solid phase. The reaction occurs in the gas phase, which is again the phase of the catalyst. An example of such a homogeneously catalyzed reaction is the Claus reaction [Eq. (1.1)], which is slowly catalyzed by water vapor at temperatures below 400°C. Above 400°C the reaction runs noncatalytically.

If the catalyst constitutes a separate phase from the reactants, we say that the catalysis is *heterogeneous*. An example of such catalysis is the acceleration of the rate of reaction (1.1) in gas phase by solid bauxite catalyst.

Thus a first classification of reactors as *homogeneous reactors* and *heterogeneous reactors* can be made.

Homogeneous catalytic reactors can be classified similarly to noncatalytic reactors. One criterion is the number of phases present while another criterion is the degree of backmixing involved. Thus we may have homogeneous gas reactors, homogeneous liquid reactors, and homogeneous gas-liquid reactors. We may also have homogeneous plug-flow tubular reactors and homogeneous continuous stirred-tank reactors (CSTRs). Of course, as mentioned in the preface, this book discusses heterogeneous catalytic reactors only.

A classification criterion for reactors containing heterogeneous solid catalysts is the movement or the lack of movement of the catalyst particles in the reactor vessel. On this basis the following types may be defined:

1. If the particles are fixed in their positions as a dense fixed bed, we have a *fixed-bed reactor.*
2. If the particles are piled up in a dense bed that moves slowly, losing some fouled particles and adding fresh ones, we have a *moving-bed reactor.* Reactors of this type are not discussed in this book because they are in many ways similar to fixed-bed reactors. However, moving bed reactors differ radically from fixed bed reactors in catalyst fouling and regeneration behavior.
3. If the catalyst particles are supported by an upflow of gas as a *fluid bed,* we have a *fluidized-bed reactor.* For reasons mentioned in the preface, this class of reactors is not discussed in this book.
4. If the catalyst particles are suspended in a liquid, we have a *suspended-bed reactor.*

There are several subclassifications of suspended-bed reactors:

1. If the catalyst is suspended in a mechanically stirred liquid, we have a *continuous stirred-tank reactor.*
2. If the catalyst is maintained in suspension in a liquid by rising gas bubbles, we have a *bubble reactor* or a *slurry reactor.*
3. If the catalyst is suspended in an upflow of liquid, we have an *ebullated-bed reactor.*

4. If the catalyst is suspended in a flow of liquid and gas strong enough to entrain these particles in the reactor system, we have a three-phase *transport reactor*.

Another criterion for classifying either homogeneous or heterogeneous reactors is their mode of operation, i.e., whether they are operated on a *batch, semicontinuous*, or *continuous* basis. However, most industrially important operations are run continuously, and batch reactors are only designed if there is a specific good reason for this mode of operation.

Still another classification criterion for reactors in general is the temperature distribution within the reactor. If the temperature is constant at all points within the reactor and does not change with time, the reactor is said to be *isothermal*. If, however, the temperature varies in different parts of the reactor, the reactor is called *nonisothermal*.

Still another classification criterion for reactors is the degree of heat exchange between the reactor and the outside. If no heat is exchanged, the reactor is called *adiabatic*, and if some degree of heat exchange occurs, the reactor is *nonadiabatic*.

Still another classification criterion for reactors is the number of phases involved in the reactions. Of course, in counting the phases the solid catalyst should not count as a phase. Reactors that handle only gases are called *gas-phase reactors*, those which handle liquids only are called *liquid-phase reactors*, and those which handle two-phase reactions are called *gas-liquid-phase reactors*. Liquid-phase reactors are not discussed in this book because they are relatively unimportant and can be considered as a special case of gas-liquid-phase reactors.

We can use several of the above criteria to classify the heterogeneous catalytic reactors discussed in this book as follows:

- Fixed-bed reactors
  - Fixed-bed gas reactors
    - Isothermal reactors
    - Adiabatic reactors
    - Nonisothermal, nonadiabatic fixed-bed (NINAF) reactors
  - Fixed-bed gas-liquid reactors
    - Trickle-bed reactors
    - Fixed-bed bubble reactors (FBBR)

- Suspended-bed reactors
  - Continuous stirred-tank reactors (CSTR)
  - Slurry reactors
  - Ebullated-bed reactors
  - Three-phase transport reactors

1.2
DESIGN DEFINITIONS

The design of a catalytic reactor involves:

1. Determining the type and shape of the reactor and calculating the dimensions which will produce a desired quantity of a product or products from a given feedstock (*process design*)
2. Making certain that the calculated reactor is thermally stable and safe and will not lead to runaway reactions (*stability study*)
3. Selecting the proper materials of construction, wall thickness, and internals so that the reactor vessel will have the structural strength to withstand the reaction conditions as well as the corrosive action of the reaction mixture (*mechanical design*)

This book is devoted mostly to the process design and only to a limited degree to the mechanical design and stability study of reactors. Mechanical design and stability are covered in overview in Chaps. 12 and 11, respectively.

1.3
GENERAL METHODS OF REACTOR DESIGN

The traditional approach to designing chemical reactors in general and catalytic chemical reactors in particular has been to try the process on a bench scale, then in pilot plants of increasing size, and finally on a full industrial scale. This certainly is cautious and safe, but also extremely time-consuming and expensive[1] (Fig. 1-1). Of course once this scale-up has been made, sufficient information has become available to design other reactors of about the same size for the same reactions or sets of reactions. But if another reactor is required for a new reaction, the same lengthy and costly process has to be repeated. This problem has led chemical engineers to devise an approach which would make it unnecessary to repeat the traditional stepwise scale-up procedure for each new reaction.

It was thought that it should be possible to design a catalytic reactor simply from the knowledge of the chemical reaction or reactions which

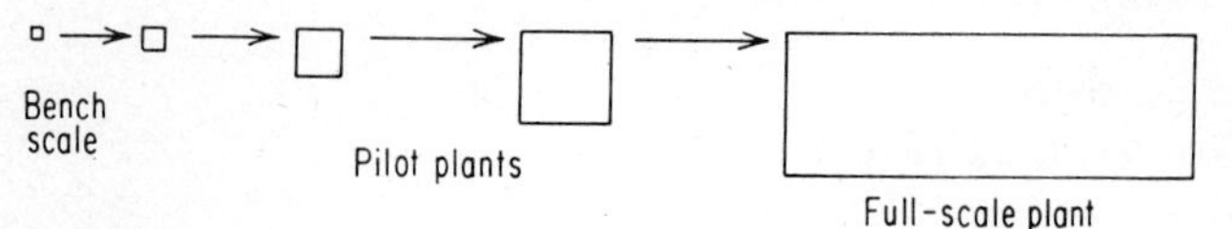

FIG. 1-1 Traditional scale-up procedure.[1] (*From Vern W. Weekman, Jr., by permission.*)

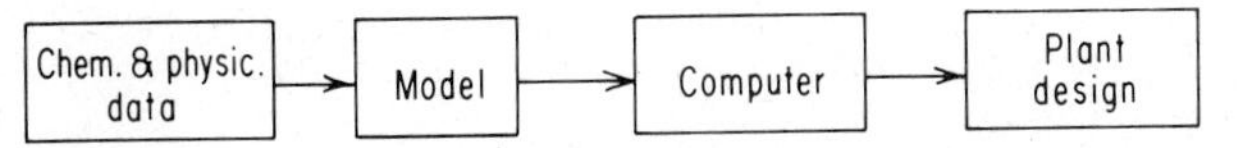

FIG. 1-2 Ideal scale-up procedure.[1] ***(From Vern W. Weekman, Jr., by permission.)***

will take place in the reactor. This is called the *a priori method* of reactor design and still is an unreached ideal for most reactions. This ideal approach includes the following steps (Fig. 1-2):

1. All necessary chemical and physical data on the process are gathered, including information on chemical kinetics and transport phenomena.
2. A chemical reaction rate model is built.
3. The above information is fed to a computer.
4. The design of the full-scale plant is prepared.

Unfortunately this ideal approach will not materialize for some time to come because reaction rate measurements are not quite precise—J factors, for example, are imprecise—and, most important of all, some processes have peculiarities and pitfalls which cannot be foreseen without operating a pilot plant for some time.

Today a compromise is made between the traditional and the ideal: a model is built from collected data and compared with the behavior of a pilot plant before progressing to full-scale plant design. In this way the number of scale-up stages is reduced and caution and safety are retained while reducing costs. The box diagram of Fig. 1-2 is modified by adding a pilot plant step with data feedback (Fig. 1-3). The additional data modify the model and we may move on with increased confidence.

1.4 PHASES OF REACTOR DESIGN

The phases of reactor design vary considerably according to the starting point. In Fig. 1-3 a completely new process is considered. If some industrial information is available, this procedure will change. In any case, each box in Fig. 1-3 represents a phase of reactor design.

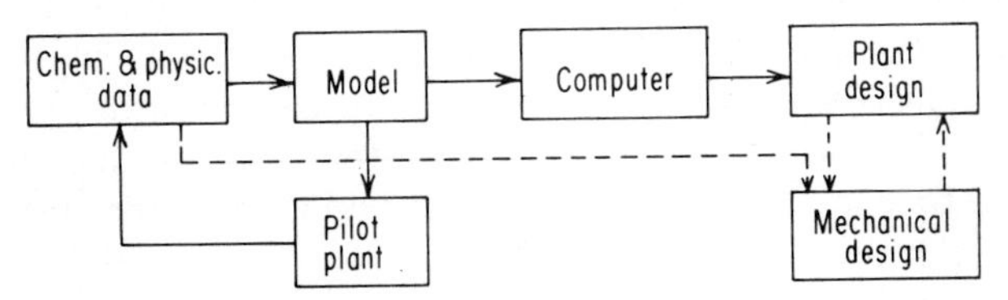

FIG. 1-3 Improved scale-up procedure for a new process.[1] ***(From Vern W. Weekman, Jr., by permission.)***

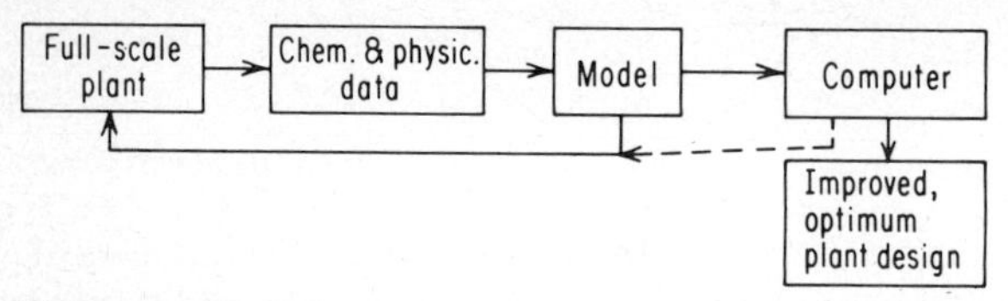

FIG. 1-4 Modeling of a commercial process.[1] (*From Vern W. Weekman, Jr., by permission.*)

We want to study each of these phases. We will begin with the modeling phase, because the kind of modeling used determines the relationship between the various phases.

Modeling of Reactors

To *model* a reactor is to write a set of mathematical equations which express the behavior of the reacting system in this reactor under various operating conditions. In a way, modeling is a simulation. The purpose of modeling is to develop thorough and detailed information on a process, which then can be used for optimizing the process both technically and economically. A thorough study of even an old and well-known process usually reveals so many unknown or even unsuspected aspects that the process can be improved by the modeling.

Let us now consider the modeling of such an old commercial process. The procedural diagram is shown in Fig. 1-4. Such a commercial process should have yielded a considerable amount of data over the years. These data are very helpful in building a mathematical model, which usually uncovers a considerable number of so far unsuspected facts. However, the process data are not enough. The kinetics and transport phenomena of the process must be studied in addition and must be included in the model. When such a model is finally completed, it is run on the computer to find the best operating conditions. If these conditions differ from those actually used in the full-scale plant, the operation of the plant is modified on the basis of the computer results to the extent that economic and other conditions allow such change. The new plant data are fed to the model and to the computer to test the model. If the new data do not exactly verify the model, or—using the model expert's vernacular—if the fit is not perfect, the model may have to be "fudged" a little, so that the new data fit. The procedure is repeated a few times until the designer is convinced that the model thus obtained really simulates and represents the process. Besides improving the operation of the modeled plant, such a study also provides an optimized design for the next plant.

There are two different approaches to modeling new processes. The first is to start the model development about the same time as the process development and to keep working along with the research and development (R & D) group until a fitting model is obtained. The steps of this approach and the interactions along the various steps are shown in Fig. 1-5. Here kinetic and transport experiments have to be performed simultaneously with process development work. Information is exchanged back and forth between the groups conducting the model study (the second line in Fig. 1-5) and the process study (the top line in Fig. 1-5). An economic model of the plant is also developed along with these studies and this model is optimized. When the plant is started up, the economic model is used for on-line optimization. After this first plant is operating successfully, data obtained from it are fed to the model until they fit it perfectly. When a second plant is built for this process, its design can be technically and economically a "bull's-eye hit."

The second approach to modeling new processes utilizes the most modern concept of modeling: no preliminary laboratory experiments are made. Instead, all kinds of data are collected and assembled in order to define the model. Only those data which are lacking in the literature are experimentally determined. Once all the needed information is on hand, the model is constructed and if it looks good, i.e., if the data used fit the model well, then an experimental model (a bench-scale or pilot-scale plant) is first built to check the fitting. This procedure is shown in Fig. 1-3. This approach, called *developing a process around a model* represents a recent trend in the U.S. petroleum industry.[2]

Modeling and optimization of reactors are outside the scope of this book although both are necessary for reactor design. Two excellent books by Luyben[3] and Franks,[4] are recommended for this phase of reactor design. A growing literature on the subject is also available.

Collection of Data

A reactor designer to whom a new design job is assigned must immediately define the reacting system and then collect all the data needed

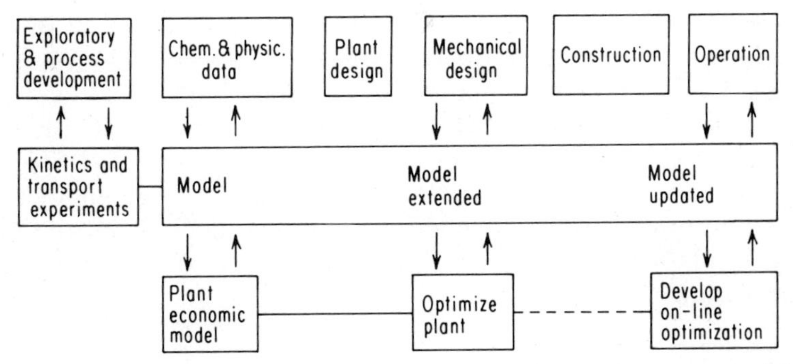

FIG. 1-5 Simultaneous process and model study for new process.[1] (*From Vern W. Weekman, Jr., by permission.*)

for writing the set of design reactions or the model, depending upon the approach to be used. Although the definition of the reacting system may sound obvious, it is anything but obvious when the feedstock is a complex mixture and when the reaction involves more than one of the feed components. An exact analysis of the feedstock must be available, with the possible ranges of variation of each component. If the reacting mixture is anything such as a coal hydrogenation product or a petroleum stream, then the numerous (possibly hundreds or thousands) of chemical compounds must be grouped in classes of compounds that behave similarly. It must be established whether the reacting system includes a single reaction, simultaneous reactions, consecutive reactions, or complex reaction systems.

The chemical properties of all reactants and products must be known so that their likely behavior in the defined reacting system can be foreseen and calculated. Similarly, various physical and thermodynamic properties of all reactants and products must be known so that the design equations or the model can be written.

Normally the reactor designer must be given all these data plus a reaction kinetic model of the reacting system. This information may be available either from the process development work or from the modeling work, depending upon the design approach used. In any case, the reactor designer *must* have this information. In most of the problems treated in this book a relatively simple kinetic model has been selected, in order not to overcomplicate the problems and in order not to deflect the reader's attention from the subject being taught. However, the reader is cautioned at this point that in most real-life design problems the kinetic model can be infinitely more complicated. It may include all kinds of complexities, such as simultaneous and consecutive reactions, reversible reactions, chain reactions, catalyst surface effects, and catalyst fouling and aging effects. It may happen that the reactor designer receives less kinetic information than is necessary and is compelled to personally obtain more information and thus become involved in discussion of the kinetics and the kinetic model of the reacting system, which subjects are outside the scope of this book. A number of very good books on reaction kinetics are available.[5–9] The literature on reaction kinetics is very extensive.

When designing a reactor around a model, the collection of data is the starting activity of the designer. In practice this is a large enough job for a group of chemists and chemical engineers, depending upon the complexity of the reacting system. Thus the designer can concentrate more on designing.

Use of a Computer

The set of simultaneous equations describing catalytic reactors of certain types can be solved only by means of a computer. In the 1960s analog computers were used for this purpose; however the job is now performed much better by digital computers. This book devotes considerable attention to the practical use of computers for the solution of reactor design problems. Chapter 2 is devoted to the discussion of general methods of numerical computation that are needed in reactor design. Also several of the design problems in other chapters are treated completely, with their computer programs and, if necessary, computer solutions.

Mechanical Design

The mechanical design of a catalytic reactor includes the selection of the proper materials of construction to hold up for an economically long period under the reaction conditions, the calculation of the correct wall thickness of the reactor vessel, and the design of internals and externals. Chapter 12 is devoted to this subject.

The mechanical design phase usually begins at the same time as the process design. Although the results of the process design are needed to size the reactor, the selection and testing of materials of construction has to start immediately. In most cases the process designer and the mechanical designer are different persons, but each must well understand the other's problems. It is not unusual for the process design of a reactor to be determined by the limitations imposed by mechanical design (see broken tie lines in Fig. 1-3).

1.5 OPERATING CONSIDERATIONS

The designers, both process and mechanical, must constantly keep in mind the way the reactor will be operated. Although the design is always aimed at the optimum steady-state operating conditions, it must also be able to meet start-up and shutdown conditions, especially the unexpected kinds. If a fixed-bed reactor has to be designed for in situ catalyst regeneration, the mechanical designer must meet not only one but two sets of temperature-pressure conditions. For example, a light aromatic pretreater reactor, filled with cobalt molybdate-on-alumina catalyst, may be operated at 200 to 250°C and say, 40 to 60 bars when on steady-state stream. However if the catalyst has to be regenerated in situ, the regeneration gases (N_2 containing 0.5% O_2) may go as high as 550°C after combustion of the coke when under strict control. If the oxygen content is permitted to exceed 0.5% in nitrogen, the combustion gases may become dangerously hot and weaken the reactor. Thus the pretreater is designed to withstand two sets of conditions:

1. 300°C at 70 bars for operation
2. 550°C at 5 bars for regeneration

1.6
WHO NEEDS REACTOR DESIGN?

Reactor design is not used only by certain professionals who practice it as their major occupation. There are quite a few other types of chemical engineers who need reactor design know-how, even if their designs may never be translated into chemical hardware. For example:

- Many catalyst manufacturers in this country have been offering to size the reactors of clients who purchase their catalysts. Some have developed specific computer programs to size certain types of reactors.
- R & D engineers must design, specify, assemble, and operate experimental reactors they will use.
- R & D engineers who have completed a process study must design full-scale reactors and estimate their costs in order to sell their new process to the management.
- Project evaluation engineers must often size reactors for processes they evaluate.
- Engineers who desire to check the design of reactors that may be purchased by their company may have to carry out independent design calculations.

The various types of chemical engineers mentioned in the above examples definitely need reactor design know-how. If they work for a corporation which employs an experienced reactor designer, they should try to obtain the services of this designer or of a good consultant in the field. If such services are not available or are needed too often, engineers may decide to learn to design their own reactors. It cannot be emphasized too strongly at this point that amateurish reactor design is both expensive and very dangerous. Anyone who wants to tackle the design of catalytic reactors must learn it properly and thoroughly, with all the mathematics and the computer work involved. The purpose of this book is actually to teach chemical engineers all the basic know-how and all the "tools of the trade" and to guide them along the road of experience gathering.

REFERENCES

1. Vern W. Weekman, "Reactor Modeling," unpublished lecture at the Catalytic Reactor Design Course at Pocono Manor, Pa., June 25–29, 1973.
2. Vern W. Weekman, Private communication.
3. William L. Luyben, *Process Modeling, Simulation, and Control for Chemical Engineers*, McGraw-Hill, New York, 1973.
4. Roger G. E. Franks, *Modeling and Simulation in Chemical Engineering*, John Wiley, New York, 1972.

5. Rutherford Aris, *Elementary Chemical Reaction Analysis,* Prentice-Hall, Englewood Cliffs, N.J., 1969.
6. Michel Boudart, *Kinetics of Chemical Processes,* Prentice-Hall, Englewood Cliffs, N.J., 1968.
7. A. R. Cooper and G. V. Jeffreys, *Chemical Kinetics and Reactor Design,* Prentice-Hall, Englewood Cliffs, N.J., 1971.
8. Octave Levenspiel, *Chemical Reaction Engineering,* 2d ed., John Wiley, New York, 1972.
9. J. M. Smith, *Chemical Engineering Kinetics,* 2d ed., McGraw-Hill, New York, 1970.

Chapter 2 METHODS OF NUMERICAL COMPUTATION

The design of fixed-bed reactors depends upon the simultaneous solution of sets of differential equations, as will be seen in the following chapters. Also, any type of reactor designed for the handling of complex reaction systems often requires the simultaneous solution of sets of differential rate equations. In the 1950s and 1960s such sets of *ordinary differential equations* (ODE) were usually solved by analog computers. In the late 60s and the 70s digital computer methods were developed to the point where they now can solve any kind of differential equations encountered in reactor design work, including sets of *partial differential equations* (PDE) occurring in the design of nonisothermal nonadiabatic fixed-bed (NINAF) reactors.

Therefore, the purpose of this chapter is to prepare the reader for setting up and solving reactor design problems by means of digital computers. The reader should be fully familiar with the Fortran IV language[1] and have sufficient mathematical background to manipulate differential equations. However, it is not necessary to be a mathematician or a numerical analyst.

2.1 TYPES OF DIFFERENTIAL EQUATIONS

Differential equations encountered in reactor design can be broadly classified into two categories, as described below.

Ordinary Differential Equations

Ordinary differential equations (ODEs) each have one independent variable x (e.g., reactor length or reactor volume) and one or more dependent variables y (e.g., reaction temperature, fractional conversion, or concentration) and may be written in the general form

$$(d\mathbf{y}/dx) = \mathbf{f}(x,\mathbf{y}) \tag{2-1}$$

where, $\mathbf{y}$ and $\mathbf{f}$ are vectors, if there is more than one dependent variable. Such ODEs will be used in the following chapters in the design of adiabatic fixed-bed reactors and of some types of trickle-bed reactors. An ODE is said to be *initial-value* if all its auxiliary conditions are written for the same value of the independent variable. ODEs used in the design of adiabatic fixed-bed reactors are typical examples of initial-value ODEs. ODEs used in the design of certain kinds of trickle-bed reactors have auxiliary conditions written for at least two values of the independent variable and are said to have *boundary conditions*. The methods used in the solution of initial-value and boundary-condition ODEs are substantially different.

Partial Differential Equations

Partial differential equations (PDEs) each have two or more independent variables x (e.g., reactor length) and r (e.g., radial coordinate) and one or more dependent variables y (e.g., fractional conversion, concentration, or temperature) and can be written in the general form for cylindrical coordinates as

$$(\partial\mathbf{y}/\partial x) = A\,[(\partial^2\mathbf{y}/\partial r^2) + (1/r)(\partial\mathbf{y}/\partial r)] + B \tag{2-2}$$

where A is a constant but B usually is a highly nonlinear quantity. More generally, for any coordinate system, Eq. (2-2) can be written as

$$(\partial y/\partial x) = A\nabla^2 y + B \tag{2-3}$$

where ∇^2 is the so-called laplacian operator.

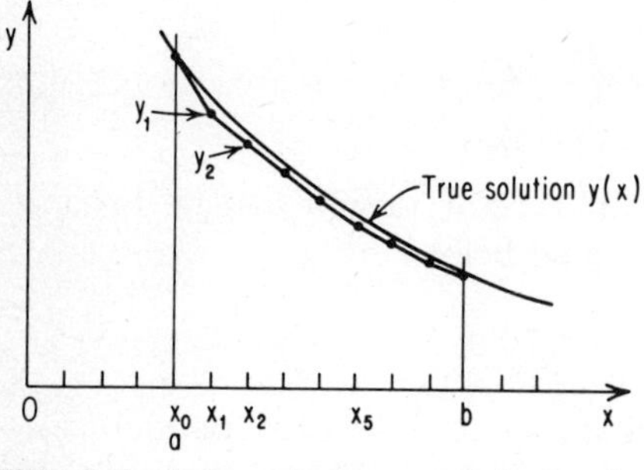

FIG. 2-1 **Approximate numerical solution of a differential equation.**

This may be of interest for spherical coordinates, i.e.,

$$(\partial y/\partial x) = A\,[(\partial^2 y/\partial r^2) + (2/r)(\partial y/\partial r)] + B \qquad (2\text{-}4)$$

because of their application to reactions in catalyst pellets. Such PDEs will be used in the design of NINAF reactors.

Detailed digital computer programs to solve reactor design problems involving differential equations of both categories will be described in the following pages. However, before going into the details of each program the principles of the algorithms on which these computer programs are based will be reviewed.

2.2 PRINCIPLES OF ALGORITHMS

An *algorithm* is a rule or calculational procedure for solving a mathematical problem that frequently involves extensive numerical operations. A number of such algorithms are used in computer programs for the solution of simultaneous ODEs or PDEs. These algorithms have a common underlying principle that the user of computer programs should know and understand.

How can one solve first-order ODEs (equations with only first-order derivatives)? Let us assume a first-order ODE, which by definition would be of the form

$$(dy/dx) = f(x,y) \qquad (2\text{-}5)$$

Solving this ODE means finding a solution $y(x)$ which satisfies both Eq. (2-5) and one specified initial condition. In general, $y(x)$ cannot be determined analytically. Instead, the interval of interest (a,b) in the independent variable x is subdivided into subintervals or discrete steps. The value of the true solution $y(x)$ is approximated for each evenly spaced value of x, so that an approximate numerical solution is obtained. This approximate solution consists of discrete values corresponding to the evenly spaced values of x, as shown in Fig. 2-1. If there are $n + 1$ evenly spaced values of x, which may be called $x_0, x_1, x_2, \ldots x_n$, the step size h would be

$$h = \frac{b - a}{n} \qquad (2\text{-}6)$$

and $x_i = x_0 + ih$ where $i = 0, 1, \ldots n$.

How can the true solution $y(x)$ be approximated? Suppose the value y_0, corresponding to the initial value x_0 of x, is known and the next value y_1, corresponding to x_1, is to be computed (see Fig. 2-2). One way of

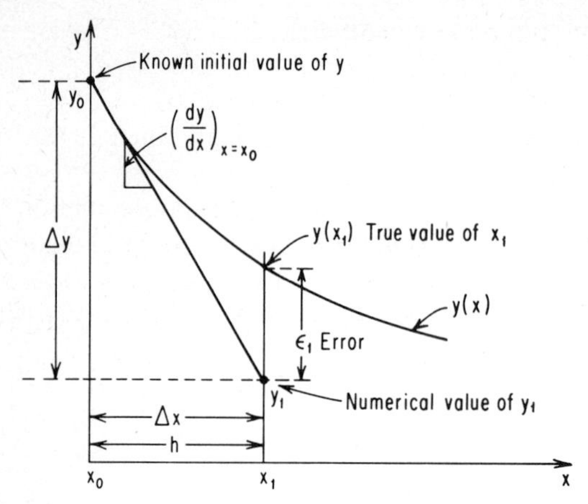

FIG. 2-2 Method of approximating a differential equation.

getting from y_0 to y_1 is to compute the tangent at the initial point y_0, which is given by the derivative at y_0 or the slope of the tangent at y_0:

$$y_1 = y_0 + \left(\frac{dy}{dx}\right)_{y=y_0} \Delta x \simeq y(x_1)$$

Referring to Fig. 2-2, what we are looking for is the true value $y(x_1)$ on the true $y(x)$ curve, but all we have from constructing the tangent at point y_0 is the numerical value y_1. Now, according to Eq. (2-5), $(dy/dx)_{y=y_0} = f(x_0, y_0)$ and we can write:

$$y_1 = y_0 + f(x_0, y_0)h \tag{2-7}$$

which is the approximate value of y_1. Here an *error* ϵ_1 is made. If one continues to approximate further values of y by this method and is not careful, the error may accumulate excessively. The essential feature of all numerical calculations of differential equations is the estimation of this error ϵ_1, since the true value $y(x_1)$ is not known. The error ϵ can be reduced if a smaller step h is selected. This can be seen from Fig. 2-2 and can be demonstrated by calculation. A simple method to estimate ϵ is that of Euler.

Euler's Algorithm

Euler's integration algorithm is

$$y_{n+1} = y_n + f(y_n, x_n)\, h + \epsilon_n \tag{2-8}$$

This expression looks like a Taylor series, since $f(y_n, x_n)$ is the derivative dy_n/dx. Thus, a few more terms can be added by Taylor expansion:

$$y_{n+1} = y_n + \frac{dy_n}{dx} \cdot h + \left[\frac{d^2y_n}{dx^2} \cdot \frac{h^2}{2!} + \frac{d^3y_n}{dx^3} \cdot \frac{h^3}{3!} + \cdots \right] \tag{2-9}$$

The added terms in the brackets may be called *truncation error.* If we want to be really accurate, we should use a large number of these terms. However, that would be too time-consuming and expensive, and we can compromise by using only the first term as a truncation error estimate, which is what Euler did. Such a procedure is called a *one-term error estimate.* The derivative dy/dx can itself be expanded in a Taylor series:

$$\frac{dy_{n+1}}{dx} = \frac{dy_n}{dx} + \frac{d^2y_n}{dx^2} \cdot \frac{h}{1!} + \cdots \tag{2-10}$$

From this expression d^2y/dx^2 can be calculated:

$$\frac{d^2y_n}{dx^2} = \frac{(dy_{n+1}/dx) - (dy_n/dx)}{h} \tag{2-11}$$

Equation (2-11) is substituted into the first term in the brackets of Eq. (2-9) and one can write:

$$\epsilon_{ne} = \left(\frac{dy_{n+1}}{dx} - \frac{dy_n}{dx} \right) \frac{h}{2!} \tag{2-12}$$

where subscript e denotes "estimated."

Equation (2-9) can then be written as

$$y_{n+1} = y_n + \frac{dy_n}{dx} \cdot h + \epsilon \tag{2-13}$$

which is the essence of the Euler algorithm.

Now, how can we convert this algorithm into a computer program? Let us assume that we have to integrate a single ODE:

$$\frac{dy}{dx} = x + y \tag{2-14}$$

with the initial value of $y(x_0) = y(0) = 0$. This initial value ODE has a known analytic solution:

$$y = e^x - x - 1 \tag{2-15}$$

In order to apply the Euler method to this ODE, we can start in Fig. 2-2 from the known point y_0 and decide up to what maximum x value, or XMAX, we will integrate. We can diagrammatically represent in Fig.

```
C                               E U L E R   M E T H O D
C        ....READ DATA AND INITIALIZE X, Y, TRUEY....
         READ (5,100) XMAX, H
         WRITE (6, 200) XMAX,H
         X = 0.
         Y = 0.
         TRUEY = 0.
         WRITE (6, 201) X, Y, TRUEY
C
C        ....EULER'S METHOD INTEGRATION....
         NSTEP = (XMAX + H/2.)/H
         DO 3 N=1, NSTEP
         Y = Y + H *(X + Y)
         X = FLOAT(N) * H
         TRUEY = EXP(X) - X - 1.
         WRITE (6, 201) X, Y, TRUEY
       3 CONTINUE
C
C        ....FORMAT FOR INPUT AND OUTPUT STATEMENTS....
     100 FORMAT (10X,F10.6,10X,F10.6)
     200 FORMAT (7H1XMAX = ,F12.6, 5X, 5H H = , F12.6)
     201 FORMAT (1H , 4HX = , F10.6, 5X, 4HY = , F16.6, 5X, 8HTRUEY = ,
        1  F16.6)
C
         END
```

```
XMAX =      1.000000          H =        0.010000
X =    0.0             Y =        0.0               TRUEY =        0.0
X =    0.010000        Y =        0.0               TRUEY =        0.000050
X =    0.020000        Y =        0.000100          TRUEY =        0.000201
X =    0.030000        Y =        0.000301          TRUEY =        0.000454
X =    0.040000        Y =        0.000604          TRUEY =        0.000811
X =    0.050000        Y =        0.001010          TRUEY =        0.001271
X =    0.060000        Y =        0.001520          TRUEY =        0.001836
X =    0.070000        Y =        0.002135          TRUEY =        0.002507
X =    0.080000        Y =        0.002857          TRUEY =        0.003286
X =    0.090000        Y =        0.003685          TRUEY =        0.004174
X =    0.100000        Y =        0.004622          TRUEY =        0.005171
X =    0.110000        Y =        0.005668          TRUEY =        0.006277
X =    0.120000        Y =        0.006825          TRUEY =        0.007496
X =    0.130000        Y =        0.008093          TRUEY =        0.008828
.
.
.
.
.
.
.
.
.
X =    0.920000        Y =        0.577848          TRUEY =        0.589290
X =    0.930000        Y =        0.592826          TRUEY =        0.604509
X =    0.940000        Y =        0.608055          TRUEY =        0.619981
X =    0.950000        Y =        0.623535          TRUEY =        0.635709
X =    0.960000        Y =        0.639270          TRUEY =        0.651696
X =    0.970000        Y =        0.655263          TRUEY =        0.667945
X =    0.980000        Y =        0.671516          TRUEY =        0.684456
X =    0.990000        Y =        0.688031          TRUEY =        0.701234
X =    1.000000        Y =        0.704811          TRUEY =        0.718282
```

FIG. 2-3 Computer program for Euler algorithm and printout of computer run.

2-3 the various computer operations that we will perform. We must first supply, or "read in," some information such as the chosen value of XMAX (we choose XMAX = 1.0) and the step size H. We should have a sufficient number of steps between the start and the end to achieve an accurate integration. Of course, the more steps, the more accurate the integration. We also conveniently print the input.

Next, we initialize the starting values of x, the computed value of y, and the true value of y, which we call TRUEY. *Initializing* means setting the initial values before the computations. We set $x = 0.$, $y = 0.$, and y_0 = TRUEY = 0. Again we ask the computer to print these initial data.

Now we calculate the number of steps NSTEP we want the Euler algorithm to use. Then we can construct the DO loop for the repeated execution of the algorithm.

```
    DO 3 N=1,NSTEP
    Y=Y+H*(X+Y)
    X=FLOAT(N)*H
    TRUEY=EXP(X)-X-1.
    WRITE(6,201)X,Y,TRUEY
  3 CONTINUE
```

where N is the counter for the number of applications of the algorithm. Here the most important statement is

```
Y=Y+H*(X+Y)
```

It is derived from Eq. (2-13) by replacing dy/dx with its value in Eq. (2-14).

An actual computer run is presented in Fig. 2-3. This is an abbreviated run. Normally, the programmer may want to ask the computer to calculate and print the errors and considerably more information of interest. But the basic idea is shown in the diagram of Fig. 2-4 and in the program of Fig. 2-3. It should be noted that an apparent discrepancy exists between the y values and the TRUEY values in the computer printout. The difference corresponds to the error ϵ_1 illustrated in Fig. 2-2. This inaccuracy can be decreased by selecting a smaller step size h. While smaller step sizes make computer calculations more accurate, they also make them more expensive, and the programmer must always compromise between the degree of accuracy needed and the price which must be paid for it.

There is, of course, another way of achieving better accuracy. One can use a better algorithm than the old Euler method. Actually, besides being somewhat inaccurate, the Euler method has limited *stability*. A solution is said to be *unstable* if errors introduced at some stage of the calculations are propagated without bound throughout subsequent cal-

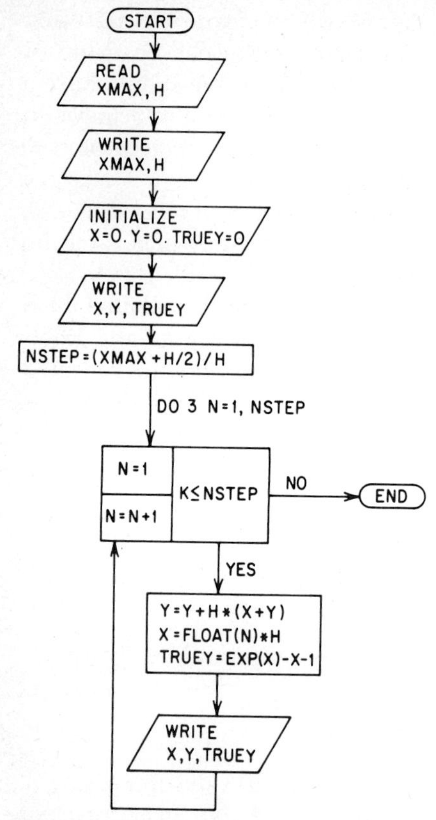

FIG. 2-4 Flow diagram of Euler algorithm.

culations. There have been numerous improvements in the Euler method. Perhaps the best known of these are the Runge-Kutta algorithms.

Runge-Kutta Algorithms

The main reason for developing improvements over the Euler algorithm has been the need for more accuracy. The Runge-Kutta algorithms satisfy this need. They exist in several variations.[2]

The improved Euler method or *Heun's method* consists of using the Euler algorithm twice in sequence. First, a preliminary estimate of y_{n+1} is obtained from

$$\mathbf{y}_{n+1} = y_n \, hf(x_n, y_n) \tag{2-16}$$

Referring to Fig. 2-5, y_{n+1} is the ordinate at $x = x_{n+1}$ of the straight line

A passing from point (x_n, y_n) with slope $f(x_n, y_n) = k_1$ Furthermore, an improved estimate $\mathbf{y}_{n+1}$ is obtained from Eq. (2-17):

$$\mathbf{y}_{n+1} = y_n + \frac{h}{2}[f(x_n, y_n) + f(x_{n+1}, \mathbf{y}_{n+1})] \tag{2-17}$$

The slope of the straight line used for this purpose is the weighted average of approximations to the derivative at the two ends of the interval. Equation (2-16) may be considered as a predicting equation for $\mathbf{y}_{n+1}$, whereas Eq. (2-17) may be considered as a correcting equation to yield the improved estimate of $\mathbf{y}_{n+1}$. Equation (2-17) can be used iteratively to give a series of corrected $\mathbf{y}_{n+1}$ values until convergence is achieved. Thus this method is called a *predictor-corrector method.*

The *Improved polygon* or *modified Euler method* also uses Euler's method twice in sequence. Referring to Fig. 2-6, an approximation is first obtained for y at the halfway point $x_n + h/2$. This value, called $\mathbf{y}_{n+½}$, is obtained from Eq. (2-18):

$$\mathbf{y}_{n+½} = y_n + \frac{h}{2} f(x_n, y_n) \tag{2-18}$$

The second step uses the equation:

$$y_{n+1} = y_n + hf\left(x_n + \frac{h}{2}, \mathbf{y}_{n+½}\right) \tag{2-19}$$

Equation (2-19) is used to evaluate $f(x,y)$ for $x = x_n + h/2$, $y = \mathbf{y}_{n+½}$ and uses this value as the average derivative over the whole interval h.

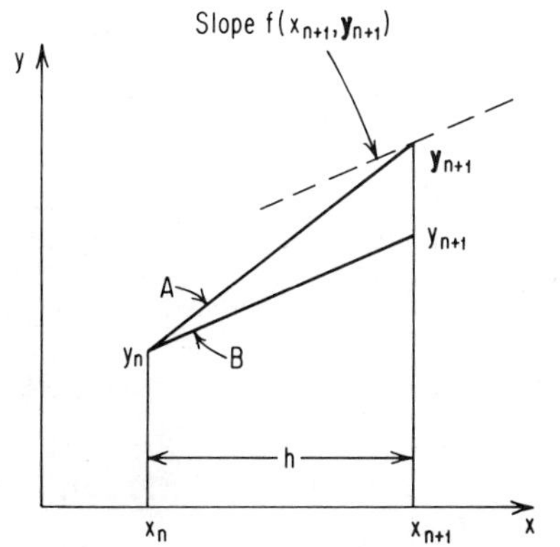

FIG. 2-5 Second-order Runge-Kutta procedure: Heun's predictor-corrector method. (*From Carnahan et al.,*[2] *by permission from John Wiley.*)

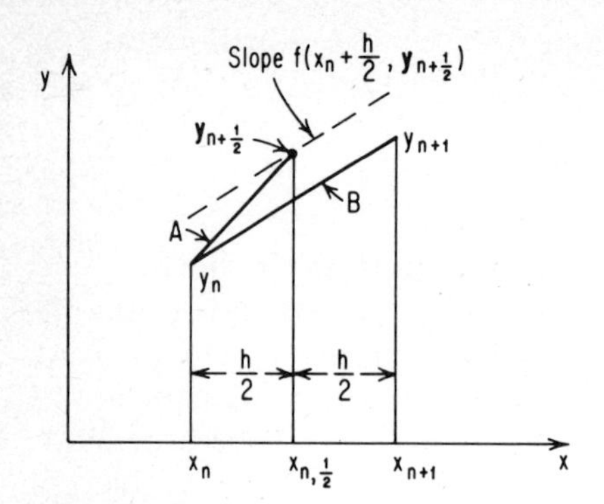

FIG. 2-6 Second-order Runge-Kutta procedure: improved polygon method. (*From Carnahan et al.,*[2] *by permission from John Wiley.*)

The terms *second-order* and *third-order* Runge-Kutta algorithm mean that approximations with accuracies equivalent to Taylor expansions of $y(x)$ retaining terms in h^2, and h^3, respectively, have been used. The order of the terms has nothing to do with the number of terms used in the error estimation.

2.3 *n*th-ORDER ORDINARY DIFFERENTIAL EQUATIONS

Up to this point only first-order ODEs, i.e., ODEs which contain only first derivatives, have been considered for integration. How can one integrate an *n*th-order ODE? The form of such an equation is

$$F(x, y, dy/dx, d^2y/dx^2, d^3y/dx^3, \ldots d^ny/dx^n) = 0 \tag{2-20}$$

Equation (2-20) is an ODE because it contains no partial derivatives, i.e., it has only one independent variable x. It is of *n*th order because the highest-order derivative is of *n*th order. An *n*th-order ODE can be written as a system of n first-order ODEs by defining $n - 1$ new variables. For example, consider the second-order equation:

$$x^2 \frac{d^2y}{dx^2} + x \frac{dy}{dx} + x^2 y = 0 \tag{2-21}$$

A new variable $z = dy/dx$ can be defined, and with it Eq. (2-21) can be rewritten as a system of two first-order ODEs:

$$\frac{dy}{dx} - z = 0 \tag{2-22}$$

$$x^2 \frac{dz}{dx} + xz + x^2y = 0 \tag{2-23}$$

Any nth-order ODE can be converted to a system of n first-order ODEs, which then can be solved simultaneously.

2.4 SIMULTANEOUS ORDINARY DIFFERENTIAL EQUATIONS

Consider a system of n simultaneous first-order ODEs in the dependent variables $y_1, y_2, \ldots y_n$:

$$\begin{aligned}
\frac{dy_1}{dx} &= f_1(x, y_1, y_2, \ldots y_n) \\
\frac{dy_2}{dx} &= f_2(x, y_1, y_2, \ldots y_n) \\
&\cdot \\
&\cdot \\
&\cdot \\
\frac{dy_n}{dx} &= f_n(x, y_1, y_2, \ldots y_n)
\end{aligned} \tag{2-24}$$

with initial conditions given at a common point x_0, i.e.,

$$\begin{aligned}
y_1(x_0) &= y_{1,0} \\
y_2(x_0) &= y_{2,0} \\
&\cdot \\
&\cdot \\
&\cdot \\
y_n(x_0) &= y_{n,0}
\end{aligned} \tag{2-25}$$

The simultaneous solution of such a system of equations is, in general, as easy as that of a single first-order equation. The algorithm selected is applied to each of the simultaneous equations in parallel at each step.

Various computer programs have been developed to solve systems of simultaneous ODEs. Most computer centers have these programs, either in their program libraries or on tapes, which may simply be called. Some programs, such as the DSS/2 program of Lehigh University,[3] are proprietary and can be used either by purchasing them or by using the host computer or one of its terminals for a fee. The use of such proprietary programs is warranted only if they offer advantages not found in openly available programs or if the user happens to have easy access to them.

2.5
PROGRAM FOR SOLVING INITIAL-VALUE ODEs

A particular fourth-order Runge-Kutta algorithm will now be discussed and used in the solution of initial-value ODE systems encountered in fixed-bed adiabatic reactor problems.

All fourth-order formulas conform to the equation

$$y_{n+1} = y_n + h(ak_1 + bk_2 + ck_3 + dk_4) \tag{2-26}$$

in which k_1, k_2, k_3, and k_4 are derivative values calculated on the interval $x_n \leqslant x \leqslant x_{n+1}$. Kutta has developed a particular algorithm in which

$$a = 1/6 \qquad b = 2/6 \qquad c = 2/6 \qquad d = 1/6$$

Then Eq. (2-26) becomes for a single equation $dy/dx = f(x,y)$:

$$y_{n+1} = y_n + \frac{h}{6}(k_1 + 2k_2 + 2k_3 + k_4) \tag{2-27}$$

where $k_1 = f(x_n, y_n)$

$k_2 = f(x_n + \tfrac{1}{2}h, y_n + \tfrac{1}{2}hk_1)$

$k_3 = f(x_n + \tfrac{1}{2}h, y_n + \tfrac{1}{2}hk_2)$

$k_4 = f(x_n + h, y_n + hk_3)$

Let us apply this algorithm to the solution of n first-order ODEs.

$$\begin{aligned} \frac{dy_1}{dx} &= f_1(x, y_1, y_2, \ldots y_n) \\ \frac{dy_2}{dx} &= f_2(x, y_1, y_2, \ldots y_n) \\ &\ \vdots \\ \frac{dy_n}{dx} &= f_n(x, y_1, y_2, \ldots y_n) \end{aligned} \tag{2-28}$$

with n initial conditions

$$y_{ji} = y_j(x_i) \qquad j = 1, 2, 3, \ldots n \tag{2-29}$$

Subscript i denotes "initial."

The development of this algorithm becomes rather lengthy and complicated. We will discuss it only briefly and will try to arrive quickly at the result, which is the FUNCTION RUNGE, the calling program that we will use without change.

We said above that Eq. (2-27) is written for a single ODE. For sets of ODEs, y, x, y_{n+1}, y_n, k_1, k_2, k_3, and k_4, can be converted to vectors with one component for each ODE, e.g.,

$$\frac{d\mathbf{y}}{dx} = \mathbf{f}(x, \mathbf{y}) \tag{2-30}$$

$$\mathbf{y}_{n+1} = \mathbf{y}_n + \frac{h}{6}(\mathbf{k}_1 + 2\mathbf{k}_2 + 2\mathbf{k}_3 + \mathbf{k}_4) \tag{2-31}$$

where $\mathbf{k}_1 = \mathbf{f}(x_n, \mathbf{y}_n)$ (2-32)

$$\mathbf{k}_2 = \mathbf{f}(x_n + h/2, \mathbf{y}_n + \tfrac{1}{2}hk_1) \tag{2-33}$$

$$\mathbf{k}_3 = \mathbf{f}(x_n + h/2, \mathbf{y}_n + \tfrac{1}{2}hk_2) \tag{2-34}$$

$$\mathbf{k}_4 = \mathbf{f}(x_n + h, \mathbf{y}_n + hk_3) \tag{2-35}$$

Equations (2-30) to (2-35) are applied in parallel at each point in the algorithm for all component ODEs. This leads to a rather lengthy and complicated development which we should avoid. The interested reader can find the entire development in the book by Carnahan et al.,[2] pages 361–375.

The block diagram of Fig. 2-7 has been designed[2] to make it easy to understand how the algorithm operates and how it communicates with the *main program.* The main program contains the ODEs that the Runge-Kutta algorithm is supposed to integrate and solve. We did not set up any main program in this chapter. However, Chaps. 5 and 7 contain a total of three such main programs that communicate with the Runge-Kutta algorithm. Let us simply assume here that our main program would contain *n* ODEs that must be solved simultaneously, and that each of these ODEs contains the variables listed in Table 2-1.

The main program sets up the number *n* of the ODEs, initializes Y for each component ODE, and initializes the independent variable x (usually the reactor length) for all the ODEs. Then the Runge-Kutta algorithm is implemented in the form of a five-step procedure that is diagrammatically explained in Fig. 2-7 and presented as a computer program entitled FUNCTION RUNGE in Fig. 2-8. The working of FUNCTION RUNGE will be explained in the following by referring to these two figures: Figs. 2-7 and 2-8.

First four variables are dimensioned. Then, the pass counter M is set to 0 and then to 1 and the *first pass* is executed. This first pass simply sets RUNGE = 1 and returns to the main program. At this signal, the main program computes the derivative values **f** and returns to FUNC-

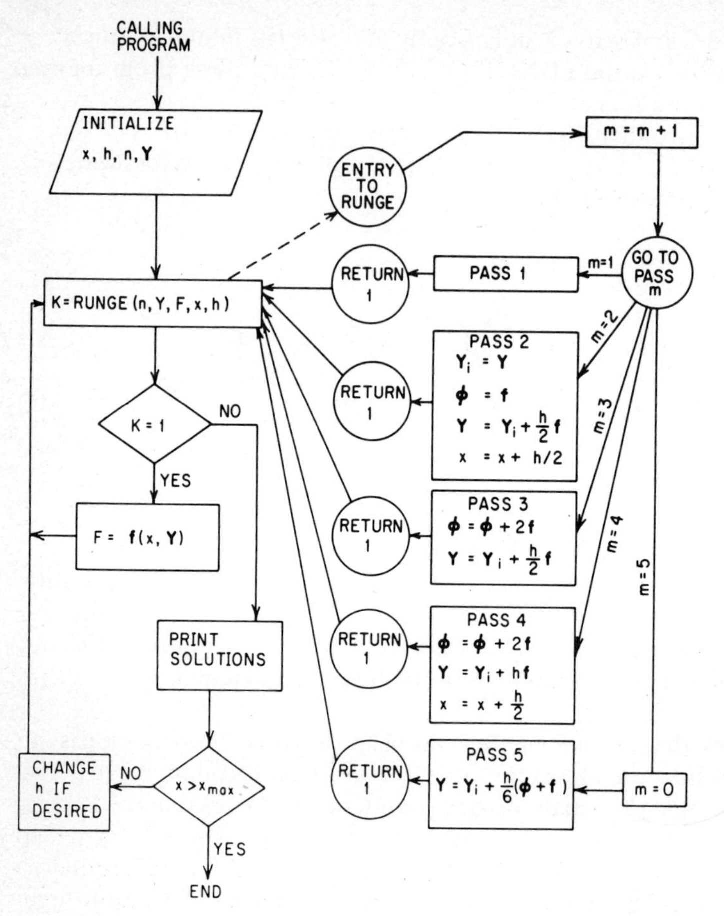

FIG. 2-7 Diagram of communications between FUNCTION RUNGE and the main calling program. (*From Carnahan et al.,*[2] *by permission from John Wiley.*)

TION RUNGE. This time the *second pass* is executed for all the ODEs by means of a DO loop which calculates

$$\mathbf{Y}_i = \mathbf{Y}$$

$$\mathbf{\Phi} = \mathbf{f}$$

$$\mathbf{Y} = \mathbf{Y}_i + \tfrac{1}{2}h\mathbf{f}$$

$$\mathrm{X} = \mathrm{X} + \tfrac{1}{2}h$$

and sets RUNGE = 1. Again we go to the main program and update derivative values at an advanced X value and come back to the FUNCTION RUNGE.

TABLE 2-1
Fortran Nomenclature Used in FUNCTION RUNGE and Corresponding Symbols Used in the Text

Fortran name	Symbol in text	Definition
N	n	Number of ODEs
Y	$\mathbf{y}$	Vector of dependent variable (solution)
F	$\mathbf{f}$	Vector of derivative approximations
X	x	Independent variable (in Chaps. 5 and 7 Z is used instead as reactor length)
H	h	Step size
M	m	Pass counter for Runge-Kutta algorithm
PHI	$\boldsymbol{\phi}$	Vector values
SAVEY	$\mathbf{Y}$	Vector of initial conditions

```
      FUNCTION RUNGE (N, Y, F, X, H)
      INTEGER RUNGE
      DIMENSION PHI(50), SAVEY(50), Y(N), F(N)
      DATA M/O/
      M = M + 1
      GO TO (1,2,3,4,5), M
C     ....PASS 1....
    1 RUNGE = 1
      RETURN
C     ....PASS 2....
    2 DO 22 J = 1, N
      SAVEY(J) = Y(J)
      PHI(J) = F(J)
   22 Y(J) = SAVEY(J) + 0.5 * H * F(J)
      X = X + 0.5 * H
      RUNGE = 1
      RETURN
C     ....PASS 3....
    3 DO 33 J = 1, N
      PHI(J) = PHI(J) + 2.0 * F(J)
   33 Y(J) = SAVEY(J) + 0.5 * H * F(J)
      RUNGE = 1
      RETURN
C     ....PASS 4....
    4 DO 44 J = 1, N
      PHI(J) = PHI(J) + 2.0 * F(J)
   44 (Y J) = SAVEY(J) + H * F(J)
      X = X + 0.5 * H
      RUNGE = 1
      RETURN
C     ....PASS 5....
    5 DO 55 J = 1, N
   55 Y(J) = SAVEY(J) + (PHI(J) + F(J)) * H/6.0
      M = 0
      RUNGE = 0
      RETURN
      END
```

FIG. 2-8 **FUNCTION RUNGE (*From Carnahan et al.,*[2] *by permission from John Wiley.*)**

In the third pass the following computations are made for all n ODEs

$$\mathbf{\Phi} = \mathbf{\Phi} + 2\mathbf{f}$$

$$\mathbf{Y} = \mathbf{Y}_i + \tfrac{1}{2}h\mathbf{f}$$

RUNGE = 1 then sends us back to the main program to revise and update derivatives **f**; X is not advanced.

In the fourth pass the following computations are made for all n ODEs

$$\mathbf{\Phi} = \mathbf{\Phi} + 2\mathbf{f}$$

$$\mathbf{Y} = \mathbf{Y}_i + h\mathbf{f}$$

$$\mathrm{X} = \mathrm{X} + h/2$$

Here RUNGE = 1 sends us back to the main program to revise and upgrade **f** at an advanced X.

In the fifth pass only one equation is computed:

$$\mathbf{Y} = \mathbf{Y}_i + (\mathbf{\Phi} + \mathbf{f})h/6$$

This time RUNGE = 0 skips the calculations of derivatives in the main program and thus completes the integration and solution of the ODEs. From there on, the main program proceeds in doing whatever else it is supposed to do with the integration results, such as calculating further dependent variables and printing the results.

The operation of FUNCTION RUNGE will be better understood when it is used in Chaps. 5 and 7 in connection with reactor design problems.

2.6 PROGRAM FOR SOLVING BOUNDARY-VALUE ODEs

Initial-value ODEs are really special cases in which all auxiliary conditions are written for the same value of the independent variable. In the general case, auxiliary conditions are written for different values of the independent variable. Such ODEs are called *boundary-value ODEs*. For example, a second-order differential equation of the form

$$F\left(x, y, \frac{dy}{dx}, \frac{d^2y}{dx^2}\right) = 0 \tag{2-36}$$

is the subject to the following boundary conditions:

$$y(a) = \alpha \qquad y(b) = \beta \tag{2-37}$$

as can be visualized in Fig. 2-9. The numerical solution of boundary-value ODEs is considerably more complicated than that of initial-value ODEs. Three types of algorithms are available, as described below.

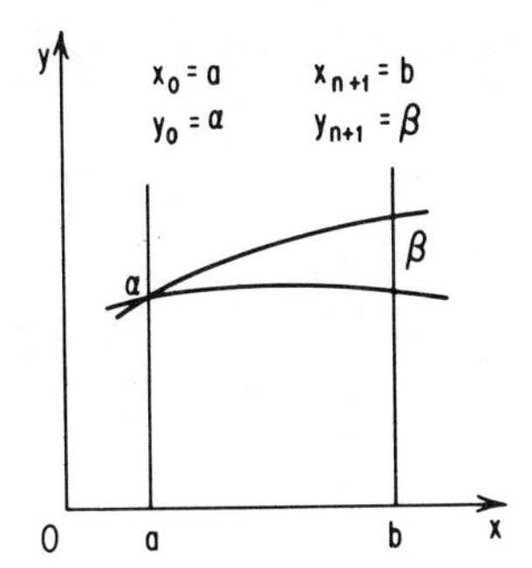

FIG. 2-9 Trial-and-error solution of a boundary-value problem. (*From Carnahan et al.,*[2] *by permission from John Wiley.*)

The Shooting Method

The shooting method consists of a trial-and-error procedure in which a boundary point having the best-known conditions is selected as the initial point. Any other missing initial conditions are assumed. The initial-value problem is then solved by one of the step-by-step procedures, such as the fourth-order Runge-Kutta algorithm (see Sec. 2.5). The initial conditions are adjusted and the problem is solved again. This process is repeated until the computed solution agrees with the known boundary conditions within specified tolerances.

The Finite Difference Method

The finite difference method consists of approximating the derivatives in the ODEs by finite difference quotients. This results in a system of difference, or algebraic, equations that require considerable computer memory. However, present-day computers can easily handle such systems.

Some ODEs can successfully be handled by means of the finite difference method, while others are too nonlinear and require the use of the method described below.

The Combined Finite Difference and Quasilinearization Method

The combined use of the finite difference method and quasilinearization as described by E. Stanley Lee[4] is recommended only in cases of complicated and nonlinear ODEs that cannot be handled by the finite difference method alone.

In most cases reactor designers do not have to use boundary-value ODEs, but there are cases when they are necessary, for example, when significant axial dispersion exists within the reactor. For integrating these equations, this book recommends either of the two methods or the combined method, as explained below.

The types of boundary-value ODEs encountered in reactor design are of the general form:

$$\frac{dC_r}{dZ} = \frac{1}{\mathrm{Pe}_{\mathrm{mal}}} \cdot \frac{d^2C_r}{dZ^2} - f_1(C_r, T_r) \tag{2-38}$$

$$\frac{dT_r}{dZ} = \frac{1}{\mathrm{Pe}_{\mathrm{ha2}}} \cdot \frac{d^2T_r}{dZ^2} + f_2(C_r, T_r) \tag{2-39}$$

where Z = dimensionless axial coordinate and independent variable

C_r = reduced molar concentration ($= C/C_0$), dimensionless dependent variable

T_r = reduced absolute temperature ($= T/T_0$), dimensionless dependent variable

f_1, f_2 = functions of C_r and T_r

Pe = Péclet number for axial dispersion, gas-liquid phase

Subscripts: mal denotes liquid-phase mass transfer

ha2 denotes two-phase heat transfer

0 denotes reactor inlet condition

The functions f_1 and f_2 are highly nonlinear functions of catalyst surface temperature T_s and may also be nonlinear functions of catalyst surface concentration C_s, depending on reaction order. In turn, in the case of first-order reactions T_s and C_s are related to bulk fluid temperature T_r and concentration C_r, respectively, through the relationships:

$$C_s = C_r\, C_0/(1 + \mathrm{Da}_m) \tag{2-39a}$$

$$\mathrm{Da}_m = \eta k/k_c a \tag{2-40}$$

$$T_s = T_0(T_r + \mathrm{Da}_h) \tag{2-41}$$

$$\mathrm{Da}_h = (-\Delta H)\mathcal{R}/a\, h\, T_0 \tag{2-42}$$

where Da_m and Da_h are Damköhler numbers for mass and heat, respectively. The reader is referred to Chap. 4 for more information on these surface-bulk relationships.

It is believed today that catalyst surface concentrations and temperatures are practically identical to corresponding bulk fluid properties in industrial-scale trickle-bed reactors. Of course, the design equations are then considerably simplified. But there certainly are also cases in which this simplification does not apply.

The boundary conditions are:

$$\text{at bed inlet} \qquad Z = 0 \qquad C_r(0) = T_r(0) = 1 \tag{2-43}$$

$$\text{at bed outlet} \qquad Z = Z_T \qquad \frac{dC_r(Z_T)}{dZ} = \frac{dT_r(Z_R)}{dZ} = 0 \tag{2-44}$$

In the following several cases, boundary-value ODEs of varying degrees of nonlinearity will be considered.

Case 1: $C_s = C$; $T_s = T$

In a first-order reaction, by assuming that $C_s = C$ and $T_s = T$ Eqs. (2-38) and (2-39) can be written as:

$$\frac{1}{\text{Pe}_{\text{ma1}}} \cdot \frac{d^2C_r}{dZ^2} - \frac{dC_r}{dZ} = b_1 \exp\,(-E/R_GT)C_rC_0 = f_3(C_r, T_r) \tag{2-45}$$

$$\frac{1}{\text{Pe}_{\text{ha2}}} \cdot \frac{d^2T_r}{dZ^2} - \frac{dT_r}{dZ} = -b_2 \exp\,(-E/R_GT)C_rC_0 = f_4(C_r, T_r) \tag{2-46}$$

where b_1 and b_2 are products of constants

E = activation energy, kJ/kmol

R_G = gas constant = 8.314 kJ/(kmol · K)

f_3, f_4 = functions of C_r and T_r

The combined finite difference and quasilinearization method must be used in this case because of the nonlinearity of the ODEs. In order to apply the *finite difference approximation method* the catalyst bed length Z_T is subdivided into M equal increments of length ΔZ as diagrammatically shown in Fig. 2-10. Since Z_T is not really known yet, it must be guessed; it is preferable to overestimate so that we do not run the risk of underestimating and repeating the whole calculation. Let $C_r(I)$ and $T_r(I)$ denote the values of C_r and T_r, respectively, at positions $I\Delta Z$; then the derivatives of Eqs. (2-45) and (2-46) can be replaced by the following difference quotients:

$$\frac{d^2C_r}{dZ^2} = \frac{1}{\Delta Z^2}\,[C_r(I + 1) - 2\,C_r(I) + C_r(I - 1)] \tag{2-47}$$

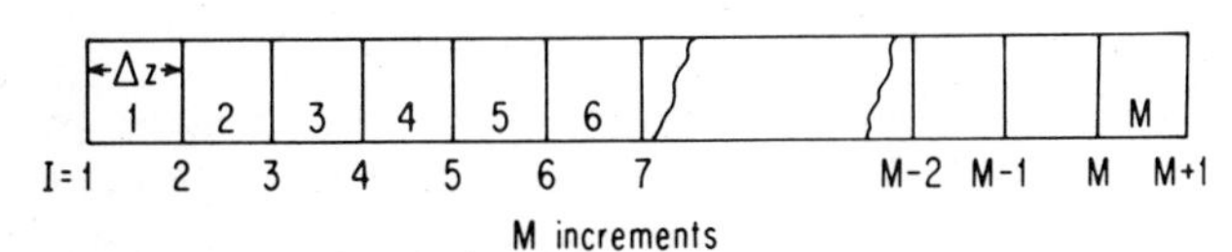

FIG. 2-10 Diagram of reactor length increments.

$$\frac{d^2T_{rx}}{dZ^2} = \frac{1}{\Delta Z^2}[T_{rx}(I+1) - 2\,T_{rx}(I) + T_{rx}(I-1)] \tag{2-48}$$

$$\frac{dC_r}{dZ} = \frac{1}{\Delta Z}[C_r(I+1) - C_r(I)] \tag{2-49}$$

$$\frac{dT_{rx}}{dZ} = \frac{1}{\Delta Z}[\,T_{rx}(I+1) - T_{rx}(I)] \tag{2-50}$$

in which $I = 1, 2, 3, \ldots, (M-1)$. The subscript x denotes an unknown value in a forthcoming iteration, while nonsubscripted T_r values are known either from the initial value or from the previous iteration.

Equations (2-49) and (2-50) are an old version of the finite difference approximation of the first derivative. It was used in this section because E. Stanley Lee used it in his work.[4] However, it is more accurate to write:

$$\frac{dC_r}{dZ} = \frac{1}{2\Delta Z}[C_r(I+1) - C_r(I-1)] \tag{2-51}$$

$$\frac{dT_{rx}}{dZ} = \frac{1}{2\Delta Z}[T_{rx}(I+1) - T_{rx}(I-1)] \tag{2-52}$$

This is done in the development of partial differential equations in Sec. 2.7. The difference in accuracy would probably be insignificant in reactor design.

Let us now replace the derivatives in Eqs. (2-45) and (2-46) by the proper difference quotients:

$$\frac{1}{\mathrm{Pe}_{\mathrm{ma1}}\,\Delta Z^2}[C_r(I+1) - 2C_r(I) + C_r(I-1)] - \frac{1}{\Delta Z}[C_r(I+1) - C_r(I)] = b_1 \exp\left(-E/R_G T_r(I) T_0\right) \cdot C_r(I) \cdot C_0 = f_3(C_r, T_r) \tag{2-53}$$

$$\frac{1}{\mathrm{Pe}_{\mathrm{ha2}}\,\Delta Z^2}[T_r(I+1) - 2T_r(I) + T_r(I-1)] - \frac{1}{\Delta Z}[T_r(I+1) - T_r(I)] = -b_2 \exp\left(-E/R_G T_r(I) T_0\right) C_r(I) \cdot C_0 = f_4(C_r, T_r) \tag{2-54}$$

Equation (2-53) is perfectly linear in C_r and does not need to be quasilinearized. However, Eq. (2-54) is not fully linear in T_r; it contains a T_r term in the exponential. Thus only Eq. (2-54) has to be quasilinearized. The function $f_4(C_r, T_r)$ can be quasilinearized by using the following equation for T_r only:

$$f(T_{rx}) = f(T_r) + \left|\frac{df(T_r)}{dT_r}\right|(T_{rx} - T_r) \tag{2-55}$$

Thus, Eq. (2-54) can be quasilinearized as follows:

$$f(T_{rx}) = -b_2 \exp(E/R_G T_0 T_r(I))C_r(I)C_0 + |(df(T_r)/dT_r)| \cdot [T_{rx}(I) - T_r(I)] \tag{2-56}$$

Here the derivative $df(T_r)/dT_r$ can be calculated by using well-known formulas:

$$df_4/dT_r = b_2\, C_r(I)\, C_0\, [d \exp(-E/R_G T_0 T_r(I))/dT_r]$$

Let $u = \exp[E/R_G T_0 R_r(I)]$. Then

$$du^{-1}/dT_r = u^{-2}(du/dT_r) = (1/\exp(2E/R_G T_0 T_r))(du/dT_r)$$

$$du/dT_r = \exp(E/R_G T_0 T_r(I))E/(R_G T_0\, T_r(I)^2)$$

Substitution of the above derivatives into Eq. (2-56) gives

$$f(T_{rx}) = -b_2 C_0 C_r(I) \exp(-E/R_G T_0 T_r(I)) \left[\frac{E(T_{rx}(I) - T_r(I))}{T_0 R_G (T_r(I))^2} - 1\right] \tag{2-57}$$

Equation (2-53) is rearranged and Eq. (2-54) is combined with Eq. (2-57) and rearranged to give

$$\begin{aligned} &C_r(I + 1)[(1/\text{Pe}_{\text{ma1}}\Delta Z^2) - (1/\Delta Z)] \\ &+ C_r(I)[(-2/\text{Pe}_{\text{ma1}}\Delta Z^2) + (1/\Delta Z) - b_1 C_0 \exp(-E/R_G T_0 T_r(I))] \\ &+ C_r(I - 1)(1/\text{Pe}_{\text{ma1}}\Delta Z^2) = 0 \end{aligned} \tag{2-58}$$

$$\begin{aligned} &T_{rx}(I + 1)[(1/\text{Pe}_{\text{ma1}}\Delta Z^2) - (1/\Delta Z)] \\ &+ T_{rx}(I)[(-2/\text{Pe}_{\text{ha2}}\Delta Z^2) + (1/\Delta Z) - (b_2 C_0 C_r(I))E \exp(-E/R_G T_0 T_r(I) \\ &/T_0 R_G T_r(I)^2)] + T_{rx}(I - 1)(1/\text{Pe}_{\text{ha2}} Z^2) \\ &= b_2 C_0 C_r(I) \exp[-E/R_G T_0 T_r(I)]\, [(-E/R_G T_0 T_r(I)^2) - 1] \end{aligned} \tag{2-59}$$

It should be noted that in Eq. (2-58) the C_r terms have no subscript x because that equation is already linear in C_r and all C_r terms in it are considered "known" or calculable by the method of Thomas, which is explained below. The C_r term in the right-hand side of Eq. (2-53) is assumed to be in the "main" increment I and not in increments $I + 1$ or $I - 1$ and is so subscripted. All the C_r and T_r terms in Eq. (2-58) and

Eq. (2-59), which do not originate from Eqs. (2-47) to (2-50), are subscripted I.

Equations (2-58) and (2-59) can be simplified and rearranged by defining the following coefficients:

$$\left.\begin{aligned}
C11 &= (\mathrm{Pe}_{\mathrm{ma1}} \cdot \Delta Z^2)^{-1} \\
C12 &= -2 \cdot C11 + (1/\Delta Z) - b_1 C_0\, CC1 \\
C13 &= C11 - (1/\Delta Z) \\
C14 &= 0 \\
C21 &= (\mathrm{Pe}_{\mathrm{ha2}} \cdot \Delta Z)^{-1} \\
C22 &= -2 \cdot C21 + (1/\Delta Z) + CC2 \cdot CC1 \\
C23 &= C21 - (1/\Delta Z) \\
C24 &= CC1 \cdot CC3 \\
\text{where } CC1 &= e^{-E/R_G T_0 T_r(I)} \\
CC2 &= \frac{-b_2 C_0 C_r(I) E}{T_0 R_G (T_r(I))^2} \\
CC3 &= b_2 C_0 C_r(I) \left[\frac{-E}{R_G T_0 (T_r(I))^2} - 1\right]
\end{aligned}\right\} \quad (2\text{-}60)$$

Substituting these coefficients in Eqs. (2-58) and (2-59)

$$C11 \cdot C_r(I-1) + C12 \cdot C_r(I) + C13 \cdot C_r(I+1) = C14 \quad (2\text{-}61)$$

$$C21 \cdot T_{rx}(I-1) + C22 \cdot T_{rx}(I) + C23 \cdot T_{rx}(I+1) = C24 \quad (2\text{-}62)$$

Note that the terms are ordered from left to right in the order of $I - 1$, I, $I + 1$. For $I = 1$, the term containing $(I - 1)$ would be zero. Because a subscript is not permitted to be zero in Fortran IV, instead of setting $I = 1, 2, 3, \ldots, M$, the values of I will be set $I = 2, 3, 4, \ldots, (M + 1)$, as shown in Fig. 2-10. Then,

$$\begin{array}{llll}
\text{at the reactor inlet} & Z = 0 & I = 1 & C_r(1) = T_r(1) = 1.0 \\
\text{at reactor outlet} & Z = Z_T & I = M + 1 & \begin{Bmatrix} C_r(M+1) = C_r(M) \\ T_r(M+1) = T_r(M) \end{Bmatrix}
\end{array} \quad (2\text{-}63)$$

When the value of I is varied, the following types of equations are obtained:

$$C11 \cdot C_r(1) + C12 \cdot C_r(2) + C13 \cdot C_r(3) = C14 \quad (2\text{-}64)$$

$$C11 \cdot C_r(I-1) + C12 \cdot C_r(I) + C13 \cdot C_r(I+1) = C14 \quad (2\text{-}65)$$

$$C11 \cdot C_r(M-1) + C12 \cdot C_r(M) + C13 \cdot C_r(M+1) = C14 \quad (2\text{-}66)$$

$$C21 \cdot T_{rx}(1) + C22 \cdot T_{rx}(2) + C23 \cdot T_{rx}(3) = C24 \quad (2\text{-}67)$$

$$C21 \cdot T_{rx}(I-1) + C22 \cdot T_{rx}(I) + C23 \cdot T_{rx}(I+1) = C24 \quad (2\text{-}68)$$

$$C21 \cdot T_{rx}(M-1) + C22 \cdot T_{rx}(M) + C23 \cdot T_{rx}(M+1) = C24 \quad (2\text{-}69)$$

Since $C_r(1) = 1$, and $T_{rx}(1) = 1.$, the terms $C11 \cdot C_r(1)$ and $C21 \cdot T_{rx}(1)$ become known quantities and can be transferred to the right-hand side of Eqs. (2-64) and (2-67). Also, because of the boundary conditions of Eq. (2-63), Eqs. (2-66) and (2-69) can be simplified and the following system of six equations is obtained:

$$C12 \cdot C_r(2) + C13 \cdot C_r(3) = C14 - C11 \quad (2\text{-}70)$$

$$C11 \cdot C_r(I-1) + C12 \cdot C_r(I) + C13 \cdot C_r(I+1) = C14 \quad (2\text{-}71)$$

$$C11 \cdot C_r(M-1) + (C12 + C13)C_r(M) = C14 \quad (2\text{-}72)$$

$$C22\, T_{rx}(2) + C23 \cdot T_{rx}(3) = C24 - C21 \quad (2\text{-}73)$$

$$C21 \cdot T_{rx}(I-1) + C22 \cdot T_{rx}(I) + C23 \cdot T_{rx}(I+1) = C24 \quad (2\text{-}74)$$

$$C21 \cdot T_{rx}(M-1) + (C22 + C23)T_{rx}(M) = C24 \quad (2\text{-}75)$$

It can be seen that the first and last equations of each set of $M - 1$ equations contain only two unknowns, and all other equations in the two sets contain three unknowns. These equations have a *tridiagonal coefficient matrix* and may be solved by using *Thomas' method.*[5,6] This method and a subroutine TRIDAG to implement it are presented by Carnahan et al.[2] This procedure is applied alternately to the mass and heat equations until C_r and T_r values for any Z do not change any more than a desired amount from one iteration to the next.

There are some problems here: the b_1 and b_2 "constants" are not really constant. Also, these quantities cannot be calculated from increment ΔZ to increment ΔZ because all increments are calculated simultaneously by the Thomas method and not in steps beginning with the reactor inlet. The only time new coefficient values are calculated is between iterative steps and then they can be picked up by the computer program for each ΔZ or each I value.

Case 2: $C_s \neq C$; $T_s \neq T$

In case of a first-order reaction, Eqs. (2-38) and (2-39) can be written as

$$\frac{dC_r}{dZ} = \frac{1}{\mathrm{Pe}_{\mathrm{ma1}}} \cdot \frac{d^2C_r}{dZ^2} - b_1\, e^{-E/R_GT_s}\, C_s \quad (2\text{-}76)$$

$$\frac{dT_r}{dZ} = \frac{1}{\mathrm{Pe}_{\mathrm{ha2}}} \cdot \frac{d^2T_r}{dZ^2} + b_2\, e^{-E/R_G T_s}\, C_s \tag{2-77}$$

where C_s is replaced by its value from Eq. (2-39a), while T_s is left as is. The following equations result:

$$\frac{1}{\mathrm{Pe}_{\mathrm{ma1}}} \cdot \frac{d^2C_r}{dZ^2} - \frac{dC_r}{dZ} = \frac{b_1 C_r C_0}{1 + \mathrm{Da}_m}\, e^{-E/R_G T_s} = f_3(C_r, T_r) \tag{2-78}$$

$$\frac{1}{\mathrm{Pe}_{\mathrm{ha2}}} \cdot \frac{d^2T_r}{dZ^2} - \frac{dT_r}{dZ} = \frac{-b_2 C_r C_0}{1 + \mathrm{Da}_m}\, e^{-E/R_G T_s} = f_4(C_r, T_r) \tag{2-79}$$

Equation (2-78) is linear in C_r and Eq. (2-79) is linear in T_r. The T_s in Eq. (2-79) can be related to T_r during local iterations. Both equations can be treated only by finite difference approximation. No quasilinearization is needed.

The simplifying coefficients are defined as follows:

$$\left.\begin{aligned}
C11 &= (\mathrm{Pe}_{\mathrm{ma1}}\Delta Z^2)^{-1} \\
C12 &= -2 \cdot C11 + (1/\Delta Z) - b_1\, CC \\
C13 &= C11 - (1/\Delta Z) \\
C14 &= 0 \\
C21 &= (\mathrm{Pe}_{\mathrm{ha2}}\Delta Z^2)^{-1} \\
C22 &= -2 \cdot C21 + (1/\Delta Z) \\
C23 &= C21 - (1/\Delta Z) \\
C24 &= -b_2 C_r(I) \cdot CC \\
\text{where } CC &= \frac{C_0\, e^{-E/R_G T_s}}{1 + \mathrm{Da}_m}
\end{aligned}\right\} \tag{2-80}$$

In Case 2, the overall iteration is not adequate to calculate new coefficient values. The values of $T_s(I)$, $C_s(I)$ and functions of other parameters related to reaction kinetics must be calculated for each I value before integrating each ODE. This must be done by an efficient *local iteration.* It is best to recalculate the temperature $T_s(I)$ by this local iteration and to compute other parameters from that recalculated temperature value. A Newton-Raphson iteration procedure required only three steps to arrive within ± 0.001 of the true figure, while a Picard iteration needed four steps for the same purpose. Iteration techniques are discussed in App. A.

Case 3: $C_s = C$; $T_s = T$; Reaction Is Second-Order

Equations (2-38) and (2-39) can be written as:

$$\frac{1}{\mathrm{Pe}_{\mathrm{ma1}}} \cdot \frac{d^2C_r}{dZ^2} - \frac{dC_r}{dZ} = b_1\, e^{-E/R_G T_0 T_r}\, C_0^2\, C_r^2 = f_3(C_r, T_r) \qquad (2\text{-}81)$$

$$\frac{1}{\mathrm{Pe}_{\mathrm{ha2}}} \cdot \frac{d^2T_r}{dZ^2} - \frac{dT_r}{dZ} = -b_2\, e^{-E/R_G T_0 T_r} C_0^2\, C_r^2 = f_4(C_r, T_r) \qquad (2\text{-}82)$$

Again, both finite difference approximation and quasilinearization are applied to both equations in the same way they were used in Case 1. The simplifying coefficients are defined as:

$$\begin{aligned}
C11 &= (\mathrm{Pe}_{\mathrm{ma1}}\Delta Z^2)^{-1} \\
C12 &= -2 \cdot C11 + (1/\Delta Z) - 2 \cdot b_1 CC1 \\
C13 &= C11 - (1/\Delta Z) \\
C14 &= -b_1 \cdot C_r(I) \cdot CC1 \\
C21 &= (\mathrm{Pe}_{\mathrm{ha2}}\, \Delta Z^2)^{-1} \\
C22 &= -2 \cdot C21 + (1/\Delta Z) - CC2 \cdot C_r(I) \cdot CC1 \cdot b_2/T_r(I) \\
C23 &= C21 - (1/\Delta Z) \\
C24 &= -b_2 \cdot C_r(I) \cdot CC1(CC2 + 1)
\end{aligned} \qquad (2\text{-}83)$$

where $CC1 = C_0^2\, \mathrm{C}_r(\mathrm{I})\, \mathrm{e}^{-E/R_G T_0 T_r(I)}$

$CC2 = E/R_G T_0 T_r(I)$

The rest of the procedure is again quite similar to that of Case 1.

A word of caution is absolutely necessary before leaving the subject of boundary-value ODEs: the foregoing algorithms do work with reaction kinetics of reasonable nonlinearity. However, if the nonlinearity exceeds certain limits, the computer program might not work. The only possible remedy I know of in such cases is to try to decrease the nonlinearity of the kinetic equations by juggling parameters.

2.7 ALGORITHMS FOR SOLVING PARTIAL DIFFERENTIAL EQUATIONS

PDEs describing NINAF reactors are of the parabolic type, i.e.,

$$\frac{dY}{dZ} = A\left(\frac{\partial^2 Y}{\partial R^2} + \frac{1}{R}\frac{\partial Y}{\partial R}\right) + C \qquad (2\text{-}84)$$

where Z is the axial coordinate, R the radial coordinate, and Y a dependent variable such as concentration or temperature.

A conventional approach to the numerical solution of PDEs is to replace the spatial derivatives in both the axial and radial coordinates with finite difference approximations. The resulting system of nonlinear algebraic equations is then solved by an iterative procedure such as the Newton-Raphson algorithm. Typically, the equations are coupled tridiagonal systems, which can be solved in a circular iterative fashion by Thomas' method. A generalized program for PDEs based on this approach has been reported by M. G. Zellner et. al.[7]

Alternatively, the radial derivatives of the PDEs can be replaced with finite difference approximations, while the axial derivatives are retained. This approach leads to a system of coupled nonlinear ODEs consisting of subsets of ODEs for each PDE. The ODEs are initial-value in the axial position if only first-order axial flow terms appear in the original PDEs. The entire system of ODEs is then integrated numerically with respect to axial position, starting at initial conditions corresponding to those at the inlet to the reactor. The dependent variables Y, i.e., the reactor temperature and concentrations, can be visualized as evolving along lines of constant radial position. Therefore this approach is often termed the *method of lines,* since the ODEs contain difference terms. The method has also been termed the *state-variable algorithm.*

The method of lines will now be illustrated in detail as applied to the solution of the PDEs that model the NINAF reactor. As we will see later in Chap. 5, these PDEs are of the form:

$$\frac{\partial C_r}{\partial Z} = \frac{1}{\mathrm{Pe}_m}\left(\frac{\partial^2 C_r}{\partial R^2} + \frac{1}{R}\frac{\partial C_r}{\partial R}\right) - f_1(R_1) \tag{2-85}$$

$$\frac{\partial T_r}{\partial Z} = \frac{1}{\mathrm{Pe}_h}\left(\frac{\partial^2 T_r}{\partial R^2} + \frac{1}{R}\frac{\partial T_r}{\partial R}\right) + f_2(R_1) \tag{2-86}$$

and have the following auxiliary conditions:

Bed inlet $\quad C_r(R, 0) = T_r(R, 0) = 1 \quad$ (2-87)

Bed centerline $\quad \partial C_r(0, Z)/\partial R = \partial T_r(0, Z)/\partial R = 0 \quad$ (2-88)

Bed wall $\quad \partial C_r(R_T, Z)/\partial R = 0 \quad$ (2-89)

$$\partial T_r(R_T, Z)/\partial R = (\mathrm{Bi})_w(T_w - T(R_T, Z)) \tag{2-90}$$

The radial derivatives in Eqs. (2-85) and (2-86) are replaced by standard second-order central difference approximations:

$$\frac{\partial^2 C_r}{\partial R^2} + \frac{1}{R}\cdot\frac{\partial C_r}{\partial R} = \frac{C_{ri+1} - 2C_{ri} + C_{ri-1}}{\Delta R^2} + \frac{1}{i\Delta R}\cdot\frac{C_{ri+1} - C_{ri-1}}{2\Delta R} \tag{2-91}$$

$$\frac{\partial^2 T_r}{\partial R^2} + \frac{1}{R} \cdot \frac{\partial T_r}{\partial R} = \frac{T_{ri+1} - 2T_{ri} + T_{ri-1}}{\Delta R^2} + \frac{1}{i\Delta R} \cdot \frac{T_{ri+1} - T_{ri-1}}{2\Delta R} \tag{2-92}$$

These approximations are written for the ith radial grid point, where $r = i\Delta R$, $i = 0, 1, 2, \ldots, N_r$, and ΔR is the radial increment and is assumed constant in the subsequent development. If Eqs. (2-91) and (2-92) are substituted in Eqs. (2-85) and (2-86), two ODEs result for each radial grid point:

$$\frac{dC_{ri}}{dZ} = \frac{1}{\mathrm{Pe}_m} \cdot \frac{C_{ri+1} - 2C_{ri} + C_{ri-1}}{\Delta R^2} + \frac{1}{i\Delta R} \cdot \frac{C_{ri+1} - C_{ri-1}}{2\Delta R} - f_1 R_1 \tag{2-93}$$

$$\frac{dT_{ri}}{dZ} = \frac{1}{\mathrm{Pe}_h} \cdot \frac{T_{ri+1} - 2T_{ri} + T_{ri-1}}{\Delta R^2} + \frac{1}{i\Delta R} \cdot \frac{T_{ri+1} - T_{ri-1}}{2\Delta R} + f_2 R_1 \tag{2-94}$$

where $i = 0, 1, 2, \ldots, N_r$

Similarly Eqs. (2-87) to (2-90) are approximated as:

$$C_{r1} = C_{r-1} \tag{2-95}$$

$$T_{r1} = T_{r-1} \tag{2-96}$$

$$C_{rNr-1} = C_{rNr+1} \tag{2-97}$$

$$\frac{T_{rNr+1} - T_{rNr-1}}{2\Delta R} = (\mathrm{Bi})_w(\mathrm{T}_w - \mathrm{T}_{rNr}) \tag{2-98}$$

Equations (2-95) to (2-98) are used to eliminate the fictitious boundary points C_{r-1}, T_{r-1}, C_{rNr+1}, and T_{rNr+1} from Eqs. (2-93) and (2-94).

The initial conditions for Eqs. (2-93) and (2-94)

$$C_{ri} = 1 \tag{2-99}$$

$$T_{ri} = 1 \tag{2-100}$$

correspond to the inlet conditions for the reactor, Eq. (2-87).

Equations (2-91) to (2-100) constitute an initial-value problem in ODEs with, in this case, a total of $2(N_r + 1)$ ODEs (two equations for each of the radial grid points $i = 0, 1, 2, \ldots, N_r$). In other words, the computational problem is now to integrate the two derivative vectors $d\mathbf{C}_{ri}(Z)/dZ$ and $d\mathbf{T}_{ri}(Z)/dZ$ that define the concentration and temperature distributions within the reactor. Any numerical integration algorithm can in principle be used to solve this initial-value problem. This book will use the fourth-order Runge-Kutta integration algorithm, which was developed in Sec. 2.3 for initial-value ODEs.

The implementation of this method presents two problems: first, at the centerline the expression $(1/i\Delta R)(C_{ri+1} - C_{ri-1})/2\Delta R$ becomes 0/0, or indeterminate; second, some of the subscripts become zero, something that the computer does not accept. Consequently, measures must be taken to solve these two problems.

In order to avoid the first problem, the PDEs for $i = 0$ must be modified. The terms $(1/R)(\partial C_r/\partial R)$ and $(1/R)(\partial T_r/\partial R)$ in Eqs. (2-85) and (2-86) can be modified by applying l'Hôspital's rule to them (i.e., differentiation of the numerator and denominator with respect to R).

$$\lim_{R \to 0} \left(\frac{1}{R}\right) \frac{\partial C_r}{\partial R} = \frac{\partial^2 C_r}{\partial R^2} \tag{2-101}$$

$$\lim_{R \to 0} \left(\frac{1}{R}\right) \frac{\partial T_r}{\partial R} = \frac{\partial^2 T_r}{\partial R^2} \tag{2-102}$$

Substitution of the relationships in Eqs. (2-85) and (2-86) gives:

$$\frac{\partial C_r}{\partial Z} = \frac{1}{\text{Pe}_m} \cdot \left(2\,\frac{\partial^2 C_r}{\partial R^2}\right) - f_1(R_1) \tag{2-103}$$

$$\frac{\partial T_r}{\partial Z} = \frac{1}{\text{Pe}_h} \cdot \left(2\,\frac{\partial^2 T_r}{\partial R^2}\right) + f_2(R_1) \tag{2-104}$$

The finite difference analog for these new equations are:

$$\frac{\partial C_r}{\partial Z} = \frac{2}{\text{Pe}_m} \cdot \frac{C_{ri+1} - 2C_{ri} + C_{ri-1}}{\Delta R^2} - f_1(R_1) \tag{2-105}$$

$$\frac{\partial T_r}{\partial Z} = \frac{2}{\text{Pe}_h} \cdot \frac{T_{ri+1} - 2T_{ri} + T_{ri-1}}{\Delta R^2} + f_2(R_1) \tag{2-106}$$

Equations (2-95) and (2-96) can be substituted into Eqs. (2-105) and (2-106), respectively, to obtain:

$$\frac{\partial C_r}{\partial Z} = \frac{4}{\text{Pe}_m} \cdot \frac{C_{ri+1} - C_{ri}}{\Delta R^2} - f_1(R_1) \qquad (\text{for } i = 0) \tag{2-107}$$

$$\frac{\partial T_r}{\partial Z} = \frac{4}{\text{Pe}_h} \cdot \frac{T_{ri+1} - T_{ri}}{\Delta R^2} + f_2(R_1) \qquad (\text{for } i = 0) \tag{2-108}$$

Thus the first problem is resolved. The second problem can also be resolved by setting $i = 1, 2, 3, 4, 5, 6$ instead of $i = 0, 1, 2, 3, 4, 5$. Then $N_r = 6$. In this way i will never become zero or negative. In order to modify Eqs. (2-93) and (2-94) for this change, the fractions $1/i\Delta R$ will be replaced by $1/(i - 1)\Delta R$. The set of equations to be integrated by FUNCTION RUNGE can then be set up as shown in Fig. 2-11.

Under certain conditions computer programs that integrate partial differential equations by the foregoing method can develop serious instability problems. In its mild form, instability becomes evident when temperature or concentration profiles begin to swing. Of course, in its

```
C       ....CALL ON THE FOURTH-ORDER RUNGE-KUTTA FUNCTION....
      2 K=RUNGE (12,Y,F,Z,H)
C       IF K=1 COMPUTE DERIVATIVE VALUES
        IF(K.NE.1) GO TO 3
        DO 10 I= 1, NR
        IF(I.NE.1)GO TO 11
        F(I,1)=(4./PEM)*(CR(I+1)-CR(I))/(DELTAR**2)-(DP*R1(I)/(CO*U))
        F(I,2)=(4./PEH)*(TR(I+1)-TR(I))/(DELTAR**2)+DHR(I)*DP
     1        /(CP*U*RHOC*TO)
        GO TO 10
     11 IF(I.EQ.NR) GO TO 12
        WALL=(TR(I+1)-TR(I-1))/(2.*DELTAR)
        F(I,1)=(1./PEM)*((CR(I+1)-2.*CR(I)+CR(I-1))/(DELTAR**2)
     1       +(1./((I-1)*DELTAR))*(CR(I+1)-CR(I-1))/(2.*DELTAR))
     2       -(DP*R1(I)/(CO*U))
        F(I,2)=(1./PEH)*((TR(I+1)-2.*TR(I)+TR(I-1))/(DELTAR**2)
     1       +(1./((I-1)*DELTAR))*WALL)
     2       +(DHR(I)*DP/(CP*U*RHOC*TO))
        GO TO 10
     12 WALL=BIW*(TW-TR(NR))
        F(I,1)=(2./PEM)*(CR(I-1)-CR(I))/(DELTAR**2)
     1        -(DP*R1(I)/(CO*U))
        F(I,2)=(2./PEH)*(TR(I-1)-TR(I))/(DELTAR**2)
     1       +(1./((I-1)*DELTAR)*WALL)
     2       +(DHR(I)*DP/(CP*U*RHOC*TO))
     10 CONTINUE
        GO TO 2
C       ....IF TR EXCEEDS TRMAX,TERMINATE INTEGRATION....
      3 IF(TR(1).LE.TRMAX) GO TO 4
        GO TO 5                        (5 is a WRITE statement)
```

FIG. 2-11 The essentials of the computer program to solve partial differential equations.

more serious form, it makes the program unworkable. Instability is usually caused by too large a $\Delta Z/\Delta R^2$ ratio. For linear PDEs there is a classical stability condition that requires $(\Delta Z/\Delta R^2)(1/\text{Pe})$ to be $<\frac{1}{2}$. For strongly nonlinear PDEs, such as Eqs. (2-85) and (2-86), that term must be much smaller still. There is apparently no universal rule for nonlinear PDEs. Since for NINAF reactors the Péclet number is constant, we can simplify the condition to $\Delta Z/\Delta R^2$. In the RDMOT2 computer program developed in Sec. 5.3 for the naphthalene oxidation process, a $\Delta Z/\Delta R^2$ ratio of $(0.1/5^2) = 0.004$ was chosen. It was observed that even a ratio as low as $(0.1/2.5^2) = 0.016$ caused mild instability. The designer must plan for a stable computer program by judiciously preselecting the proper $\Delta Z/\Delta R^2$ ratio. Both the increase of ΔR and the decrease of ΔZ should result in a greater number of computer calculations, hence in greater computing costs. However, increasing ΔR might get us to a given ratio more cheaply, since ΔR is squared.

2.8 HANDLING OF SEVERAL PARALLEL REACTIONS

Up to this point we have considered algorithms that would handle a single chemical reaction. Processes that include several parallel reactions are quite common in coal hydrogenation and in petroleum refining. In Sec. 7.2 we will discuss in detail the design of an industrial-size trickle-bed reactor for petroleum oil hydrodesulfurization and that of a laboratory trickle-bed reactor for the same process. Both designs will handle four parallel reactions. The first one will be designed as a plug-flow reactor in a manner quite similar to that used for an adiabatic fixed-bed gas reactor and will use the same algorithm. The second one, however, will be designed as a backmixed trickle-bed reactor and will require a more complex algorithm than was discussed in Sec. 2.6.

We want to extend the Case 2 boundary condition algorithm of Sec. 2.6 to a process with n parallel first-order reactions. The mass equations can be collectively expressed as:

$$\frac{dC_r(J)}{dZ} = \frac{1}{\mathrm{Pe}_{\mathrm{ma1}}} \frac{d^2C_r(J)}{dZ^2} - f_1(C_r(J), T_r) \qquad (2\text{-}109)$$

where $J = 1, 2, 3, \ldots n$

$J = 1$ will denote sulfur concentration

$J = 2$ will denote oxygen concentration

$J = 3$ will denote nitrogen concentration

$J = 4$ hydrocrackables concentration

$J = 5$ unsaturates concentration

The heat equation can be written:

$$\frac{dT_r}{dZ} = \frac{1}{\mathrm{Pe}_{\mathrm{ha2}}} \cdot \frac{d^2T_r}{dZ^2} + f_2\left(\sum C_r(J), T_r\right) \qquad (2\text{-}110)$$

The simplifying coefficients are defined as follows:

$C11 = (\mathrm{Pe}_{\mathrm{ma1}}\, \Delta Z^2)^{-1}$ for all reactions

$C121 = -2 \cdot C11 + (1/\Delta Z) - b_{11}\, C_0 \exp\left(-E_1/R_GT_s\right)/(1 + \mathrm{Da}_{m1})$

$C122 = -2 \cdot C11 + (1/\Delta Z) - b_{12}\, C_{\mathrm{ox0}} \exp\left(-E_2/R_GT_s\right)/(1 + \mathrm{Da}_{m2})$

$C123 = -2 \cdot C11 + (1/\Delta Z) - b_{13}\, C_{N0} \exp\left(-E_3/R_GT_s\right)/(1 + \mathrm{Da}_{m3})$

$C124 = -2 \cdot C11 + (1/\Delta Z) - b_{14}\, C_{HY0} \exp\left(-E_4/R_GT_s\right)/(1 + \mathrm{Da}_{m4})$

$C125 = -2 \cdot C11 + (1/\Delta Z) - \mathrm{b}_{15}\, \mathrm{C}_{HC0} \exp\left(-E_5/R_GT_s\right)/(1 + \mathrm{Da}_{m5})$

$C13 = C11 - (1/\Delta Z)$ same for all reactions

$C14 = 0$ same for all reactions

$C21 = (\mathrm{Pe}_{\mathrm{ha2}}\, \Delta Z^2)^{-1}$

$C22 = -2 \cdot C21 + (1/\Delta Z)$

$C23 = C21 - (1/\Delta Z)$

$$C24 = -\frac{d_p \varepsilon_L \sum (\Delta H_j \, R_j/\mathrm{Da}_{mj})}{T_0(\varepsilon \rho c_p u + \varepsilon_L \rho_L \, c_{pL} u_L)}$$

where $R_j = \eta \, A_j \exp(-E_j/R_G T_s) \, C_{0j} \, C_r(J,I)$

In case of several parallel first-order reactions, the calculation of the heat transfer becomes somewhat complicated. Equation (4-23) becomes:

$$ha(T_s - T) = \sum (-\Delta H_i)\mathcal{R}_i$$

or

$$T_s = T + \frac{\sum (-\Delta H_i)\mathcal{R}_i}{h \cdot a} \tag{2-111}$$

Here, $\mathcal{R}_i$ occurs on the catalyst surface, where conditions are different from those in the bulk gas phase in the case of small-scale trickle-bed reactors.

Thus
$$\mathcal{R}_i = \eta_i \, A_i \exp(-E_i/R_G T_s) \, C_{si} \tag{2-112}$$

since
$$C_{si} = C_{ri} \, C_{0i}/(1 + \mathrm{Da}_{mi}) \tag{2-113}$$

$$\mathrm{Da}_{mi} = \eta k_i/k_c \, a \tag{2-114}$$

$$\mathcal{R}_i = \frac{\eta_i A_i \exp(-E_i/R_G T_s) \, C_{ri} \, C_{0i}}{1 + (\eta_i A_i/k_c a) \exp(-E_i/R_G T_s)} = \frac{\eta_i k_i \, C_{ri} \, C_{0i}}{1 + (\eta_i k_i/k_c a)} \tag{2-115}$$

$$T_s = T + \sum \left[\eta_i \, (\Delta H_i) \, k_i \, C_{ri} \, C_{0i} / \left(1 + \frac{\eta_i \, k_i}{k_c \, a} \right) \right] / (h \, a) \tag{2-116}$$

This information is needed in the Newton-Raphson iteration in the laboratory-size trickle-bed algorithm in Sec. 7.2.

The iterative calculation of T_s according to Newton-Raphson can be made by means of the formula:

$$T_{s,i+1} = \frac{f(T_{si}) - T_{si} \, f'(T_{si})}{1 - f'(T_{si})} \tag{2-117}$$

where T_{si} = the T_s value calculated at any increment i

$T_{s,i+1}$ = the T_s value calculated for the next increment $i + 1$

$f(T_{si})$ = the T_{si} function or the expression giving the T_{si} value [in this case, Eq. (2-116)]

$f'(T_{si}) = df(T_{si})/dT_{si}$

Since we already have $f(T_{si})$ [Eq. (2-116)], let us calculate $f'(T_{si})$. In these calculations we can eliminate the subscript i from T_{si}. The only term in Eq. (2-116) that contains T_s is k_i, which we can expand into

$$k_i = A_i \exp(-E_i/R_G T_s)$$

Then

$$\frac{df(T_s)}{dT_s} = \frac{1}{ha} \sum \eta_i(-\Delta H_i)C_{ri}C_{0i}A_i \frac{d}{dT_s}\left[\frac{\exp(-E_i/R_G T_s)}{1 + (\eta_i A_i/k_c a)\exp(-E_i/R_G T_s)}\right] \tag{2-118}$$

In order to obtain the derivative of the expression in the brackets let us set:

$$u = \exp(-E_i/R_G T_s) \qquad \text{and} \qquad v = 1 + (\eta_i A_i/k_c a)\exp(-E_i/R_G T_s)$$

The well-known formula for $d(u/v)/dT_s$ is of course

$$\frac{d(u/v)}{dT_s} = \frac{v(du/dT_s) - u(dv/dT_s)}{v^2} \tag{2-119}$$

Let us calculate each term of Eq. (2-119):

$$du/dT_s = \exp(-E_i/R_G T_s)E_i/R_G T_s^2 \tag{2-120}$$

$$dv/dT_s = (\eta_i A_i E_i/k_c a R_G T_s^2)\exp(-E_i/R_G T_s) \tag{2-121}$$

Substituting Eqs. (2-120) and (2-121) into Eq. (2-119) and simplifying gives:

$$d(u/v)/dT_s = \exp(-E_i/R_G T_s)(E_i/R_G T_s^2)/[1 + \eta_i k_i/k_c a)\exp(-E_i/R_G T_s)]^2 \tag{2-122}$$

and substituting Eq. (2-122) into the brackets of Eq. (2-118) gives:

$$f'(T_s) = \frac{(1/ha)\sum \eta_i(-\Delta H_i)C_{ri}C_{0i}A_i E_i \exp(-E_i/R_G T_s)}{R_G T_s^2[1 + (\eta_i A_i/k_c a)\exp(-E_i/R_G T_s)]^2} \tag{2-123}$$

With these results the *internal* Newton-Raphson iteration can be performed. The use of the full program is illustrated in Chap. 7.

The number of *overall* iterations (not the *internal* Newton-Raphson iterations) is usually 3 for a single-reaction process. For the four-parallel-reaction process described in Sec. 7.2 the number of overall iterations is 11.

NOMENCLATURE

a	Ratio of external surface area to catalyst particle volume, m^{-1}
A	Frequency factor
C	Molar concentration, $kmol/m^3$
Da	Damköhler number, dimensionless

E	Activation energy, kJ/kmol
f	Derivative value in the Runge-Kutta algorithm
f_3, f_4	Functions of C_r and T_r
h	Step size
I	Longitudinal increment in finite difference approximation method; integer
k	Reaction rate constant
$k_1, k_2, \ldots$	Coefficients of the Runge-Kutta algorithm
k_c	Liquid-catalyst mass-transfer coefficient, m/s
M	Number of longitudinal reactor increments
n	Total number of terms in a series, or the number of a typical member of a series
$\mathrm{Pe}_{\mathrm{ha2}}$	Péclet number for heat, two-phase (gas and liquid) axial dispersion
$\mathrm{Pe}_{\mathrm{ma1}}$	Péclet number for mass, axial dispersion, liquid-phase (see Chap. 7)
R	Reduced radial coordinate, dimensionless
R_G	Gas constant = 8.314 kJ/(kmol · K)
$\mathcal{R}$	Rate of global reaction, kmol/(m^3 · s)
T	Absolute temperature, K
x	Independent variable
y	Dependent variable
z	Variable = dy/dx
Z	Reduced longitudinal coordinate, dimensionless
Z_T	Reduced total reactor length, dimensionless
ΔH	Heat of reaction, kJ/kmol (positive if endothermic, negative if exothermic)
ϵ	Error
ε	Void fraction
η	Intraphase effectiveness factor, dimensionless

Subscripts

e	Estimated
h	Heat

Nr	Label of the outermost radial increment near the reactor wall
0	Initial or inlet
r	Reduced
s	Catalyst surface
x	Unknown value

REFERENCES

1. Daniel D. McCracken, *A Guide to Fortran IV Programming,* 2d ed. John Wiley, New York, 1972.
2. B. Carnahan, H. A. Luther, and J. O. Wilkes, *Applied Numerical Methods,* John Wiley, New York, 1969.
3. William E. Schiesser, "DSS/2 (Differential Systems Simulator, Version 2)," Lehigh University, 1982.
4. E. Stanley Lee, "Quasilinearization, Difference Approximation, and Nonlinear Boundary Value Problems," *AIChE J.*, **14**:490–496 (1968).
5. Leon Lapidus, *Digital Computation for Chemical Engineers*, McGraw-Hill, New York, 1962, p. 254–255.
6. Matthew G. Zellner, "DSS Distributed Systems Simulator," Ph.D. thesis, Lehigh University, 1970.
7. Matthew G. Zellner, Fred P. Stein, Robert W. Coughlin, and William E. Schiesser, "A DSS Study of the Kinetics of Adsorption and Chemical Reaction," *Proceedings of the 1970 Summer Computer Simulation Conference, Denver, June 10–12*, 1970, pp. 284–294.

Chapter 3 CATALYTIC KINETIC MODELS

This chapter briefly reviews the general area of heterogeneous catalytic kinetics and the modeling of catalytic reactions. Such a review is necessary because reactor designers may have to pass judgment on the value and completeness of kinetic information they receive. For this, they must fully understand the entire subject. This chapter provides a bird's-eye view of the field and an introduction to further studies. Reaction modeling is actually the initial phase of reactor design.

The task of reaction modeling is usually a difficult one, because of complex kinetic mechanisms involving parallel and consecutive reactions, chain reactions, catalytic surface inhibition and poisoning, and catalyst aging. If heat and mass transfer relations both inside the catalyst pores and outside the catalyst pellets are added to that, the modeler faces a herculean task.

3.1 CATALYSIS

The catalyst plays an important role in just about any aspect of the chemical reactions which occur on its surface. Thus we must first briefly review the science of catalysis (if such a thing is possible at all) in order to understand catalytic reaction rates, which we will review in Sec. 3.2.

Definition of a Catalyst

A *catalyst* is a material which initiates and enhances the rate of a chemical reaction without being consumed by that reaction. While the catalyst per se does not appear in the overall reaction statement (for example, $SO_2 + \frac{1}{2}O_2 \rightarrow SO_3$), it does not follow that the catalyst is not a partici-

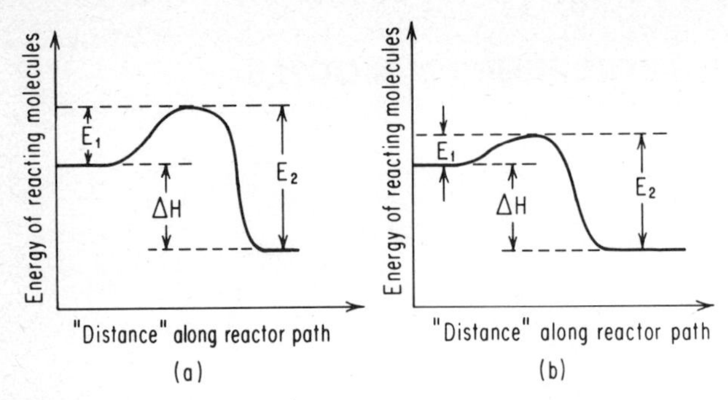

FIG. 3-1 Comparison between (*a*) a noncatalyzed and (*b*) a catalyzed reaction.

pant. In fact, it participates in many cases and alters the path of the reaction. For example, SO_2 oxidation is catalyzed by V_2O_5 as follows:

$$V_2O_5 + SO_2 \rightarrow V_2O_4 + SO_3 \tag{3-1}$$
$$V_2O_4 + \tfrac{1}{2}O_2 \rightarrow V_2O_5 \tag{3-2}$$

The catalyst V_2O_5 participates but is then regenerated.

A catalyst may also be defined as an agent which lowers the free energy of activation of a thermodynamically permitted reaction. Figure 3-1 presents two diagrams of the energy of a reaction, one run thermally (at left) and the other catalytically (at right). An exothermic reaction has been selected as an example. The reaction must first overcome an energy barrier by expending the activation energy E_1. Once the energy level of the reactants has been increased to the height of the barrier, the reaction can proceed and an energy $\Delta H = E_2 - E_1$ is produced. In the case of the noncatalyzed reaction (left), the amount of energy E_1 to be expended is quite large, but catalysis reduces E_1 to a much lower level although ΔH is unchanged. In nontechnical terms, the catalyst may be considered to "drill tunnels" through the energy mountain.

Classification of Catalysts

Roughly, catalysts are classified as *homogeneous* and *heterogeneous*. *Homogeneous* catalysts, which are not discussed in this book, exist in the same phase as the reactants. *Heterogeneous* catalysts exist in a different phase than the reactants. Commonly, heterogeneous catalysts are solid substances catalyzing gas- and/or liquid-phase reactions. This book discusses exclusively these solid catalysts.

Heterogeneous catalysts are classified according to various criteria. According to their electrical conductivity, they are classified as follows:

Commercial catalysts usually do not belong exclusively to any single

Conductors	Semiconductors	Insulators
Pt, Pd, Fe metals	NiO, ZnO Conductivity increases with temperature	MgO, Al_2O_3, SiO_2-Al_2O_3, solid acids
Electron-exchange between metal and adsorbate	Electron transfer at high temperatures	
Chemisorb all gases O_2, H_2	O_2, H_2	Chemisorb hydrocarbons
Metals generally found in transition groups		
Good oxidation-reduction catalysts	Good oxidation-reduction catalysts	Good isomerization, cracking, alkylation, dehydration catalysts

class. For example, the dual function catalysts may have two specific functions on one particle, each belonging to another group. For example:

Pt/SiO_2-Al_2O_3

Metal/acid

Conductor/insulator

Hydrogenation site/acidic site

The classification of catalysts has been discussed in great detail by R. W. Coughlin.[1]

Properties of Heterogeneous Catalysts

In heterogeneous catalysis at least one reactant must be chemisorbed. If we call two catalytically active sites on a catalyst surface X_1 and X_2, the reaction of two chemical species A and B over the catalyst giving a product P can be formulated as follows (Fig. 3-2):

FIG. 3-2 Chemisorption of species A and B on a catalyst surface.

$$A + B \xrightarrow[\text{Catalyst}]{X} P \qquad (3\text{-}3)$$

$$A + X_1 \rightarrow AX_1 \qquad (3\text{-}4)$$

$$B + X_2 \rightarrow BX_2 \qquad (3\text{-}5)$$

$$AX_1 + BX_2 \rightarrow P + X_1 + X_2 \qquad (3\text{-}6)$$

$$\overline{A + B \rightarrow P} \qquad (3\text{-}7)$$

The overall result of Eqs. (3-4) to (3-6) will be Eq. (3-7), which is identical to Eq. (3-3). This cycle can be repeated many times but eventually the site deteriorates. Thus no fixed relationship exists between reactant consumption and site X. If only A is chemisorbed, we have:

$$A + X_1 \rightarrow AX_1 \qquad (3\text{-}4)$$

$$B + AX_1 \rightarrow P + X_1 \qquad (3\text{-}8)$$

$$\overline{A + B \rightarrow P} \qquad (3\text{-}7)$$

The reaction velocity or rate depends on the amount of active catalyst exposed to the reacting fluid. However, in heterogeneous catalysts the intrinsic relationship between observed reaction rate parameters and catalyst concentration cannot be anticipated a priori. Hence catalytic reaction rates are expressed per gram of catalyst formulation.

Catalysts can only speed up a reaction that is thermodynamically possible. They cannot change the thermodynamic equilibrium; they can only alter the path. Consequently, a catalyst that speeds up the forward reaction also speeds the reverse reaction if placed on the other side of the equilibrium.

Another important property of the catalysts is their ability to alter yields and selectivities by speeding up some reactions more than others. For example, ethyl alcohol undergoes dehydration or dehydrogenation as follows:

$$CH_3{-}CH_2{-}OH \xrightarrow{Al_2O_3} H_2O + \underset{\text{Ethylene}}{CH_2{=}CH_2} \qquad (3\text{-}9)$$

$$CH_3{-}CH_2{-}OH \xrightarrow{Cu} H_2 + \underset{\text{Acetaldehyde}}{CH_3{-}\underset{H}{C}{=}O} \qquad (3\text{-}10)$$

Alumina speeds up Reaction (3-9) while copper speeds up Reaction (3-10).

The *reaction mechanism* is not always known definitely. The oxidation of SO_2 is catalyzed by V_2O_5 according to:

$$SO_2 + \tfrac{1}{2}O_2 \xrightarrow{V_2O_5} SO_3 \tag{3-11}$$

The mechanism is believed to follow Eqs. (3-1) and (3-2). This is a *model,* in other words, a hypothesis. We do not know for certain whether it represents reality.

If we compare a thermal reaction, which gives a multitude of products, with the same reaction over a catalyst, we often see that many fewer products are produced. In other words, the catalyst makes the reaction more selective. For example, thermal hydrogenation of ethylene gives a chain reaction and produces not only ethane but also other gases. On the other hand, catalytic hydrogenation of ethylene gives only ethane.[2] Boudart[3] compared the thermal and the catalytic rates of this reaction:

$$r(\text{homogeneous}) = 10^{27} \exp(-180{,}540/RT)p_{H_2} \tag{3-12}$$

$$r(\text{catalytic}) = 2 \times 10^{27} \exp(-54{,}390/RT)p_{H_2} \tag{3-13}$$

At $T = 600$ K, the rate ratio is:

$$\frac{\text{Catalytic}}{\text{Noncatalytic}} = 2 \exp[(180{,}540 - 54{,}390)/600R]$$

$$= 1.921 \times 10^{11} \tag{3-14}$$

We can see that the catalytic reaction is more than 11 orders of magnitude faster than the thermal, or homogeneous, reaction.

Some catalysts are dispersed on the surface of *catalyst supports,* while others are used alone and undiluted. Some supports are catalytically inactive or inert and some are not; some supports actually affect the catalyst. The actual catalytically active material is called the *catalytic agent.* Additives which improve the catalytic agent are called *promoters.* Promoters can work physically or chemically. For example, alumina in iron catalysts for ammonia synthesis prevents the sintering of crystallites. This is an example of a physical promoter.

It is not always possible to measure the *intrinsic reaction rate* directly on the active sites of the catalyst. For one thing, the sites may be on inner pores of the catalyst particles. What is normally measured is the *global reaction rate,* which comprises the following events (Fig. 3-3):

- *Transport of reactants:* Interphase and intraphase (*Interphase* means "in the space outside of the catalyst particle"; *intraphase* means "inside the pores of the catalyst particles.") This is the diffusional step (see Sec. 3.4).

- *Chemisorption:* Rate $= k_a\, C_A(1 - \theta)$.
- *Surface reaction:* Rate = chemical reaction rate $= k\theta_A\theta_B = kC_AC_B$.
- *Desorption:* Rate $= k_d\, \theta_{prod}$

where k_a = absorption rate constant
k_d = desorption rate constant
C = molar concentration, kmol/m^3
θ = surface coverage or fraction of catalyst surface covered by adsorbed species
Subscripts A,B denote species A,B
Subscript prod denotes product

- *Transport of products:* interphase and intraphase.

In these steps only the bulk concentrations can be measured. The first and third steps are familiar mass-transfer processes. The second step, which involves adsorption on a solid surface, is discussed below.

Let us now digress for a while and take a closer look at the adsorption phenomenon, which is so crucial to the understanding of catalysis.

There are two types of gas adsorption on catalyst surfaces:

- *Physical adsorption:* At some temperatures and pressures a gas can be adsorbed on a solid, covering it entirely. The binding forces between the adsorbing species and the site are of the van der Waals type. This adsorption resembles liquefaction. If we know that the adsorbed gas forms a monolayer, this may give us a method for measuring the adsorbing surface area.
- *Chemisorption:* Some gases are strongly adsorbed on certain sites of a surface; here the bond is chemical.

Table 3-1 shows the main characteristics of and differences between physical adsorption and chemisorption. Physical adsorption isotherms are used to determine the surface area of catalysts by the BET (Brunauer-Emmett-Teller) method.[4]

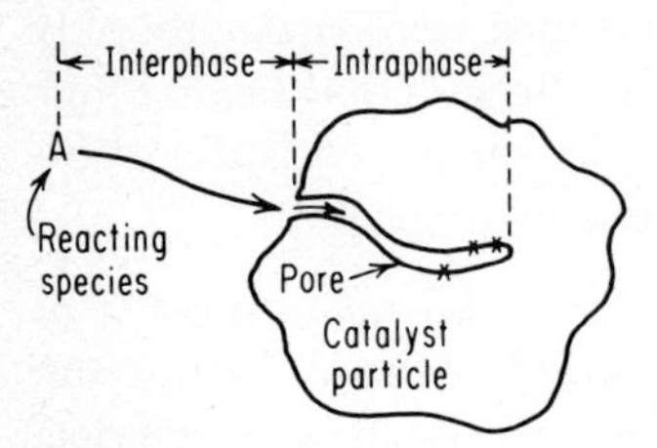

FIG. 3-3 Interphase and intraphase events in the global catalytic reaction.

TABLE 3-1
Comparison of physical adsorption with chemisorption

	Physical adsorption	Chemisorption
Adsorbent	All solids	Some solids
Adsorbate	All gases below critical point	Some chemically reactive gases
Temperature range	Low temperatures	Generally high temperatures
Heat of adsorption	Low, $\approx \Delta H_{liq}$	High, $\approx$ reaction ΔH
Rate and activation energy	Very rapid, low E	Nonactivated, low E; activated, high E
Coverage	Multilayer	Monolayer
Reversibility	Highly reversible	Often irreversible
Importance	For determining surfaces and pore sizes	For determining surface concentration, rates of adsorption and desorption; for estimating active center area; and for elucidation of surface reaction kinetics.

The nature of the chemisorbed complex is still obscure. It cannot yet be measured.

There are several models (theories) of the relationships among surface coverage θ, concentration C_A, and adsorption rates. For example in the Langmuir model:

$$\text{Adsorption rate} = k_a\, p(1 - \theta) \tag{3-15}$$

$$\text{Desorption rate} = k_d \theta \tag{3-16}$$

where p = partial pressure.

At equilibrium the adsorption and desorption rates are equal

$$k_a\, p(1 - \theta) = k_d \theta \tag{3-17}$$

We may set $(k_a/k_d) = K$, where K is the adsorption equilibrium constant, and combine it with Eq. (3-17) to calculate the surface coverage:

$$\theta = \frac{K \cdot p}{1 + K \cdot p} \tag{3-18}$$

This is the *Langmuir isotherm*. Some reactions obey this model, others obey the *Freundlich isotherm*:

$$\theta = K \cdot p^{1/n} \qquad n > 1 \tag{3-19}$$

Still other reactions obey other isotherms. They will not all be discussed here. The interested reader is advised to consult standard textbooks on chemical engineering kinetics[5–7]; the articles by Brunauer, Love, and Keenan,[8] Halsey and Taylor,[9] and Beeck[10]; and perhaps books by Rideal[11] and Hayward and Trapnell.[12]

Perhaps the most important property of a heterogeneous catalyst is its *porosity*. A good catalyst may have several hundred square meters of inner pore surface area per gram of catalyst. This inner surface area of catalysts can be measured by various classical methods (such as the BET and mercury porosimeter methods), and from the results it is possible to calculate the pore distribution, the mean pore radius, and similar information. As we will discuss later on, the pore structure has a strong effect on diffusion phenomena and hence on reaction kinetics. The pore structure also has a strong effect on the poisoning and the selectivity of catalysts.

When some chemical species are chemisorbed on a catalyst surface and stay there, we say that the catalyst is *poisoned* because it loses part of its activity. Some poisons such as coke are temporary and can be removed by heating or by burning. Other poisons are more permanent; when they are involved, the whole catalyst must be replaced (e.g., sulfur on platinum).

$$\text{If } \alpha = \text{fraction of pore surface poisoned and}$$

$$F = \frac{\text{reaction rate poisoned}}{\text{reaction rate unpoisoned}}$$

Curves 1 and 2 in Fig. 3-4 are ordinary cases of *selective poisoning*. Curve 3 shows *non-selective poisoning*. Here, the surface is still available and the relationship is linear:

$$F = 1 - \alpha$$

Curve 4 in Fig. 3-4 represents *antiselective poisoning*: $F = (1 - \alpha)^{1/2}$. By fast reaction the poison is distributed homogeneously into the pore structure and more of the inner surface of the catalyst can be used by the reaction. Catalyst poisoning considerably affects the *selectivity* of catalysts.[13]

Catalyst poisoning has been widely studied. Some of the basic work was done by Maxted[14] in England. Current progress has often been reviewed by John Butt in voluminous articles.[15,16]

The poisoning or deactivation behavior of catalysts must be well stud-

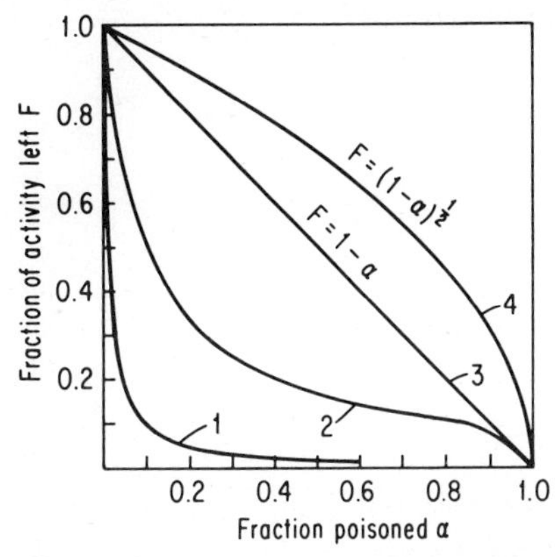

FIG. 3-4 Selectivity of catalyst pore poisoning. (***Reproduced with the permission of the Academic Press and Dr. Ahlborn Wheeler.***[13])

ied and known before any reactor design can begin. There is no amount of a priori knowledge that can make up for the lack of such information.

3.2 CATALYTIC REACTION RATE MODELS

There are two well-known models for a catalytic reaction rate. The first one is that of *Langmuir-Hinshelwood/Hougen-Watson* (*L-H/H-W*).[17] The other is the *power law.* The L-H/H-W model gives for a reaction of the type

$$A + B \rightarrow D \tag{3-20}$$

the reaction rate:

$$r = \frac{k\,K_1K_2C_AC_B}{[1 + K_1C_A + K_2C_B + K_3C_D]^2} \tag{3-21}$$

where C_A, C_B, and C_D are the molar concentrations of species A, B, and D, respectively. The constants K_1, K_2, and K_3 are adsorption equilibrium constants and k is the reaction rate constant. In Eq. (3-21) there are too many coefficients that are difficult to determine. For the same reaction [Eq. (3-20)] the power law is:

$$r = k\,C_A^{\alpha}\,C_B^{\beta}\,C_D^{\gamma} \tag{3-22}$$

The power law has only one temperature-dependent coefficient k. One usually operates at a narrow temperature range of interest. It is at best very difficult to prove whether the one or the other model is closer to reality. In general it does not make much sense to retain a complicated model if the existing data can be made to fit the simpler power law just as well.

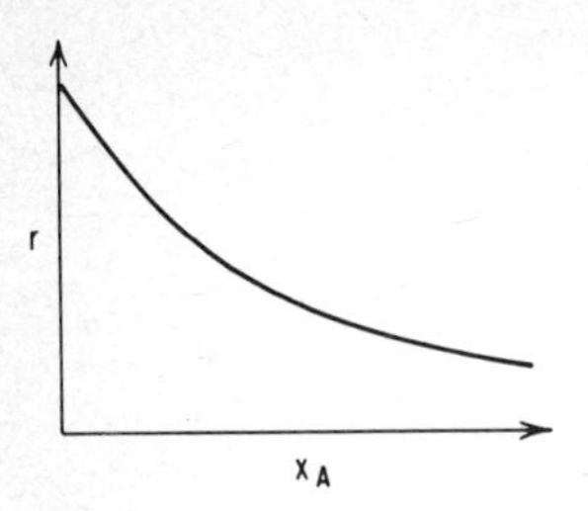

FIG. 3-5 Normal reaction.

The factor k in Eq. (3-22) is called the *reaction rate constant* and is given by the well-known *Arrhenius equation*:

$$k = A \exp(-E/RT) \tag{3-22a}$$

where E = activation energy, kJ/kmol (see Fig. 3-1)
R = gas constant = 8.314 kJ/(kmol · K)
T = absolute temperature, K
A = frequency factor or preexponential factor (the dimension of this parameter depends on the order of the reaction)

A catalyst affects both the activation energy and the frequency factor of the reaction rate constant.

Mezaki and Kittrell have shown that it is possible to distinguish between various reaction models by using linear regression techniques. From the viewpoint of the reactor designer, there can be no justification in using anything but the power law unless the other model has been significantly differentiated by a better curve fit.

In Eq. (3-22) r is the reaction rate, which is usually expressed as a derivative such as $r = -dC_A/dt$, which is the consumption of the species A during the differential time dt. It also may be expressed as the rate of formation of a species, such as $r = dC_D/dt$. In this case the sign in front of the derivative is positive. The reaction rate constant k is related to temperature by the *Arrhenius equation* [Eq. (3-22*a*)].

Reaction Order

The *order of reaction* is the value of the exponent of the concentration term of a rate expression. For example, some reaction rates are independent of any concentration. Then Eq. (3-22) can be simplified to

$$r = k \tag{3-23}$$

Such reactions are termed *zero-order,* since Eq. (3-23) can also be written as

$$r = kC_A^0 C_B^0 C_D^0 = k(1)(1)(1)$$

If a reaction rate is proportional to a single concentration term and is thus described by an equation of the form

$$r = kC_A \tag{3-24}$$

the reaction is said to be *first-order* with respect to reactant A. Some reactions may be *second-order:*

$$r = kC_AC_B \tag{3-25}$$

$$r = k\,C_A^2 \tag{3-26}$$

There are also reactions of *fractional order,* such as the hydrodealkylation of toluene to benzene and methane:

$$C_6H_5CH_3 + H_2 \longrightarrow C_6H_6 + CH_4 \tag{3-27}$$

$$r = k\,C_{tol} \cdot C_{H_2}^{0.5} \tag{3-28}$$

The reaction order has no relationship to stoichiometry. The only time the order coincides with stoichiometry is when the reaction occurs "as written."

Normal and Autocatalytic Reactions

A reaction is called *normal* if its rate falls off with conversion x_A (Fig. 3-5). There are some reactions for which the rate may go up with increasing conversion x_A and then fall off after having reached a maximum. This is typical of *autocatalytic reactions*[18] (Fig. 3-6). Carbon monoxide oxidation and many aromatic oxidation reactions are autocatalytic:

$$CO + \tfrac{1}{2}\,O_2 \xrightarrow{\text{Pt, Pd, Rd, Ru}} CO_2 \tag{3-29}$$

In an autocatalytic reaction, the rate at the start is low because little product is present. It increases to a maximum as more product is formed

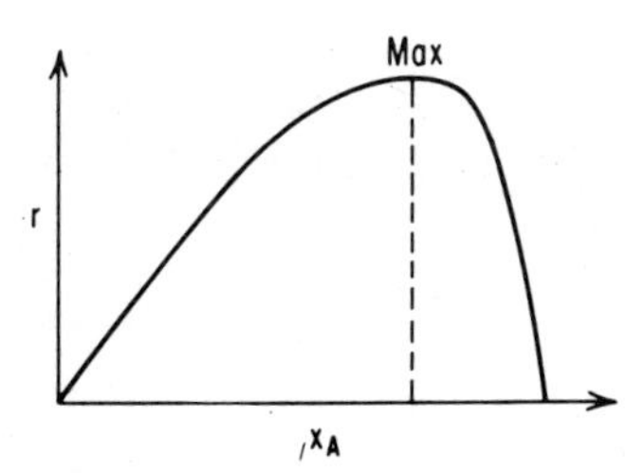

FIG. 3-6 Autocatalytic reaction.

and then drops again to a low value as reactant is consumed. The rate expression is usually of the form

$$-r_A = k\,C_A^{\alpha} \cdot C_{\text{product}}^{\pi} \qquad (3\text{-}30)$$

Here at the right-hand side of the maximum the order is negative.

3.3 DETERMINATION OF REACTION RATE

The reactor designer needs an accurate expression for the catalytic reaction rate which has been determined for the catalyst to be used. Although in most cases someone else will make this determination, it is important that the reactor designer knows how it was done.

The expression needed is of the general type:

$$\text{Rate} = r = f\,(C_A, C_B, C_D, T, A, E)_{\text{cat}} \qquad (3\text{-}31)$$

where A,B = reactants
C = molar concentration, kmol/m^3
D = reaction product
T = absolute temperature, K
A = frequency factor
E = activation energy, kJ/kmol

This expression represents the *intrinsic reaction rate.*

There are a number of methods for determining catalytic reaction rates. Some are batch, some are semibatch, and some are continuous.

The Differential Flow Reactor

This method of measuring the reaction rate uses a long, thin tube which has been packed with a small amount of catalyst. It contains thermocouples to measure the temperature before and after the catalyst bed. The tube must be kept absolutely *isothermal* by a liquid at constant temperature surrounding the tube. High heat transfer is essential for isothermality (Fig. 3-7).

A series of experiments is carried out in this tube at absolutely isothermal conditions while trying to keep the conversion low, so that it may be considered *differential conversion.* The concentration C_A of a key reactant is analyzed before and after conversion, and actual molar con-

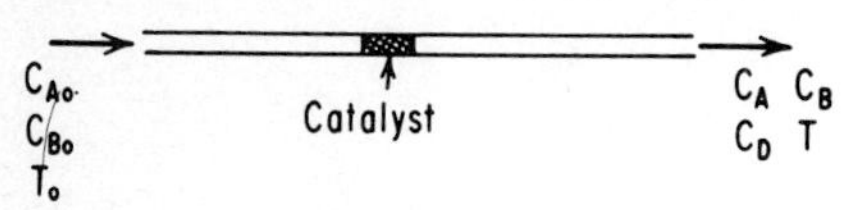

FIG. 3-7 Schematic representation of a differential flow reactor.

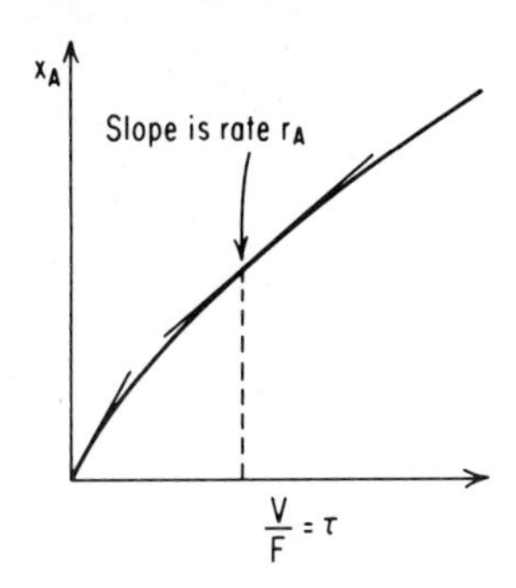

FIG. 3-8 Reaction rate as slope of conversion vs. space time curve.

centrations at reaction conditions are calculated. From these concentrations, one calculates *conversion* x_A:

$$\frac{C_A}{C_{A0}} = \frac{1 - x_A}{1 + \varepsilon_A x_A} \quad \text{or} \quad x_A = \frac{1 - (C_A/C_{A0})}{1 + (\varepsilon_A C_A/C_{A0})} \tag{3-32}$$

where C_{A0} is the molar concentration of reactant A at the inlet to the reactor and ε_A is the fractional change in volume of the system during complete conversion of reactant A and is defined by

$$\varepsilon_A = \frac{V'_{x_A=1} - V'_{x_A=0}}{V'_{x_A=0}} \tag{3-33}$$

In Eq. (3-33) V' is the volume of the reactants and $V'_{x_A=1}$ means the value of V' when $x_A = 1$. Now we can plot x_A versus V/F, where F is the volumetric feed rate in cubic meters per second. The V/F ratio is defined by

$$\frac{V}{F} = \tau = \text{space time} \tag{3-34}$$

We can graphically obtain the derivatives of the curve in Fig. 3-8. Each derivative, or slope at a tangent, is the reaction rate r_A at the corresponding space time and concentration. We can plot these rate data versus C_A (Fig. 3-9). If the points fall on a straight line, we can say that r_A is directly proportional to C_A, or first-order with respect to C_A. If the points fall on a straight line but the straight line is parallel to the abscissa, we can tell that r_A is independent of C_A, or zero-order. If the points fall on a curve, then we may have a case of second-order or fractional-order reaction. The shortest way of determining the reaction order α in such a case is to consider, as in Fig. 3-10,

$$r_A = k\, C_A^{\alpha} \tag{3-35}$$

$$\ln r_A = \ln k + \alpha \ln C_A \tag{3-36}$$

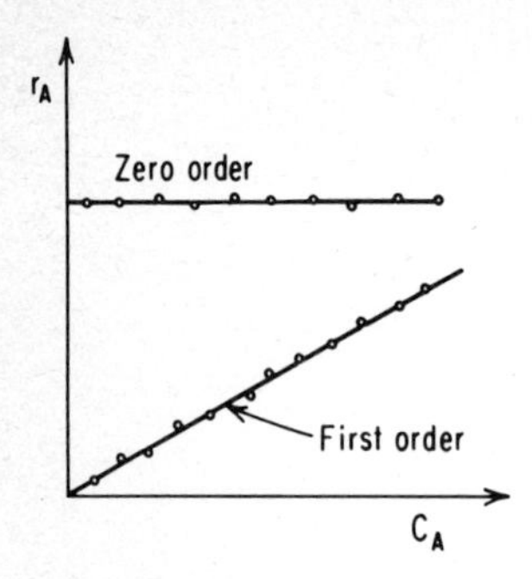

FIG. 3-9 Determination of reaction order.

and to plot $\ln r_A$ versus $\ln C_A$. The slope of the line represents the reaction order α. Of course this method will work for fractional-order reactions and for second-order reactions of the type $r_A = kC_A^2$ but will not work for second-order reactions of the type

$$r_A = k\, C_A\, C_B \tag{3-25}$$

Here we can write:

$$\ln r_A = \ln k + \ln C_A C_B \tag{3-37}$$

and plot $\ln r_A$ against $\ln C_A C_B$ as shown in Fig. 3-11. If the reaction is of the type of Eq. (3-25), the plot will be a straight line.

The main drawback of the differential reactor is that it must work with small conversions, and consequently extremely good analyses of inlet and outlet streams are required. These are not always available.

One of the best procedures commonly used in searching for a rate equation is *differential analysis,* which uses a differential reactor and is more convenient with complex rate expressions.

The design equation for plug-flow reactors

$$F_{A0}\, dx_A = -r_A\, dV \tag{3-38}$$

can be rearranged to

$$-r_A = \frac{dx_A}{dV/F_{A0}} \tag{3-39}$$

- One makes a series of runs in the packed bed of Fig. 3-7, using fixed feed concentration C_{A0} but varying F_{A0} such that a wide range of values for V/F_{A0} and x_A is obtained.
- One plots x_A vs. V/F_{A0} for all runs (Fig. 3-8).
- One fits the best curve to the x_A vs. V/F_{A0} data, making it pass through the origin.

- The rate of reaction at any value of x_A is the slope of the curve at that value. For each x_A value one can find a rate value and a C_A value.
- Now all one has to do is to plot r_A vs. C_A or ln A vs. ln C_A as in Figs. 3-9 and 3-10, respectively.

Differential reactors are discussed in detail by Levenspiel,[18] Smith,[7] and Hougen and Watson.[17]

The Integral Flow Reactor—Integral Analysis

The same packed laboratory reactor shown in Fig. 3-7 can be used as an integral flow reactor. However, more catalyst can be packed into it, so that 20% conversion is obtained. Again, the reactor is operated under isothermal conditions. Another commonly used procedure in searching for a rate equation is *integral analysis* which uses the integral flow reactor.

A specific mechanism with its corresponding rate equation is put to the test by integrating the rate equation for the reactor flow conditions. For this:

- A series of runs is made in a packed bed, with fixed feed concentration C_{A0} but with varying catalyst volume V and/or feed rate F_{A0}, in such a manner that a wide range of V/F_{A0} vs. x_A data are obtained.
- A rate equation is selected for testing and used in integrating the plug-flow performance equation to give

$$\frac{V}{F_{A0}} = \int_0^{x_A} \frac{dx_A}{-r_A} \tag{3-40}$$

- For each experimental run, the left and the right sides of Eq. (3-38) are evaluated numerically.
- The results are plotted one against the other and tested for linearity.

Integral analysis provides a straightforward and fast method for test-

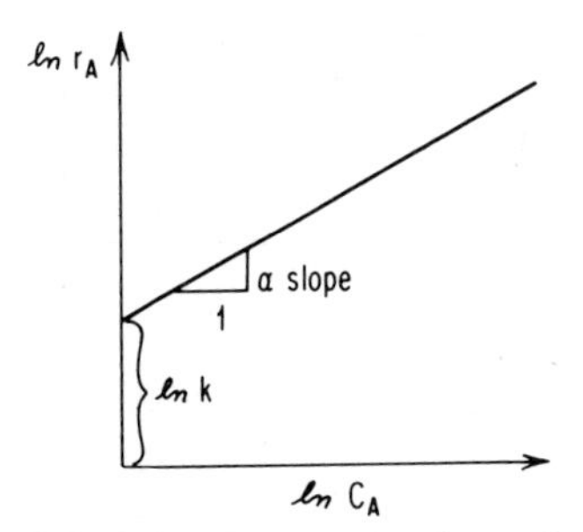

FIG. 3-10 Determination of reaction order and reaction rate constant k for rates depending on a single concentration C_A.

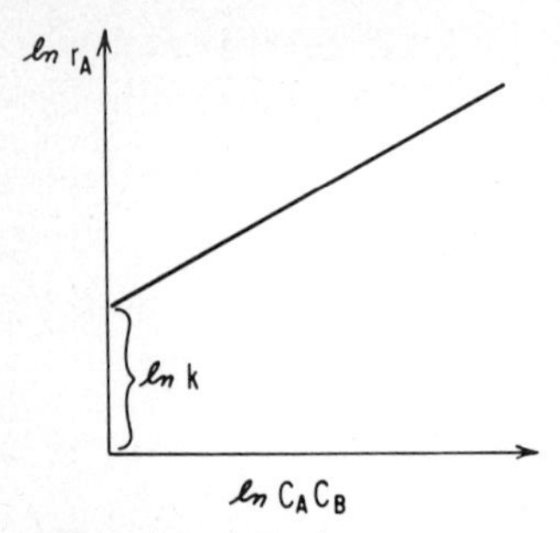

FIG. 3-11 Determination of reaction order and reaction rate constant k for rates depending on two concentrations, C_A and C_B.

ing simple rate expressions. However, with increasing complexity, the integrated forms of the rate expressions become too messy.

In the tubular packed integral reactor, ideally the gas flow, as represented by either the feed rate F_A or the Reynolds number, should be constant and the reactor length should be varied. However, this is frequently not done, because it is inconvenient to repack a laboratory reactor for every data point.[19] Instead, a fixed length of packed bed is used while attempting to maintain the pressure, the temperature, and the reactants ratio constant and varying only the flow rate. After such a series of experiments is completed, further series are run by varying the flow rate at other levels of constant reactant ratio.[7] This type of reactor must be kept absolutely isothermal or the data obtained from it will be worthless.

According to J. J. Carberry,[5,19] a tube diameter equivalent to 5 to 6 particle diameters are the maximum to have in the tube to be certain that isothermality is maintained. However, this conflicts with the general packed-bed rule that a minimum of 8 to 15 particle diameters is necessary to minimize wall effects. This means that no matter what is done some error will be made.

The Continuous Stirred-Tank Reactor (CSTR)

The CSTR can be used in the laboratory as a tool for reaction rate determination. It is normally used for homogeneous reactions. If it is perfectly mixed, the reaction rate can be obtained by materials balance (Fig. 3-12):

$$r_A = \frac{C_{A0} - C_A}{\tau} \tag{3-41}$$

In order to adapt the CSTR to heterogeneous catalysts, Carberry developed his basket-type experimental CSTR.[20] In this reactor, catalyst pellets are placed in wire baskets, which rotate around a vertical axis in a cylinder full of the reactant gases. The performance equation becomes:

$$\frac{V}{F_{A0}} = \frac{x_A}{-r_A} \tag{3-42}$$

from which

$$-r_A = \frac{F_{A0}x_A}{V} \tag{3-43}$$

Here, each run gives directly a value for the rate at the composition of the exit fluid.

There is an alternate design for a similar reactor with a fixed catalyst and recirculated gases. However this alternate design costs considerably more than the Carberry reactor.

The Recycle Reactor

The recycle reactor can also be used in the laboratory as a tool for reaction rate determination. It uses a plug-flow reactor and converts it to a backmixed reactor by adding a recycle (Fig. 3-13). Again a specific kinetic equation is tested by inserting it into the performance equation for recycle reactors

$$\frac{V}{F_{A0}} = (R + 1)\int_{Rx_A/(R+1)}^{x_A} \frac{dx_A}{-r_A} \tag{3-44}$$

The equation is integrated and a plot of the left-hand and right-hand sides of Eq. (3-44) then tests the linearity.

At high recycle ratio R the reactor approaches a CSTR. The most critical part of the reactor is the pump. According to J. J. Carberry,[21] the best pump is the all-glass pump developed by M. Boudart.

The CSTR and the recycle reactor do not give the best yields, but at this stage of learning, no one cares about yields—it is the rate constants that are desired.

Laboratory reactors will be discussed in greater detail in Chap. 10.

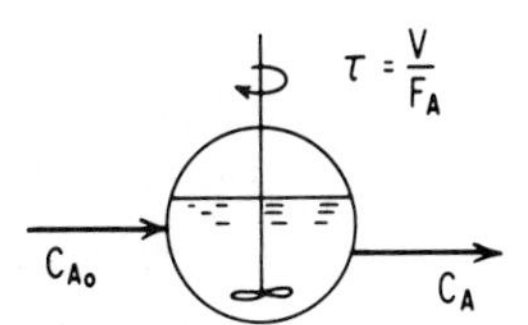

FIG. 3-12 Schematic representation of a continuous stirred-tank reactor (CSTR).

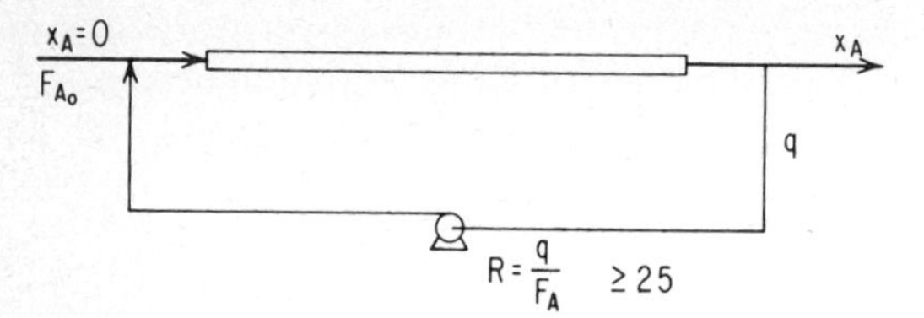

FIG. 3-13 Schematic representation of a recycle reactor.

3.4 EFFECTS OF PORE STRUCTURE AND TRANSPORT PHENOMENA ON REACTION KINETICS

Most solid catalysts are porous pellets, some having internal surface areas as large as 300 m^2/g or more. This sort of porous structure strongly affects the kinetics of chemical reactions, not only with respect to reaction rate but also by favoring certain products over others. We say that pore structure affects the *selectivity* of the reaction.

A typical heterogeneous catalyst pellet is a small solid (spherical, cylindrical, or irregular in shape) containing a multitude of pores. In Fig. 3-14 such a pellet is shown with exagerated pores. Gases or liquids which surround the pellet diffuse into the pores, where they react on catalytically active sites; the products of the reaction diffuse back to the bulk phase and are transported by the bulk phase.

Because the actual catalytic reaction takes place on the active sites of the catalyst surface, which are mostly inside the pores, both the temperature and the concentrations may vary between the bulk phase and the pores.

All properties related to the space inside the pellets are called *intraphase* properties, while all properties related to the space between pellets are called *interphase* properties.

The Global Rate of Reaction

The *global* rate of reaction is the rate that can be measured. It includes also the mass transfer. The simple case is a nonporous solid catalyst plate, as shown in Fig. 3-15. A reactant of initial concentration C_0 may approach the solid. The solid is assumed to be covered by a fictitious film of thickness δ, which represents a sort of resistance to the reaction on the surface. The reactant will penetrate the film and will be adsorbed on the surface; its surface concentration will then be C_s. The rate of surface reaction will be:

$$\mathcal{R} = k\, C_s^{\alpha} = k_g a\, (C_0 - C_s) \qquad (3\text{-}45)$$

where k = reaction rate constant (units vary according to α)
α = reaction order
k_g = mass-transfer coefficient, m/s
a = the ratio of surface available per unit volume of reactor space, m^2/m^3

Equation (3-45) simply states that the number of moles of reactant consumed by the surface reaction is equal to the number of moles transferred through the film to the catalyst surface. The coefficient k_g is a phenomenological coefficient, which is also related to the diffusivity D of the reactant by:

$$k_g = D/\delta \tag{3-46}$$

With increasing flow or with increasing Reynolds number Re:

$$\delta \rightarrow 0 \qquad k_g \rightarrow \infty$$

Let us solve Eq. (3-45) for C_s. If $\alpha = 1$, Eq. (3-45) is first-order. Then C_s can be extracted from it:

$$C_s = \frac{C_0}{1 + (k/k_g a)} \tag{3-47}$$

Substituting C_s from Eq. (3-47) into the rate equation $\mathcal{R} = kC_s$ gives:

$$\mathcal{R} = \frac{k\, C_0}{1 + (k/k_g a)} \tag{3-48}$$

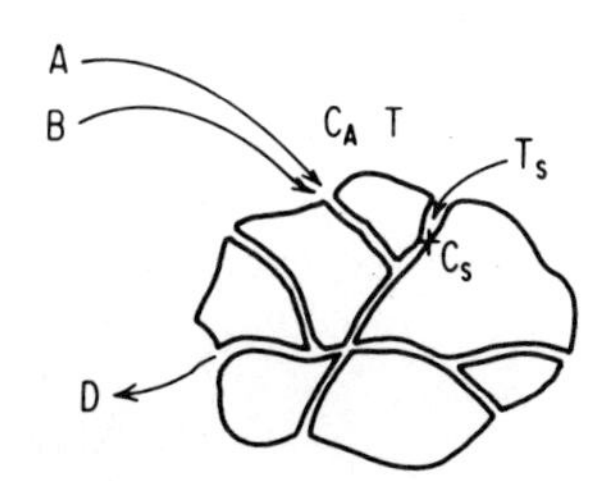

FIG. 3-14 Schematic representation of a porous catalyst pellet.

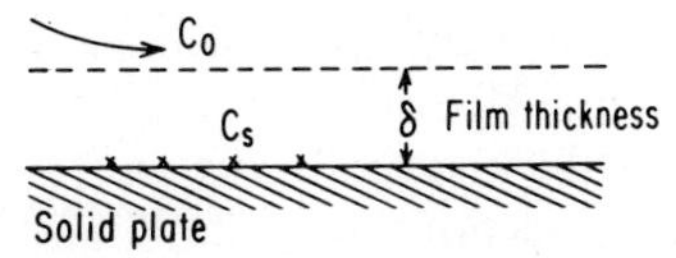

FIG. 3-15 Schematic representation of a nonporous catalyst.

In Eq. (3-48), the expression $k/[1 + (k/k_g a)]$ is the experimental value of the rate constant. Thus, this whole expression, not just k, is the rate constant.

At low temperatures $k_g a > k$; $(k/k_g a) \rightarrow 0$; $\mathcal{R} = kC_0$ and

$$k_{\text{experimental}} = k_{\text{intrinsic}}$$

At higher temperatures $k_g a < k$; $k/[1 + (k/k_g a)] = (k \cdot k_g a)/(k_g a + k) \rightarrow (k \cdot k_g a/k) = k_g a$; $\mathcal{R} = k_g a\, C_0$ and

$$k_{\text{experimental}} \neq k_{\text{intrinsic}}$$

To express the relationship between the experimentally measurable *global reaction* and the *intrinsic reaction rate* we will define an *external effectiveness factor* η_x[5,21]:

$$\mathcal{R} = \eta_x\, k\, C_0 \tag{3-49}$$

where

$$\eta_x = \frac{1}{1 + (k/k_g a)} \tag{3-50}$$

The dimension of k for first-order reaction is seconds^{-1}. Here the ratio $k/k_g a$ is dimensionless and is called the *Damköhler number* (Da). It expresses the relationship of the chemical reaction to the mass transfer.

The external effectiveness factor η_x should not be confused with the intraphase effectiveness factor η.

If η_x is plotted against the Damköhler number on a double logarithmic chart, the curve on Fig. 3-16 is obtained. The factor η_x can also be computed in cases of reaction orders different from 1 and plotted on the same Fig. 3-16. We see that the diffusion intrusion is the more serious, the higher the order of reaction.[22]

If we investigate the Arrhenius relationship of the experimentally measured reaction rate

$$k_x = \eta_x k \tag{3-51}$$

by plotting $\ln k_x$ against $1/T$ in Fig. 3-17, we see that at low temperatures (high $1/T$), the slope of the curve is $-E/R_G$, where E is the activation energy of the catalytic intrinsic reaction. At intermediate T we have a mixed phase with a flatter curve. At very high temperatures (low $1/T$) most of the reaction will occur in the bulk gas phase rather than on the surface, and we will be measuring the intrinsic reaction rate in bulk gas phase. Then E will be the activation energy of the thermal reaction and $k_{\text{experimental}} = k_{\text{intrinsic, thermal}}$. This means that if the measured activation en-

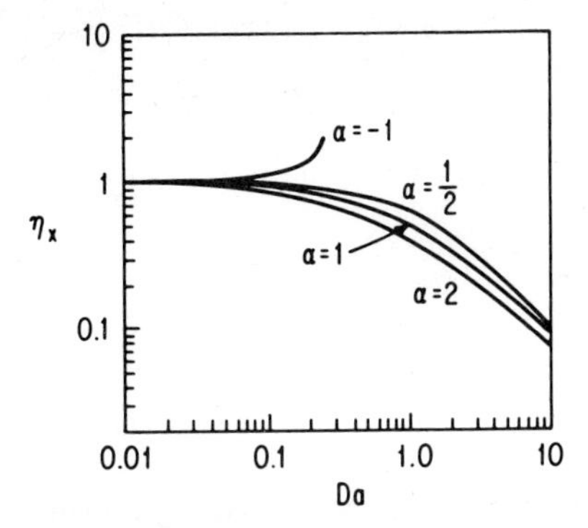

FIG. 3-16 Plot of the isothermal external catalytic effectiveness factor for reaction order α as a function of the Damköhler number Da. (*From Cassiere and Carberry,*[22] *by permission from the American Society for Engineering Education.*)

ergy E is found to be low in studying a reaction, considerable diffusion is involved.

$$\mathrm{Da}\ \eta_x = \frac{k}{k_g a} \cdot \frac{1}{1 + (k/k_g a)} \tag{3-52}$$

Equation (3-52) works with all reaction orders. In a pure diffusion region, all reactions appear to be first-order. By obtaining η_x from observable rate data, it is possible to calculate the real order of the reaction.

Let us consider again a flat catalyst plate (Fig. 3-18). However, let this be a porous plate instead of the nonporous one of Fig. 3-15. With the porous plate we can study the intraphase aspect of the heterogeneous reaction rate. In order to correlate the observable reaction rate constant $k_{\text{experimental}}$ with $k_{\text{intrinsic}}$, we define an *effectiveness factor* η

$$\eta = \frac{\frac{1}{L} \int k\, C^{\alpha}\, dl}{k_s C_s} \tag{3-53}$$

which under isothermal conditions tends to

$$\eta_i = \frac{\frac{1}{L} \int C^{\alpha} dl}{C_s} \leqslant 1.0 \tag{3-54}$$

Here dl is a differential distance and L is a characteristic dimension of the particle:

$$L = \frac{\text{volume of particle}}{\text{external surface area}} = \frac{1}{a}$$

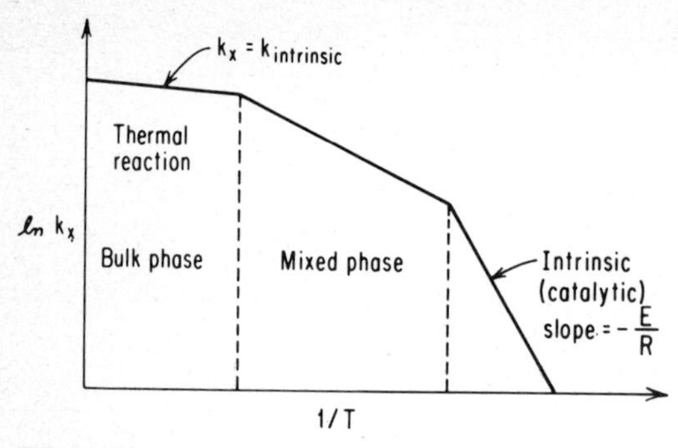

FIG. 3-17 Arrhenius plot for the experimentally measured reaction rate constant k_x in a nonporous catalyst.

Thus

$$k_g a \equiv k_g / L$$

At nonisothermal conditions

$$\eta_{\text{nonisothermal}} \lesseqgtr 1.0$$

The rate of diffusion of the reactant equals that of its consumption by the reaction; therefore we can write

$$D \frac{d^2C}{dl^2} = kC^{\alpha} \tag{3-55}$$

For first-order reaction, $\alpha = 1$ and we have:

$$D \frac{d^2C}{dl^2} = kC \tag{3-56}$$

We may use the dimensionless forms of some quantities:

$$f = \frac{C}{C_s} \qquad z = \frac{1}{L} \tag{3-57}$$

With these quantities, Eq. (3-56) becomes

$$D \frac{d^2(fC_s)}{d(zL)^2} = k \frac{C}{C_s} \quad \text{or} \quad \frac{d^2 f}{dz^2} = \left(L^2 \frac{k}{D}\right) f \tag{3-58}$$

The value of the quantity in parentheses on the right-hand side of Eq. (3-58) is equated to φ^2, φ being the well-known *Thiele modulus*.[23] Analytical solution of Eq. (3-58) by a complicated and lengthy procedure gives:

$$\eta_i = \frac{\tanh \varphi}{\varphi} \tag{3-59}$$

where tanh φ is the *hyperbolic tangent* of φ. A hyperbolic tangent of a quantity φ is given by the relationship:

$$\tanh \varphi = \frac{e^{\varphi} - e^{-\varphi}}{e^{\varphi} + e^{-\varphi}} \tag{3-60}$$

Let us plot tanh φ against φ in Fig. 3-19. We see that tanh φ increases almost proportionally to φ up to about $\varphi = 1$, and then flattens out and approaches $\tanh \varphi = 1$ asymptotically. Thus

$$\text{for } \varphi < 1 \qquad \tanh \varphi \cong \varphi$$
$$\text{for } \varphi > 3 \qquad \tanh \varphi = 1$$

Let us now plot η against φ in Fig. 3-20 on double logarithmic paper. We see that for $\varphi < 0.2$, $\eta \cong 1$. Then the curve begins declining; above about $\varphi = 2$ it becomes a straight line and Eq. (3-59) gives $\eta_i = 1/\varphi$.

When the modulus φ is small, the effectiveness is close to unity and the experimental reaction rate approaches the intrinsic reaction rate:

$$\Re = \eta_i k C_s \rightarrow k C_s$$

where the rate is directly proportional to the intrinsic rate constant k.

When, however, $\varphi > 3$, the effectiveness factor is quite small and equals $1/\varphi$. The experimental reaction rate is given by:

$$\Re = kC_s/\varphi = kC_s/L(k/D)^{0.5} = (kD)^{0.5}\, C_s/L \tag{3-61}$$

We see that for low effectiveness factors the experimentally measured reaction rate $\Re$ becomes proportional to the square root of the reaction rate constant. This means that the reaction slows down.

When the natural logarithm of k_x for a reaction over a porous catalyst is plotted against $1/T$ in Fig. 3-21, we observe no effect of particle size at low temperatures, where diffusion is negligible. The slope of the Arrhenius line is $-E/R$ and the true activation energy E is obtained. However, at high temperature (low $1/T$), where diffusion in pores be-

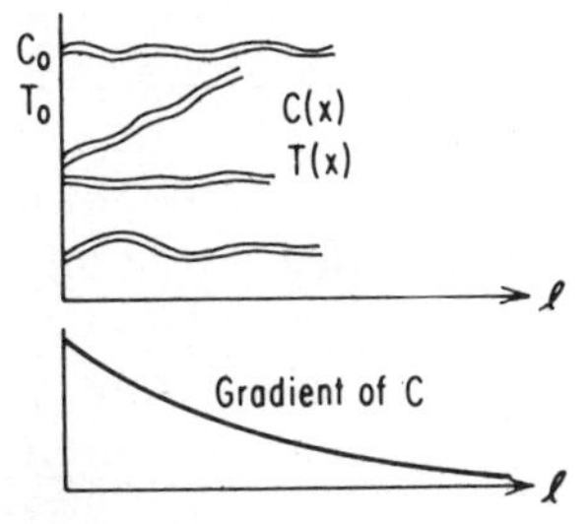

FIG. 3-18 **Concentration gradients in a porous catalyst plate as a function of distance *l* from exterior surface.**

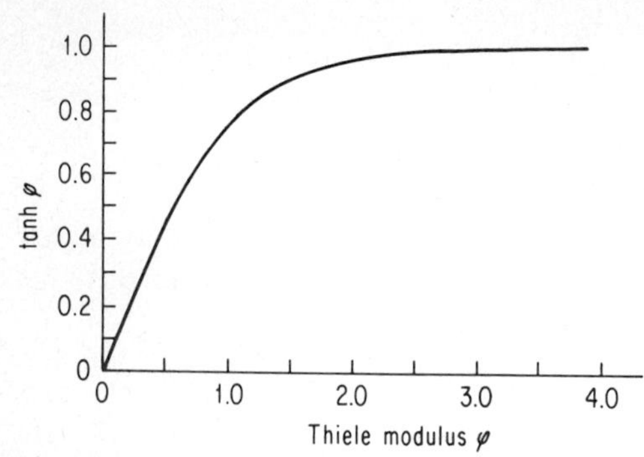

FIG. 3-19 Plot of tanh φ vs. φ.

comes significant, the slope of the Arrhenius line is $-E/2R$, or half the value at low temperatures. Hence the apparent activation energy measured at high temperatures would be half the true activation energy.

For further information on kinetics and effectiveness of porous catalysts, the reader is referred to the excellent treatment of the subject in Carberry's book.[5]

Yield and Selectivity in Complex Reaction Systems

Let us consider two types of reaction systems: consecutive reactions and simultaneous reactions[24]:

$$A \xrightarrow{k_1} B \xrightarrow{k_2} C \qquad\qquad A \begin{matrix} \xrightarrow{k_1} B \\ \xrightarrow[k_2]{} C \end{matrix}$$

Consecutive reactions Simultaneous reactions

In the above schematic equations, subscripts 1 and 2 denote the first and the second reaction, respectively. In *consecutive reactions,* the product B of the first reaction becomes the feed to the second. In *simultaneous reactions,* however, fractions of the same species A react simultaneously according to the two different reaction rates and produce products B and C.

The *yield* Y of a reaction is the ratio of the rate of generation r_B of a desired product to the rate of consumption r_A of a key reactant at any point within the reactor.

The *selectivity* S at any point of a reactor is the rate of generation r_B of a desired product to the rate of generation r_C of some undesired product.

$$Y = r_B/r_A \qquad S = r_B/r_C \tag{3-62}$$

Yield and selectivity are important parameters for the reactor designer.
Under isothermal conditions we can set

$$k_1/k_2 = K' \tag{3-63}$$

The reaction step 1 is assumed to be α order, while the reaction step 2 is β order. The expressions for yield and selectivity can be written as follows[24]:

$$\text{Yield}\begin{cases} Y_c = -(dC_B/dC_A) = 1 - (1/K')(C_B^{\beta}/C_A^{\alpha}) & (3\text{-}64)\\ Y_s = -(dC_B/dC_A) = 1/(1 + C_A^{\beta-\alpha}/K') & (3\text{-}65)\end{cases}$$

$$\text{Selectivity}\begin{cases} S_c = (dC_B/dC_C) = K'(C_A^{\alpha}/C_B^{\beta}) - 1 & (3\text{-}66)\\ S_s = (dC_B/dC_C) = K'\,C_A^{\alpha-\beta} & (3\text{-}67)\end{cases}$$

where subscript c and s denote consecutive and simultaneous systems, respectively.

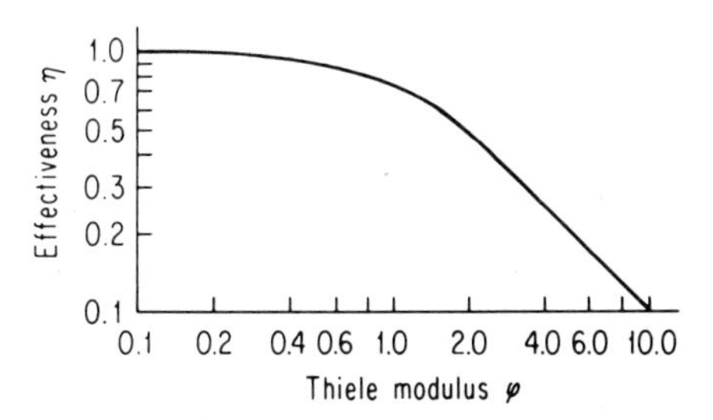

FIG. 3-20 Plot of effectiveness factor versus Thiele modulus.

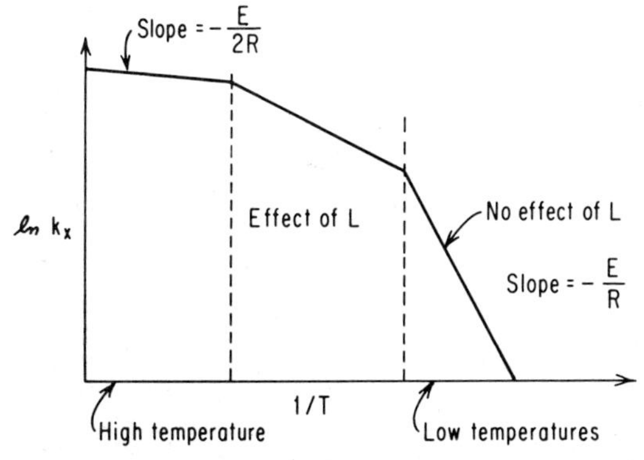

FIG. 3-21 Arrhenius plot for the experimentally measured reaction rate constant k_x in a porous catalyst.

Under nonisothermal conditions we can write:

$$K = (k_1/k_2) = K_0 \exp\left[\frac{E_2 - E_1}{RT_0}\left(\frac{T_0}{T} - 1\right)\right] \tag{3-68}$$

where subscript 0 refers to isothermal conditions.

By setting $t = (T/T_0)$, which is the reduced temperature, and

$$\Delta\epsilon = \frac{E_2 - E_1}{RT_0}$$

we obtain a simpler expression:

$$K' = K_0 \exp\left[\Delta\epsilon\left(\frac{1}{t} - 1\right)\right] \tag{3-69}$$

Here $\Delta\epsilon$ refers to apparent rather than intrinsic E difference. Thus yield and selectivity depend on relative reaction order and activation energy difference $\Delta\epsilon$ for a given ΔH change and thermal capacity of the fluid.

For simultaneous reactions, yield is $\Delta\epsilon$-dependent and sensitive to relative order as long as $\alpha \neq \beta$.

NOMENCLATURE

a	Ratio of external surface area to particle volume, m^{-1}
A	Frequency factor or preexponential factor (dimension depends on reaction order)
C	Molar concentration, $kmol/m^3$
C_0	Initial or inlet molar concentration, $kmol/m^3$
C_s	Molar concentration on the surface of the catalyst, $kmol/m^3$
Da	Damköhler number, dimensionless
E	Activation energy, kJ/kmol
f	Dimensionless concentration $= C/C_s$
F	Volumetric feed rate, m^3/s or rate ratio of poisoned to nonpoisoned reactions, dimensionless
k	Reaction rate constant
k_a	Adsorption rate constant
k_d	Desorption rate constant
k_g	Mass-transfer coefficient, m/s
k_x	Experimentally measured reaction rate
K	Adsorption equilibrium constant

K'	Ratio of reaction rates = k_1/k_2
l	Distance from porous catalyst surface, m
L	Ratio of particle volume to external surface area, m
p	Partial pressure, Pa or bars (1 bar = 10^5 Pa)
r	Reaction rate
R	Gas constant = 8.314 kJ/(kmol · K) or recycle ratio in recycle reactor
Re	Reynolds number, dimensionless
$\mathcal{R}$	Rate of global reaction, kmol/(m^3 · s)
S	Selectivity, dimensionless
t	Time, s (unless specifically indicated otherwise)
T	Absolute temperature, K
V	Catalyst volume, m^3
V'	Volume of reactants, m^3
x	Conversion, dimensionless
Y	Yield, dimensionless
z	Dimensionless distance from catalyst surface = $1/L$
α	Reaction order or fraction of pore surface poisoned
$\Delta\epsilon$	Apparent activation energy difference
ε	Fractional change in volume of the system during complete conversion
η	Intraphase effectiveness factor, dimensionless
η_i	Intrinsic effectiveness factor under isothermal conditions, dimensionless
η_x	External effectiveness factor, dimensionless
θ	Surface coverage of catalysts, i.e., fraction of catalyst surface covered by an adsorbed chemical species
τ	Space time
φ	Thiele modulus

Subscripts

A B	Species A, B
C	Consecutive

Prod	Product
S	Simultaneous

REFERENCES

1. Robert W. Coughlin, "Classifying Catalysts—Some Broad Principles," *Ind. Eng. Chem.* **59**(9):45–57 (1967).
2. R. Winkoop and R. H. Wilhelm, "Kinetics of Tubular Flow Reactors—Hydrogenation of Ethylene on Cu-MgO Catalyst," *Chem. Eng. Progr.* **46:**300–310 (1950).
3. Michel Boudart, "Kinetics and Mechanism of Catalytic Reactions," *Ind. chim. belge,* **23:**383–396 (1958). (*Note:* Data were converted to SI units by the author of this book.)
4. S. Brunauer, P. H. Emmett, and E. Teller, "Adsorption of Gases in Multimolecular Layers," *J. Am. Chem. Soc.,* **60:**309–319 (1938).
5. James J. Carberry, *Chemical and Catalytic Reaction Engineering*, McGraw-Hill, New York, 1976.
6. A. R. Cooper and G. V. Jeffreys, *Chemical Kinetics and Reactor Design,* Prentice-Hall, Englewood Cliffs, N.J., 1971.
7. J. M. Smith, *Chemical Engineering Kinetics,* 2d ed., McGraw-Hill, New York, 1970.
8. S. Brunauer, K. S. Love, and R. G. Keenan, "Adsorption of Nitrogen and the Mechanism of Ammonia Decomposition over Iron Catalysts," *J. Am. Chem. Soc.,* **64:**751–758 (1942).
9. G. Halsey and H. S. Taylor, "The Adsorption of Hydrogen on Tungsten Powders," *J. Chem. Phys.,* **15:**624–630 (1947).
10. Otto Beeck, "Catalysis and the Adsorption of Hydrogen on Metal Catalysts," *Advan. Catalysis,* **2:**151–195 (1950).
11. E. Rideal, *Surface Chemistry*, Cambridge Press, 1930.
12. D. Hayward and B. M. W. Trapnell, *Chemisorption,* Butterworth, London, 1964.
13. Ahlborn Wheeler, "Reaction Rates and Selectivity in Catalyst Pores," *Advan. Catalysis,* **3:**250–326 (1951).
14. Edward B. Maxted, "The Poisoning of Metallic Catalysts," *Advan. Catalysis,* **2:**129–178 (1951); "The Nature of Chemisorption Bonds. I. Some Observed Regularities," *J. Chem. Soc.,* 1987–1991 (1949); E. B. Maxted and A. Marsden, "Catalytic Toxicity and Chemical Structure. VI. Poisoning of Pt-Metals by Metals," *Ibid.,* 469–474 (1940); E. B. Maxted and Robert W. D. Morrish, "Catalytic Toxicity and Chemical Structure. V. Simple Anions Containing Toxic Elements," *Ibid.,* 252–256 (1940); "Catalytic Toxicity and Chemical

Structure. VII. Elimination of Catalyst Poisons by Conversion into Derivatives of Shielded Type," *Ibid.,* 132–136 (1941).

15. John B. Butt, "Catalyst Deactivation," in *Chemical Reaction Engineering,* Advances in Chemistry Series, no. 109, 1972, pp. 259–496.
16. John B. Butt and R. M. Billimoria, "Catalyst Deactivation," in *Chemical Reaction Engineering Reviews—Houston,* American Chemical Society, Symposium Series no. 72, 1978, pp. 288–322.
17. Olaf A. Hougen and Kenneth M. Watson, *Chemical Process Principles,* part 3: *Kinetics and Catalysis,* John Wiley, New York, 1947.
18. Octave Levenspiel, *Chemical Reaction Engineering,* 2d ed., John Wiley, New York, 1972.
19. James J. Carberry, Unpublished notes from the First Catalytic Reactor Design Course at Lehigh University, Bethlehem, Pa., June 21, 1971.
20. James J. Carberry, "Designing Laboratory Catalytic Reactors," *Ind. Eng. Chem.,* **56**(11):39–46 (1964).
21. James J. Carberry: Unpublished notes from the "Catalytic Reactor Design Course" at Pocono Manor, Pa., June 19, 1972.
22. G. Cassiere and James J. Carberry, "The Interphase Catalytic Effectiveness Factor: Activity, Yield and Non-isothermality," *Chem. Eng. Educ.,* Winter pp. 22–26, 1973.
23. E. W. Thiele, "Relation between Catalytic Activity and Size of Particles," *Ind. Eng. Chem.,* **31**(7):916–920 (1939).
24. James J. Carberry, "Yield in Chemical Reaction Engineering," *Ind. Eng. Chem.,* **58**(10):40–58 (1966).

Chapter 4 TRANSPORT PHENOMENA IN FIXED-BED GAS REACTORS

Fixed-bed gas reactors will be the subject of this and next chapter. First, the concept of *fixed bed* must be defined.

4.1 DEFINITION

A fixed-bed reactor is a chemical reactor containing a bed of solid catalyst particles that is filled into a usually cylindrical vessel and stays there until it is dumped. However, the stay of the solid catalyst in the reactor vessel is by no means eventless. The catalyst activity changes with time. Normally activity declines from some kind of surface fouling, coking, or poisoning. It is also possible for activity to increase at the beginning before it starts to decline. The designer must make a judgment as to how much the activity should be allowed to decrease before something has to be done with the catalyst. Either the catalyst charge is dumped and a fresh catalyst charge is filled into the reactor, or the spent catalyst is regenerated in situ. The choice is of course dictated by economics (price of catalyst, loss of on-stream time by regeneration in situ, cost of regeneration equipment, etc.) It is also possible to dump the catalyst, regenerate it somewhere else, and recharge it later.

Most catalysts lose some of their activity on regeneration. Figure 4-1 shows the change in catalyst activity with time in a typical fixed-bed reactor. In the first hours and days of the operation activity declines fairly rapidly, but thereafter the rate of decline is slower. When activity reaches a point at which it is uneconomical to use the fouled catalyst, the bed is regenerated, either in situ or outside the reactor. When the regenerated catalyst is put back on stream, its initial activity is somewhat below the initial activity of the first period of use. Consequently, after

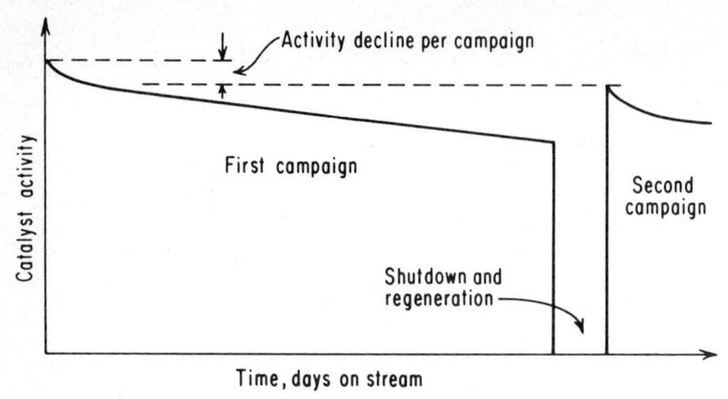

FIG. 4-1 Change in catalytic activity in a fixed bed.

a number of regenerations the catalyst bed must be dumped and fresh catalyst must be charged. That is the extent to which a so-called fixed bed is really fixed.

4.2 CLASSIFICATION OF FIXED-BED GAS REACTORS

Fixed-bed gas reactors can be classified into three categories:

1. *Isothermal* reactors, which remain at the same constant temperature at every point.
2. *Adiabatic* reactors, which exchange no heat with the surroundings. If an exothermic reaction is run in an adiabatic reactor, the temperature of the gas stream will increase from the inlet toward the outlet. If, on the other hand, an endothermic reaction is run in the same reactor, the fluid temperature will drop along the reactor length.
3. *Nonisothermal, nonadiabatic fixed-bed* gas reactors, which are sidewall-cooled or sidewall-heated and usually are bundled up like heat exchanger tubes. This type of reactor has an extremely long, awkward name, which can be shortened to the more convenient acronym *NINAF reactor*. The acronym is made up of the first letters of the full name.[1] The temperature in NINAF reactors varies from one point to another and heat is exchanged with the surroundings through the side wall.

In order to begin with the process design of any type of reactor, the designer must have complete information on transport phenomena in the reactor. Therefore, this chapter will discuss this kind of information for fixed-bed gas reactors.

Transport phenomena in a fixed bed of catalyst can be classified in two categories: those which occur in the void space in the catalyst bed are called *interphase phenomena*, while those which occur inside the catalyst pores and on the surface of the catalyst are called *intraphase phenomena*.

4.3
INTERPHASE TRANSPORT IN FIXED-BED GAS REACTORS

Interphase transport phenomena in fixed-bed gas reactors include momentum transport phenomena, mass-related transport phenomena, and heat-related transport phenomena. The expression *mass-related* strictly means "concentration-related."

Interphase Flow of Gas

We are interested in the resistance to gas flow when a gas is passing through a fixed bed and in the uniformity of this flow.

Pressure Drop across Fixed-Bed Gas Reactors

The resistance to the gas flow is measured by the pressure drop across the bed. The pressure drop is given by the well-known Ergun law[2]

$$(\Delta P/Zg_c) = 150 \times 10^{-5}(1 - \varepsilon)^2 \mu u_m/(\varepsilon^3 d_p^2) + 1.75 \times 10^{-5}(1 - \varepsilon) G u_m/(\varepsilon^3 d_p) \quad \text{bars/m} \qquad (4\text{-}1)$$

where ΔP = pressure drop, force units, bars

Z = height of bed, m

g_c = force-to-mass conversion factor = 1.0 kg · m/(N · s^2)

G = mass flow rate of fluid = $u\rho$, kg/(s · m^2)

ε = fractional void volume in bed, dimensionless

μ = absolute viscosity of fluid, Pa · s = kg/(m · s)

u_m = superficial fluid velocity based on empty reactor cross section, measured at average pressure between inlet and outlet, m/s

d_p = effective diameter of particles, m, as defined by

$$d_p = 6\,A_c\,Z(1 - \varepsilon)/S_t \qquad (4\text{-}2)$$

A_C = cross-sectional area of the empty reactor, m^2

S_t = total geometric surface area of the solids (catalysts), m^2

u = superficial fluid velocity based on empty reactor cross section, m/s

ρ = density of fluid (gas), kg/m^3

The bar, which is very close to 1 atm, was selected as the SI unit for pressure. This is what required the factor of 10^{-5} in the right-hand side of Eq. (4-1).

Radial Distribution of Axial Flow Rate

It was first learned in the early 1950s that the distribution of gas flow through packed beds of catalyst is not uniform. Schwartz and Smith[3] found that gas flow at the reactor wall and at the reactor center is the lowest and that it increases considerably along a ring located approximately one catalyst particle diameter from the reactor wall. Figure 4-2 shows four velocity profiles in pipes packed with 1/8-in (3.17-mm) and ¼-in (6.35-mm) "square cylinders" (a square cylinder is a cylinder with equal height and diameter). The abscissa represents the radial position or the ratio $2r/D_T$ and the ordinate represents v/u where:

r = distance from reactor axis or radial position, m

D_T = reactor inside diameter, m

v = point velocity at a distance r from the axis, m/s

u = average or superficial velocity through the reactor, m/s

This profile becomes flatter with increasing D_T and decreasing particle diameter d_p. For small aspect ratio D_T/d_p the maximum flow was found to be as high as double the flow at the reactor axis. On the other hand, for aspect ratios greater than 30 and a uniform velocity through the reactor, the profile diverged no more than 20% from the true flow profile.

This study suggested that the void fraction ε (the ratio of voids to the total bed volume) in a packed bed is constant at its minimum value up to a distance of two particle diameters from the wall. Then ε increases up to 1.0 at the wall. This conclusion has been verified by M. R. Shaffer.[4] Benenati and Brosilow[5] showed that the void fraction in a bed of spheres decreased from 1.0 at the wall to a minimum of 0.23 according to a damped oscillation function toward the center of the reactor.

Schlünder[6] calculated the gas flow in the high and low void areas of the reactor cross section and estimated the fraction f of the cross-sectional area with the larger voids near the wall:

$$f \cong 2d_p/D_T \tag{4-3}$$

In most industrial-size gas reactors f should be ≤ 0.01. Consequently, the reactor designer can for all practical purposes assume the gas flow in commercial catalyst beds to be uniform. The error by doing so would probably be much less than the error caused by inadvertently stepping

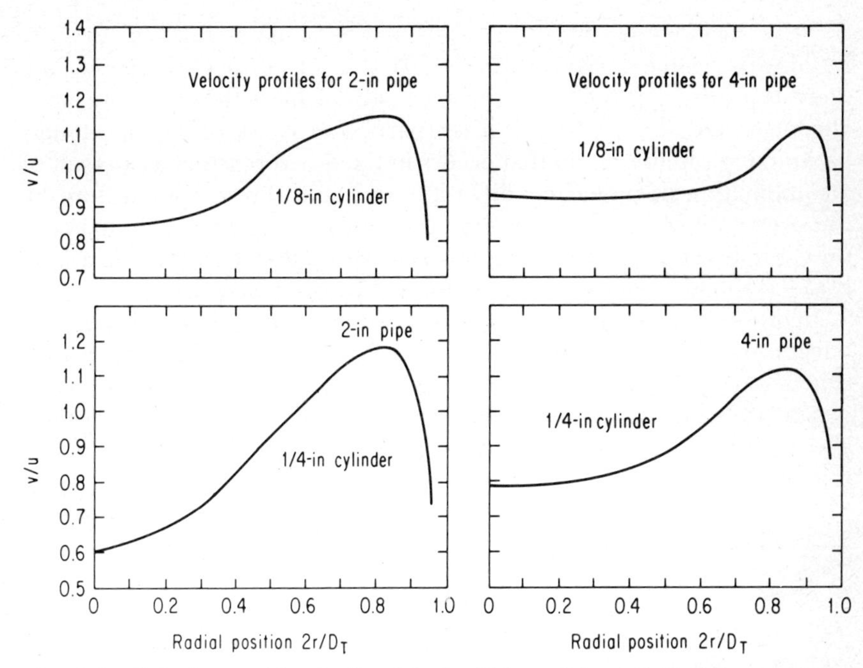

FIG. 4-2 Velocity profiles in fixed beds. (*Adapted from C. E. Schwartz and J. M. Smith, "Flow Distribution in Packed Beds," Ind. Eng. Chem.*, **45**:*1214–1215 (1953), by permission.*)

on the catalyst bed during catalyst charging and thus compressing some parts of the bed.

For most laboratory and pilot-plant reactors f will be greater than 0.3. The nonuniformity of gas flow through such reactors does not present any serious design problems, since such reactors are almost always overdesigned to allow experimentation over a broad range of parameters. However, it is of serious concern to those who must interpret the data collected in these small reactors. This is one area where the reactor designer should very carefully scrutinize the pilot data obtained to make certain that proper allowance has been made for the correct flow conditions in the pilot-plant reactor results.

Interphase Mass Transport Phenomena

Phenomena related to the transport of mass, i.e., variation in concentration of chemical species, in the void space of fixed-bed gas reactors include the radial dispersion of mass, the axial dispersion of mass, and interphase mass transfer.

Radial Dispersion of Mass

Besides the radial variation of the bulk flow of gas in the catalyst bed, there is a different type of radial variation of mass flow, namely *radial dispersion.* Radial dispersion is just a particular aspect of a general mass backmixing phenomenon that occurs in fixed-bed reactors as a result of a combination of molecular diffusion and bulk flow turbulence in the tortuous path of the fluid through the catalyst bed. The backmixing in the axial direction is called *axial dispersion* and that in the radial direction is called radial dispersion. The latter will be discussed first.

In industrial-size reactors in which no heat is exchanged with the outside, radial dispersion of mass does not create any significant concentration gradients and hence is neglected in design. However, radial dispersion must be taken in consideration in NINAF reactors, in which both concentration gradients and temperature gradients exist in the radial direction.

Radial dispersion of mass in fixed-bed gas reactors is usually expressed by a dimensionless group, the *radial Péclet number* for mass flow[7,8]:

$$\mathrm{Pe}_m = d_h\, u/\mathcal{D}_r \tag{4-4}$$

with $d_h = D_T/[1.5\,(D_T/d_p)(1 - \varepsilon) + 1]$ (4-5)

where d_h = hydraulic diameter, m

u = superficial velocity of gas, m/s

d_p = catalyst particle diameter, m

D_T = reactor inside diameter, m

$\mathcal{D}_r$ = radial dispersion coefficient, m^2/s

Pe_m is the product of the Reynolds and Schmidt numbers:

$$\mathrm{Re} \cdot \mathrm{Sc} = \mathrm{Pe}_m \tag{4-6}$$

At low Reynolds numbers Pe_m is proportional to Re. However, at turbulent flow ($\mathrm{Re} > 40$) Pe_m becomes independent of Re and acquires a constant value of about 10. Although different theories and experimental results suggest a constant between 8 and 12, the reactor designer can confidently use the value $\mathrm{Pe}_m = 10$. This subject is thoroughly discussed in Chaps. 4 and 10 of Carberry's book.[8]

Axial Dispersion of Mass

The mass dispersion in the axial direction can be expressed in two ways:

1. A backmixed fixed-bed can be compared with a system of perfectly mixed reactors in series, such as a series of CSTRs. If it is completely backmixed, we can say that it is equivalent to one CSTR. As we

increase the number n of CSTRs in series, the corresponding fixed-bed system becomes less and less backmixed, and finally an infinity of CSTRs in series ($n = \infty$) corresponds to a perfect plug-flow reactor, in which there is no backmixing at all.

2. The backmixing in a fixed-bed reactor can also be expressed by an *axial Péclet number for mass* Pe_a which is a dimensionless group

$$\mathrm{Pe}_a = d_p u / \mathcal{D}_a \tag{4-7}$$

where $\mathcal{D}_a$ = axial dispersion coefficient for mass in square meters per second.

Carberry and Wendel[9] studied and discussed the significance of Pe_a in adiabatic as well as in nonadiabatic fixed-bed reactors. They found that the effects of axial dispersion of mass and heat upon conversion appear to be negligible for practical industrial bed lengths. For any bed length Z_T greater than about 50 particle diameters,

$$\mathrm{Pe}_a = 2.0 \tag{4-8}$$

Only very shallow industrial reactors or small laboratory reactors deviate from this fixed value. Thus, axial dispersion in fixed beds can be completely neglected in reactor design. It will be seen in Chaps. 5 and 7 that axial dispersion is completely omitted from design calculations.

The two types of expressions of axial dispersion of mass are related as follows[10,11]:

$$n = Z_T \, \mathrm{Pe}_a / 2d_p \tag{4-9}$$

where n is the number of equivalent CSTRs and Z_T is the reactor bed length in meters.

Interphase Mass Transfer

The concentration of the key reactant on the external catalyst surface in a fixed-bed gas reactor is related to the concentration of the same reactant in the bulk gas phase by the equation:

$$k_g a \, (C - C_s) = \eta_1 k_1 C_s^{\alpha} = \mathcal{R} \tag{3-45}$$

where k_g = interphase mass-transfer coefficient, m/s

a = ratio of external particle-surface-area/particle-volume, m^{-1}

C_s = concentration of key reactant on exterior particle surface, $\mathrm{kmol/m^3}$

η_1 = effectiveness factor of reaction 1

k_1 = reaction rate constant of reaction 1

α = reaction order

The left-hand side of Eq. (3-45) expresses the interphase mass transfer and the right-hand side expresses the depletion of the key reactant by the global reaction $\mathcal{R}$ as observed from the catalyst surface. The left-hand side of Eq. (3-45) is the product of a driving force, $C - C_s$, by a constant value $k_g a$. Since the constant a can be easily measured for any catalyst, we will be mainly interested in k_g. Some aspects of the relationship represented by Eq. (3-45) have already been discussed in Sec. 3.4, including the derivation of the Damköhler number from it. In Sec. 5.3 we will use this relationship in the design of the NINAF reactor in the form

$$C = C_s\,[(\eta_1\, k_1/k_g a) + 1] = C_s\,[\mathrm{Da}_m + 1] \qquad (4\text{-}10)$$

This is the desired relationship between the bulk gas concentration C and the concentration C_s of the key reactant on the catalyst surface. This relationship is further improved by making it dimensionless. Let us divide both sides of Eq. (4-10) by the inlet concentration C_0 and let us set:

$C_s/C_0 = C_{rs}$ = reduced concentration on catalyst surface
$C/C_0 = C_r$ = reduced concentration in the bulk gas phase

Thus, we can write:

$$C_r = C_{rs}\,[1 + (\eta_1\, k_1/k_g a)] = C_{rs}\,(1 + \mathrm{Da}_m) \qquad (4\text{-}11)$$

where Da_m = Damköhler number for mass. Da_m relates the effective reaction rate to the interphase mass transfer. In the following we will be mainly interested in the interphase mass transfer coefficient k_g and in its calculation.

Ergun[12] and Carberry[13,14] reviewed past studies on k_g and Carberry arrived at the following correlation, based on a "developing boundary layer concept":

$$J_D = (k_g/u)\varepsilon\,\mathrm{Sc}^{2/3} = 1.15\,\mathrm{Re}^{-1/2} = J_H = (h/\rho c_p u)\,\mathrm{Pr}^{2/3} \qquad (4\text{-}12)$$

where J_D = J factor for mass
J_H = J factor for heat
u = superficial velocity, m/s
ε = void fraction, dimensionless
Sc = Schmidt number = $\mu/\rho D_{1m}$, dimensionless
μ = viscosity, Pa · s
D_{1m} = molecular diffusion coefficient for diffusing species in multiple component mixtures, m^2/s
ρ = gas density, kg/m^3

Re = Reynolds number = $d_p G/\mu$, dimensionless
G = mass velocity of gas, $kg/(m^2 \cdot s)$
d_p = catalyst particle diameter, m
h = interphase heat transfer coefficient, $kJ/(m^2 \cdot s \cdot K)$
c_p = heat capacity, $kJ/(kg \cdot K)$
Pr = Prandtl number = $c_p \mu/\lambda_g$, dimensionless
λ_g = thermal conductivity of gas, $kJ/(s \cdot m \cdot K)$

Equation (4-12) shows that the mass-transfer coefficient k_g correlates not only with the flow characteristics of the gas, as expressed by the Reynolds number, but also with the heat-transfer coefficient h. The applicability of this correlation has some limits, however:

1. It is applicable below the Reynolds number corresponding to turbulent boundary-layer development, which probably has a value of several hundred.[13]
2. It is applicable in the region where radiant heat transfer is negligible. Radiant heat transfer would at least do away with the correlation between mass and heat transfer. The effect of radiant heat will be discussed further below.

Interphase Heat Transport

Heat transport phenomena in the void spaces of the catalyst bed include the radial dispersion of heat, the transfer of heat between the catalyst surface and the bulk gas, and radiant heat transfer in the bed.

Radial Dispersion of Heat

The general backmixing phenomenon in fixed-bed reactors, which we already discussed in relation to mass dispersion, also causes some radial dispersion of heat. This heat dispersion is of no practical consequence in isothermal and adiabatic gas reactors. However, it must be definitely taken into account in sidewall-cooled NINAF reactors.

The radial dispersion of heat is expressed by a radial Péclet number for heat flow:

$$\mathrm{Pe}_h = d_p u/K_r \tag{4-13}$$

where K_r is the radial dispersion coefficient for heat in square meters per second. The value of Pe_h lies between 5 and 10. In Chap. 5 we used a value of $\mathrm{Pe}_h = 7$.

Interphase Heat Transfer

The temperature of a key reactant on the external catalyst surface in a fixed-bed gas reactor is related to the temperature in the bulk gas phase by the equation:

$$ha\,(T_s - T) = (-\Delta H)\,\Re \qquad (4\text{-}14)$$

where h = interphase heat transfer coefficient, kJ/(m^2 · s · K)

$(-\Delta H)$ = reaction heat, kJ/kmol

T = temperature of the gas in the bulk phase, K

T_s = temperature on catalyst surface, K

a = surface area-to-volume ratio for the catalyst, m^{-1}

Equation (4-14) can be rearranged into

$$T_s = T + [(-\Delta H)\Re/ha] \qquad (4\text{-}15)$$

which can be made dimensionless by dividing both sides by the inlet temperature T_0:

$$(T_s/T_0) = (T/T_0) + [(-\Delta H)\Re/T_0ha] \qquad (4\text{-}16)$$

If we set (T_s/T_0) equal to T_{rs}, the reduced surface temperature of catalyst, and (T/T_0) equal to T_r, the reduced temperature in the bulk gas phase, we can write

$$T_{rs} = T_r + \frac{(-\Delta H)\Re}{ahT_0} \qquad (4\text{-}17)$$

The term $(-\Delta H)\Re/ahT_0$ is another dimensionless group relating the heat produced by reaction (numerator) to the interphase heat transfer (denominator) and is called the *Damköhler number for heat*:

$$\mathrm{Da}_h = (-\Delta H)\Re/ahT_0 \qquad (4\text{-}18)$$

Equation (4-17) will be used in the NINAF reactor design problem in Chap. 5.

The interphase heat transfer coefficient can be calculated from the correlation of the J_D and J_H factors in Eq. (4-12). As mentioned above, Eq. (4-12) is not applicable to turbulent flow conditions or to high temperatures at which radiant heat transfer becomes significant. Martin[15] used a different approach to obtain h. He had observed that for low Péclet numbers most of the experimentally obtained particle-to-fluid heat transfer coefficients in packed beds were several orders of magnitude below the values predicted for a single spherical particle in cross flow. Martin attempted to establish a relationship between the heat transfer coefficient of the single particle and that of the packed bed and to calculate the latter from the former. In the range Pe > 100 the Nusselt number of a packed bed can be calculated from the following equations:

$$\mathrm{Nu} = [1 + 1.5(1 - \varepsilon)] \cdot \mathrm{Nu}_p \tag{4-19}$$

$$\mathrm{Nu}_p = 2 + F \cdot (\mathrm{Pe}/\varepsilon)^{1/2}\,\mathrm{Pr}^{-1/6} \tag{4-20}$$

where Nu is the Nusselt number for the packed bed $= hd_p/\lambda$ and Nu_p is the Nusselt number for a single sphere and equals $h_p d_p/\lambda$, λ being thermal conductivity. In the laminar region the factor F has values between 0.6 and 0.664 as found by different workers. For intermediate turbulence levels, F can be calculated from Gnielinski's correlation[16]:

$$F = 0.664\left\{1 + \left[\frac{0.0557\,(\mathrm{Re}/\varepsilon)^{0.3}\,\mathrm{Pr}^{2/3}}{1 + 2.44(\mathrm{Pr}^{2/3} - 1)(\mathrm{Re}/\varepsilon)^{-0.1}}\right]^2\right\}^{0.5}$$

$$(\mathrm{Pr} > 0.6) \tag{4-21}$$

Here h_p is the interphase heat transfer coefficient for a single sphere and h is the interphase heat transfer coefficient for a fixed bed in kilojoules per square meter per second per kelvin.

Calculations with the above equations show that for the same superficial velocity and for intermediate Reynolds numbers, the heat transfer coefficient of a packed bed of spheres is about 3 times that of a single sphere. Equations (4-19) to (4-21) assume uniformity of flow rate throughout the packed bed. The question of flow uniformity through packed-bed gas reactors was discussed under radial distribution of axial flow rate. If this assumption is not true, local heat and mass transfer coefficients must be used in radial increments when making design calculations.

Radiant Heat Transfer

Radiant heat transfer was studied by Vortmeyer[17,18] in West Germany, among others. He showed that, at temperatures where radiant heat becomes significant, heat transfer in fixed-bed gas reactors can be calculated by using the following differential equation:

$$u\rho c_p(dT/dz) - [(d(\lambda_a + \lambda_r)/dz](dT/dz) = (-\Delta H) \tag{4-22}$$

where u = superficial gas velocity, m/s

ρ = density, kg/m^3

c_p = specific heat of the gas, kJ/(kg · K)

λ_a = axial heat conductivity, kJ/(m · s · K)

λ_r = radiation conductivity, kJ/(m · s · K)

When boundary conditions are defined and Eq. (4-22) is integrated simultaneously with a mass differential equation of the type:

$$dC/dz = -f(C, T) \tag{4-23}$$

we obtain the temperature profile and the concentration profile in an adiabatic reactor. Equation (4-22) is valid only for moderately exothermic reactions; it cannot be used for reactors with steep temperature rises. The value of λ_r can be estimated from:

$$\lambda_r = \frac{2B + \epsilon(1 - B)}{2(1 - B) - \epsilon(1 - B)} \cdot 4\, k_B\, T^3 d_p \tag{4-24}$$

where B = radiation passage number, defining the fraction of the incident radiation that is allowed to pass through the packing, dimensionless

ϵ = emission coefficient of the particle surface, dimensionless

k_B = Boltzmann's constant

d_p = catalyst particle diameter, m

Vortmeyer[17] calculated $B = 0.1$ and confirmed it by comparison with other studies. A reasonable value for ϵ is given by the same author as $\epsilon = 1/3$. The value of λ_a, which measures heat transport by ordinary conduction and convection, must be obtained by some other means.

In NINAF reactors that are cooled from the sidewalls, similarly to heat exchanger tubes, significant temperature profiles occur in the packed bed. Such temperature profiles are shown in Fig. 4-3, where the radial

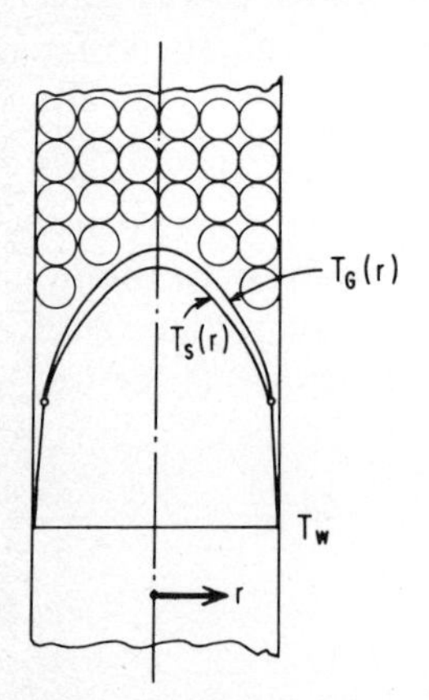

FIG. 4-3 Typical temperature profile of a NINAF reactor. (*From E. U. Schlünder, "Transport Phenomena in Packed Bed Reactors," in D. Luss and V. W. Weekman, Jr. (eds.), Chemical Reaction Engineering Reviews—Houston, American Chemical Society Symposium Series 72, 128 (1978) by permission.*)

profile of catalyst surface temperatures is shown by the curve marked $T_s(r)$ and the radial profile of bulk gas temperatures is shown by the curve marked $T_G(r)$. Catalyst particles are shown as spheres. However, other particle shapes would not change the temperature profiles considerably.

Heat Transfer between Reactor Walls and Packed Beds

Schlünder[6] derived the following formula to calculate the *heat transfer coefficient* h_w between catalyst packing and tube walls in NINAF reactors:

$$h_w = (4\lambda/d_p)\left[\left(\frac{\sigma}{d_p} + 1\right)\ln\left(1 + \frac{d_p}{\sigma}\right) - 1\right] + \epsilon C_s(T_m/100)^3 \quad (4\text{-}25)$$

where $\sigma = 4\,\sigma_0(2 - \gamma)/\gamma$

ϵ = radiation emissivity

C_s = radiation of the blackbody

λ = heat conductivity of the gas

σ_0 = mean free path of gas molecules

γ = accommodation coefficient

T_m = average temperature between the wall and the first layer of the packed bed

An extensive study of some 5000 data from various authors revealed unsuspected complexities in the relationships of h_w to other reactor parameters such as Pe_h and D_T/Z_T. Schlünder concedes that much about h_w is not yet fully understood.

4.4 INTRAPHASE TRANSPORT IN FIXED-BED GAS REACTORS

Gaseous chemical species move in catalyst pores by diffusion. The interested reader is referred to various thorough treatments of pore diffusion by Thiele,[19] Weisz and Prater,[20] Wheeler,[21] Satterfield,[22] Chap. 9 in Carberry,[8] and Smith.[23]

Intraphase Mass Transfer

When a chemical reaction occurs on the internal pore surface of a catalyst pellet, a concentration gradient is created between the outside bulk gas phase and the inside of the porous catalyst. Since the reactants are consumed in the pore reaction, the concentration of key reactant decreases from the outside toward the inside of the pores. The movement of the chemical species by diffusion through the pores and the return of the reaction products by the same path but in the reverse direction constitute a mass transfer resistance to the reaction. A reaction which occurs only on the outside surface of a catalyst is always much faster than the same reaction would be if it occurred inside deep pores. The ratio of the reaction rate in a porous catalyst to the rate on a nonporous catalyst is called the *effectiveness factor* η. Of course we have to assume that both the porous and the nonporous catalyst are made of the same material and have the same surface area. Furthermore we must assume that the concentrations and temperatures over both catalysts are the same. The rate of a reaction that has no mass transfer resistance to overcome is called the *intrinsic* reaction rate. That would be the rate of the reaction catalyzed on the outside particle surface.

In a porous catalyst one always measures the global reaction rate, which is much slower than the intrinsic rate. One rough, but practical, way of measuring the intrinsic rate is to crush the catalyst to a very fine powder so that all the internal surface area is exposed to the full bulk-phase concentration and temperature.

Effectiveness factors were briefly discussed in Sec. 3.4. We will add only a short discussion of the Biot number for mass.

The *Biot number for mass* (Bi_m) is a dimensionless group that relates interphase mass transfer to intraphase mass transfer.

$$\mathrm{Bi}_m = k_g a/\mathcal{D}_i \tag{4-26}$$

where $\mathcal{D}_i$ is the intraphase diffusivity in square meters per second. Biot numbers are obtained by equating bulk mass transfer to mass diffusive flow:

$$k_g(C_0 - C_s) = -\mathcal{D}\frac{dC_s}{dz}\bigg|_{z=a} \tag{4-27}$$

This expression can be converted to a dimensionless one by setting $C_{rs} = (C_s/C_o)$ and $Z = z/a$, replacing C_s and z by the dimensionless parameters, and rearranging:

$$\frac{1 - C_{rs}}{(dC_{rs}/dZ)}\bigg|_{Z=1} = -\frac{1}{k_g a/\mathcal{D}} = \frac{1}{\mathrm{Bi}_m} \tag{4-28}$$

Thus Biot numbers are obtained

$$\mathrm{Bi}_m = k_g a/\mathcal{D}_i \tag{4-26}$$

Values for Bi_m can be calculated from three sources:

1. The value of k_g is calculated from Carberry's correlation [Eq. (4-12)].

2. The value of a can be measured for each catalyst.
3. $\mathcal{D}_i$ can be estimated from the practical methods for estimating diffusivities given by Satterfield.[22]

The Bi_m values range[8] from 10^2 to 10^5.

Intraphase Heat Transfer

Heat phenomena in fixed-bed gas reactors include temperature gradients through the catalyst particles and the bulk gas phase and heat transport through the packed bed and the wall.

Since the chemical reaction occurs on the internal and external surfaces of the catalyst particle, the heat generated by an exothermic reaction must be removed from inside the catalyst to maintain the desired reaction temperature. In the case of endothermic reactions, the heat consumed inside the particle must be replaced, or else the catalyst would cool and the reaction would slow down or even stop entirely. Thus temperature gradients are created between the inside and the outside surfaces of the particle and between the catalyst particle and the bulk gas phase.

Intraphase Temperature Gradients

The temperature gradient ΔT_i between the centerline of the catalyst pellet and the catalyst outside surface is called the *intraphase temperature gradient.* This gradient is expressed according to Prater[24] by

$$\Delta T_i = T - T_s = -\Delta H \, D_e(C_s - C)/\lambda \qquad (4\text{-}27)$$

where T = temperature at all points of the particle having a reactant concentration C, K

T_s = temperature at the surface of the catalyst, K

$-\Delta H$ = heat of reaction, kJ/kmol (negative values mean exothermic reaction)

D_e = effective diffusivity of the particle, m^2/s

λ = thermal conductivity of the catalyst, kJ/(s · m · K)

C = molar concentration of key reactant, $kmol/m^3$

C_s = molar concentration of key reactant on the catalyst surface, $kmol/m^3$

It is advantageous to discuss both intraphase and interphase temperature gradients together in this section.

Interphase Temperature Gradients

The external temperature gradient ΔT_x between the catalyst surface and the bulk gas phase is called the *interphase temperature gradient.* This gradient is obtained by a heat balance across the fluid film[25]

$$h(T_s - T) = \mathcal{R}(-\Delta H) \tag{4-28}$$

where h = interphase heat transfer coefficient
T = bulk gas temperature
$\mathcal{R}$ = observable global reaction rate

From Eq. (4-28) we can obtain:

$$\Delta T_x = T_s - T = \mathcal{R}(-\Delta H)/h \tag{4-29}$$

All three quantities in the right-hand side of this equation can be evaluated.

It is also of interest to know the ratio of the external gradient ΔT_x to the total temperature gradient ΔT_o. Carberry[25] calculated this ratio as follows:

$$\frac{\Delta T_x}{\Delta T_o} = \frac{(\mathrm{Bi}_m/\mathrm{Bi}_h)\eta_0\,\mathrm{Da}}{1 + \eta_0\,\mathrm{Da}\,[(\mathrm{Bi}_m/\mathrm{Bi}_h) - 1]} \tag{4-30}$$

where η_0 = overall effectiveness factor
Bi_m = Biot number for mass
Bi_h = Biot number for heat
Da = Damköhler number

In Eq. (4-30), $\Delta T_x/\Delta T_o$ is expressed in terms of an observed rate η_0 Da and the ratio of Biot numbers. We will discuss thermal Biot numbers further below. The significance of this ratio derives from the fact that ΔT_x makes up a far larger fraction of ΔT_o than does ΔT_i. Thus, in fixed-bed gas reactors the major seat of thermal resistance is likely to be external.

Thermal Biot Numbers

In analogy to Biot numbers for mass, there is a Biot number for heat (Bi_h), defined by

$$\mathrm{Bi}_h = ha/\lambda \tag{4-31}$$

where λ = thermal conductivity of the catalyst particle, $kJ/(m \cdot s \cdot K)$
h = interphase heat transfer coefficient, $kJ/(m^2 \cdot s \cdot K)$
a = outside surface area-to-volume ratio of the catalyst, m^{-1}

This *thermal Biot number* relates interphase heat transfer (numerator) to intraphase heat transfer (denominator). Its values range[8] between 10 and 10^3. Thermal Biot numbers are derived as described below.

For the outside surface of the catalyst particle, where the interphase borders on the intraphase, we can write:

$$h(T_s - T) = -\left.\frac{\lambda dT}{dz}\right|_{z=a} \qquad (4\text{-}32)$$

where T_s = catalyst surface temperature, K
T = bulk gas temperature, K
h = interphase heat transfer coefficient, $kJ/(m^2 \cdot s \cdot K)$

in dimensionless form with $T_{rs} = T_s/T$ we have:

$$\frac{T_{rs} - 1}{(dT_{rs}/dz)_{z=1}} = \frac{1}{ha/\lambda} = \frac{1}{\text{Bi}_h} \qquad (4\text{-}33)$$

There is also a *wall Biot number* (Bi_w) defined by:

$$\text{Bi}_w = h_w D_T/(2K_r \rho c_p) \qquad (4\text{-}34)$$

which relates the heat transfer through the main body of the catalyst bed (numerator) to the heat transfer through the wall (denominator). Here K_r is the radial dispersion coefficient for heat and can be calculated from the Pe_h number.

Obviously the concept of Bi_w is only applicable to NINAF reactors, since there is no heat transfer through the walls of adiabatic reactors. Values of Bi_w range[8] between 10^{-1} and 10^2.

Intraphase and Interphase Heat Transfer

Interphase heat transfer has already been discussed above. Because of the necessity of reviewing the joint treatments of interphase and intraphase heat transfer, it must be discussed again here.

Heat transport through the bulk gas phase in fixed-bed gas reactors can be characterized by a heat transport coefficient h, which we can define as a flux divided by a driving force:

$$h = \frac{\text{diffusive flux of heat}}{T_s - T} \qquad (4\text{-}35)$$

The diffusive heat flux can then be expressed for both the bulk gas phase (interphase) and the solid catalyst phase (intraphase), according to Fourier's law:

$$q_G = -\lambda_{G0}\,\partial T/\partial z \tag{4-36}$$

$$q_s = -\lambda_{s0}\,\partial T_s/\partial z \tag{4-37}$$

where λ_{G0} = apparent heat conductivity in gas phase
λ_{s0} = apparent heat conductivity in catalyst (solid) phase
T = bulk gas temperature, K
T_s = temperature of catalyst surface, K
z = space variable
q_G = interphase heat flux
q_s = intraphase heat flux

The evaluation of these thermal fluxes require that a transport model be developed and that the boundary conditions be well defined (see pp. 200–201 of Ref. 8). Schlünder[6] has discussed a "most widely used model" for heat transport through catalyst beds. This model assumes that: (1) both the gas and solid phases follow Fourier's law, and (2) both heat fluxes q_G and q_s penetrate through the fixed bed along the radial space variable r simultaneously and independently. The total heat flux q is then:

$$q = -\lambda_{s0}(\partial T_s/\partial r) - \lambda_{G0}(\partial T/\partial r) \tag{4-38}$$

In the absence of any chemical reaction $T_s = T$ and

$$q = -(\lambda_{s0} + \lambda_{G0})(\partial T/\partial r) \tag{4-39}$$

Assumption (1) is arbitrary and has yet to be experimentally verified. Assumption (2) has been verified by Schlünder,[6] who reviewed this apparently quite complex model.

NOMENCLATURE

a — External particle surface-area/particle-volume ratio, m^{-1}

A_c — Cross-sectional area of the empty reactor, m^2

B — Radiation passage number, or fraction of the incident radiation that is allowed to pass through the packing, dimensionless

Bi_h — Biot number for heat, dimensionless

Bi_m — Biot number for mass, dimensionless

c_p	Heat capacity or specific heat of gas, kJ/(kg · K)
C_0	Inlet concentration, kmol/m^3
C_r	Reduced concentration, dimensionless
C_{rs}	Reduced surface concentration, dimensionless
C_s	Molar concentration of key reactant on exterior particle surface, kmol/m^3, or radiation of the blackbody
d_h	Hydraulic diameter, m
d_p	Catalyst particle diameter, m
D_e	Effective diffusivity of the particle, m^2/s
D_{1m}	Molecular diffusion coefficient for diffusing species in multiple component mixtures, m^2/s
D_T	Reactor inside diameter, m
$\mathcal{D}_a$	Axial dispersion coefficient for mass, m^2/s
$\mathcal{D}_i$	Intraphase diffusivity, m^2/s
$\mathcal{D}_r$	Radial dispersion coefficient for mass
Da_h	Damköhler number for heat, dimensionless
Da_m	Damköhler number for mass, dimensionless
f	Fraction of the reactor cross-sectional area with larger voids, dimensionless
g_c	Force-to-mass conversion factor = 1.0 kg · m/(N · s^2)
G	Mass flow rate of gas, kg/(s · m^2)
h	Interphase heat transfer coefficient, kJ/(m^2 · s · K)
h_p	Interphase heat transfer coefficient for single sphere, kJ/(m^2 · s · K)
h_w	Heat transfer coefficient between catalyst packing and tube walls, kJ/(m^2 · s · K)
k_1	Rate constant of reaction 1
k_B	Boltzmann's constant
k_g	Interphase mass-transfer coefficient, m/s
K_r	Radial dispersion coefficient for heat, m^2/s
n	Number of CSTR equivalents
Nu	Nusselt number for packed bed, dimensionless
Nu_p	Nusselt number for single sphere, dimensionless
Pe_a	Mass Péclet number for axial dispersion, dimensionless

Pe_h	Radial Péclet number for heat, dimensionless
Pe_m	Radial Péclet number for mass, dimensionless
Pr	Prandtl number, dimensionless
q_G	Interphase heat flux, $kJ/(m^2 \cdot s)$
q_s	Intraphase heat flux, $kJ/(m^2 \cdot s)$
r	Radial position or distance from reactor axis, m
Re	Reynolds number, dimensionless
$\mathcal{R}$	Global rate of reaction, $kmol/(s \cdot m^3)$
Sc	Schmidt number, dimensionless
S_t	Total geometric surface area of catalyst, m^2
T	Absolute temperature of the bulk gas phase, K
T_0	Inlet temperature of the bulk gas phase, K
T_m	Average temperature between the wall and the first layer of the packed bed, K
T_r	Reduced bulk gas temperature = T/T_0, dimensionless
T_{rs}	Reduced surface temperature = T_s/T_0, dimensionless
T_s	Absolute temperature at the catalyst surface, K
u	Superficial fluid velocity based on empty reactor cross section, m/s
u_m	Superficial gas velocity based on empty reactor cross section between inlet and outlet, m/s
v	Point velocity at a distance r from the axis, m/s
z	Longitudinal reactor coordinate
Z_T	Total reactor length, m
$(-\Delta H)$	Reaction heat, kJ/kmol
ΔP	Pressure drop, force units, bar
ΔT_i	Intraphase temperature gradient, K
ΔT_o	Overall thermal gradient, K
ΔT_x	Interphase temperature gradient, K
η_1	Effectiveness factor of reaction 1
α	Reaction order
ε	Void fraction or fractional void volume in bed, dimensionless
ϵ	Emission coefficient of the particle surface, dimensionless

λ	Thermal conductivity of the catalyst particle, kJ/(s · m · K)
λ_a	Axial thermal conductivity, kJ/(s · m · K)
λ_g	Thermal conductivity of gas, kJ/(s · m · K)
λ_r	Radiation conductivity, kJ/(m · s · K)
μ	Absolute viscosity of gas, Pa · s
ρ	Density of gas, kg/m^3
σ_0	Mean free path of gas molecules, m

REFERENCES

1. M. Orhan Tarhan and William E. Schiesser, "Computer-Aided Design of Nonisothermal Nonadiabatic Fixed-Bed (NINAF) Gas Reactors," paper presented at the 74th AIChE National Meeting in New Orleans, March 11–15, 1973.
2. Sabri Ergun, "Fluid Flow Through Packed Columns," *Chem. Eng. Progr.* **48:**89–94 (1952).
3. C. E. Schwartz and J. M. Smith, "Flow Distribution in Packed Beds," *Ind. Eng. Chem.* **45:**1209–1218 (1953).
4. M. R. Shaffer, M.S. thesis, Purdue University, Lafayette, Ind. (1952).
5. R. F. Benenati and C. B. Brosilow, "Void Fraction Distribution in a Bed of Spheres," *AIChE J.* **3:**359–361 (1962).
6. E. U. Schlünder, "Transport Phenomena in Packed-Bed Reactors," in *Chemical Reaction Engineering Reviews—Houston,* American Chemical Society, Symposium Series 72, 1978, pp. 110–161.
7. Richard H. Wilhelm, "Rate Processes in Chemical Reactors," *Chem. Eng. Progr.* **49:**150–154 (1953).
8. James J. Carberry, *Chemical and Catalytic Reaction Engineering,* McGraw-Hill, New York, 1976.
9. James J. Carberry and Martin M. Wendel, "A Computer Model of the Fixed-Bed Catalytic Reactor—The Adiabatic and Quasi-Adiabatic Cases," *AIChE J.* **9:**129–133 (1963).
10. James J. Carberry, "First Order Rate Processes and Axial Dispersion in Packed Bed Reactors," *Can. J. Chem. Eng.* **36:** 207–209 (1958).
11. James J. Carberry and R. H. Bretton, "Axial Dispersion of Mass in Flow Through Fixed Beds," *AIChE J.* **4:**367–375 (1958).
12. Sabri Ergun, "Mass-Transfer Rate in Packed Columns—Its Analogy to Pressure Loss," *Chem. Eng. Progr.* **48:**227–236 (1952).
13. James J. Carberry, "A Boundary-Layer Model of Fluid-Particle Mass Transfer in Fixed Beds," *AIChE J.* **6:**460–463 (1960).

14. James J. Carberry and Donald White, "The Role of Transport Phenomena in Catalytic Reactor Behavior," *Ind. Eng. Chem.* **61**(7):27–35 (1969).

15. Holger Martin, "Low Peclet Number Particle-To-Fluid Heat and Mass Transfer in Packed Beds," *Chem. Eng. Sci.* **33:**913–919 (1978).

16. Volker Gnielinski, "Berechnung mittlerer Wärme- und Stoffübergangskoeffizienten an laminar und turbulent überströmten Einzelkörpern mit Hilfe einer einheitlichen Gleichung," *Forsch. Ingr.-Wesen.* **41:**145–153 (1975).

17. D. Vortmeyer and C. J. Börner, "Die Strahlungsdurchlasszahl in Schüttungen," *Chem.-Ingr.-Tech.* **38:**1077–1079 (1966).

18. D. Vortmeyer, "Der Energietransport durch Wärmestrahlung in Festbetten mit exothermer Reaktion," *Ber. Bunsenges, physik. Chem.* **74:**127–130 (1970).

19. E. W. Thiele, "Relation between Catalytic Activity and Size of Particles," *Ind. Eng. Chem.* **31**(7):916–920 (1939).

20. Paul Burg Weisz and C. D. Prater, "Interpretation of Measurements in Experimental Catalysis," in *Advances in Catalysis,* Vol. 6, Academic Press, New York, 1954 pp. 143–146.

21. Ahlborn Wheeler, "Reaction Rates and Selectivity in Catalyst Pores," in P. H. Emmett (ed.), *Catalysis,* Vol. 2, Reinhold, New York, 1955, Chap. 2, pp. 105–165.

22. Charles N. Satterfield, *Mass Transfer in Heterogeneous Catalysis,* MIT Press, Cambridge, 1970, Chap. 1.

23. J. M. Smith, *Chemical Engineering Kinetics,* 2d ed. McGraw-Hill, New York, 1970, Chap. 11.

24. Charles D. Prater, "The Temperature Produced by Heat of Reaction in the Interior of Porous Particles," *Chem. Eng. Sci.* **8:**284–286 (1958).

25. James J. Carberry, "On the Relative Importance of External-Internal Temperature Gradients in Heterogeneous Catalysis," *Ind. Eng. Chem. Fundamentals* **14:**129–131 (1975).

Chapter 5 PROCESS DESIGN OF FIXED-BED GAS REACTORS

This chapter deals with the process design of various types of fixed-bed reactors. Isothermal reactors are treated first, mainly in order to introduce a simple procedure. As we progress through the treatment of adiabatic and—later—NINAF reactors, things will become increasingly complex.

5.1 ISOTHERMAL REACTORS

There are various ways of making a fixed-bed gas reactor behave isothermally. It is hard to imagine a chemical reaction that has a reaction heat of zero. By definition such a reaction would not occur at all. Consequently, one way to obtain an isothermal reactor is to achieve perfect heat transfer with the surroundings so that all points of the fixed bed may be maintained at the same temperature. This may be nearly achieved only in very small laboratory reactors.

Sometimes the reactant is diluted in the feed and the heat of reaction is hardly noticeable. In such cases a fixed bed may be operated practically as an isothermal reactor. Also, a very weakly exothermic or endothermic reaction behaves practically like an isothermal reaction. Thus isothermal reactors are not designed very often for full-scale plants. In spite of this, we will discuss the design of an isothermal reactor as an introductory and relatively simple example.

General Design Procedure

The general procedure for designing isothermal gas reactors consists of setting up rate equations and a design equation. Rate equations may be expressed in the practical power law form:

$$\mathcal{R} = \eta r_v = \eta A \exp(-E/RT)\, C_a^{\alpha} C_b^{\beta} \tag{5-1}$$

where
$\mathcal{R}$ = apparent reaction rate, kmol/(s · m^3)
r_v = intrinsic reaction rate, kmol/(s · m^3)
η = intraphase effectiveness factor, dimensionless
C = molar concentration of reactant or product, kmol/m^3
A = frequency factor
E = activation energy, kJ/kmol
R = gas constant = 8.314 kJ/(kmol · K)
T = absolute temperature, K

Subscripts a and b relate to the concentrations of particular reactants or products in a reaction of the type

$$\text{A} + \text{B} + \ldots \rightarrow \text{P} + \text{Q} + \ldots$$

Superscripts α and β are exponents indicating reaction order.

Sometimes the rate equations are expressed in terms of partial pressures instead of concentrations:

$$r_{vp} = A \exp(-E/RT)\, p_a^{\alpha} p_b^{\beta} \tag{5-2}$$

where p is the partial pressure of a reactant or product in bars.

The relationship between r_v and r_{vp} is given by:

$$r_{vp} = r_v(\dot{R}T)^{\alpha+\beta} \tag{5-3}$$

where $\dot{R}$ is the gas constant (expressed in different units from R) = 0.08314 m^3 · bar/(kmol · K).

In most "real-life cases" the reacting system is not a simple one. There is more than one reaction going on and these reactions are consecutive, simultaneous, parallel, or combinations of these types. However we will simplify our first problem by assuming a single reaction.

The so-called design equation is the same for all types of fixed-bed reactors. It is developed as follows: Let us consider a fixed-bed reactor of cross-sectional area A_c and bed height z (Fig. 5-1). Let us consider a differential volume dV of this fixed bed limited by two parallel surfaces, each perpendicular to the axis oz of the cylindrical bed. If the distance between these cross-sectional surfaces is a differential dz, the differential volume dV will be:

$$dV = A_c\, dz \tag{5-4}$$

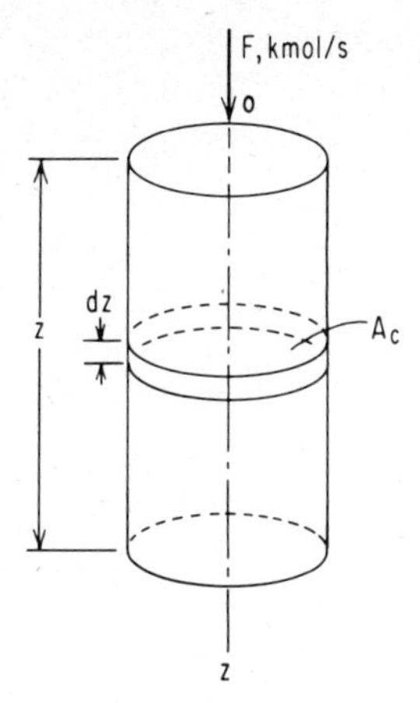

FIG. 5-1 Development of the design equation for isothermal or adiabatic fixed-bed reactors.

Let us assume that F kmol/s of a feedstock containing y_0 mole fraction of the key reactant enters the reactor and that the fractional conversion of that reactant is x. Let us also designate the rate of chemical reaction occurring in the reactor as r_v. The dimensions of this rate are kilomoles per second per cubic meter. The volume includes both the catalysts and the voids. The balance between the incoming and the outgoing materials can be written:

$$\text{Incoming moles} = \text{outgoing moles} + \text{accumulating moles} + \text{moles disappearing by reaction} \tag{5-5}$$

In steady-state operation no material accumulates in or is depleted from the reactor. Equation (5-5) can then be expressed as

$$Fy_0 = Fy_0(1 - dx) + r_v\, dV \tag{5-6}$$

Here Fy_0 is the number of moles of the key reactant and $1 - x$ is the unreacted fraction of Fy_0 when leaving the differential volume dV, thus $Fy_0(1 - dx)$ is the unreacted feed leaving dV and $r_v dV$ is the extent of reaction occurring in differential volume dV. Equation (5-6) can be rearranged to give

$$\begin{aligned} Fy_0 - Fy_0 + Fy_0\, dx &= r_v\, dV \\ Fy_0\, dx &= r_v\, dV \end{aligned} \tag{5-7}$$

or on replacing dV by its value in Eq. (5-4)

$$Fy_0\, dx = r_v\, A_c\, dz \tag{5-8}$$

In addition to the rate and design equations, it is necessary to develop a pressure drop equation to compute the pressure at every point of the reactor. The pressure drop is given by the Ergun law, discussed in Sec. 4.3:

$$\frac{\Delta P}{Z} = 150 \times 10^5 \frac{(1-\varepsilon)^2}{\varepsilon^3} \cdot \frac{\mu\, u_m}{g_c\, d_p^2} + 1.75 \times 10^5 \frac{1-\varepsilon}{\varepsilon^3} \cdot \frac{G\, u_m}{d_p g_c} \text{ bar/m} \quad (4\text{-}1)$$

The value of $\Delta P/Z$ can be calculated at the start, and at every step proper pressure corrections can be made.

Once the design equation, rate equation, and pressure drop equation have been set up, the designer must express the concentration or partial pressure terms in the rate equation in terms of the fractional conversion x and simultaneously solve the three equations for the reactor height Z. If there is more than one rate equation, that system of rate equations must be prepared for use in the simultaneous solution. This preparation will be discussed further below in the treatment of NINAF reactors.

Example: Design of an Isothermal Reactor

Let us consider a simple hydrogenation reaction

$$\underset{\text{Ethylene}}{H_2C{=}CH_2} + H_2 \rightarrow \underset{\text{Ethane}}{CH_3{-}CH_3} \quad (5\text{-}9)$$

This is an exothermic reaction, but it can be run in a very small isothermal reactor, which was done by Wynkoop and Wilhelm.[1] These investigators used a copper-magnesia catalyst, which they prepared and packed in a 9.35-mm ID, 280-mm-long yellow brass reactor tube provided with a water jacket. By recirculating 37.85 L/min of water through this jacket, a water film coefficient of more than 5.67 kJ/(m^2 · s · K) and a practically constant tube-wall temperature were obtained. Experiments made at various constant temperatures in the 9 to 79°C range in this reactor showed that the reaction of Eq. (5-9) is first-order with respect to hydrogen. The rate equation can then be written by setting

$$\alpha = 1 \qquad \beta = 0 \qquad a = H_2 \qquad A \exp(-E/RT) = k \qquad C_a^\alpha = C_H$$

k being the *reaction rate constant.* Thus Eq. (5-1) becomes

$$r_v = k\, C_{\text{H}} \quad (5\text{-}10)$$

in which η is implicitly set equal to 1. The reactor volume can be calculated by simultaneously solving the design and rate equations [Eqs.

(5-7) and (5-10), respectively]. (In this small reactor ΔP can be neglected.) This can be done, if C_H is expressed in terms of x.

Let us combine Eq. (5-7) and Eq. (5-10) and rearrange:

$$F\, y_0\, dx = k\, C_H\, dV$$

$$\frac{dV}{Fy_0} = \frac{dx}{k \cdot C_H} \tag{5-11}$$

Since the reaction involves a change in volume, we must take account of it in order to integrate Eq. (5-11). Let us consider the reaction

$$aA + bB \rightarrow pP + qQ \tag{5-12}$$

where a, b, p, and q are stoichiometric coefficients, A and B are reacting species, and P and Q are reaction products. Suppose the feedstock consists only of A and B, not necessarily in the stoichiometric proportion. Let A be the limiting reactant, i.e., $N_A^0/N_B^0 < a/b$, where N is the number of moles passing through the reactor per unit time and let the superscript 0 denote *inlet* and let the subscripts T and A denote *total* and *ethylene*. Initially we have:

$$N_T^0 = N_A^0 + N_B^0 \tag{5-13}$$

where $N_A^0 = y_0\, N_T^0 \qquad N_B^0 = (1 - y_0)\, N_T^0 = \dfrac{1 - y_0}{y_0} N_A^0$ (5-14)

After a fractional conversion x_A:

$$\begin{aligned} N_T &= N_A + N_B + N_P + N_Q \\ &= N_A^0(1 - x_A) + N_B^0 - \frac{b}{a} N_A^0\, x_A + \frac{p}{a} N_A^0\, x_A + \frac{q}{a} N_A^0\, x_A \\ &= N_T^0 - N_A^0\, x_A \left(1 + \frac{b}{a} - \frac{p}{a} - \frac{q}{a}\right) \\ &= N_T^0 - N_T^0\, y_0\, x_A \left(\frac{a + b - p - q}{a + b}\right)\left(\frac{a + b}{a}\right) \end{aligned} \tag{5-15}$$

If we set $d' = \dfrac{(p + q) - (a + b)}{a + b}$ (5-16)

$$\begin{aligned} N_T &= N_T^0 + N_T^0\, y_0 \frac{a + b}{a} d' x_A \\ N_T &= N_T^0 \left(1 + y_0 \frac{a + b}{a} d' x_A\right) \end{aligned} \tag{5-17}$$

In the case of ethylene hydrogenation:

$$1 \text{ mol ethylene} + 1 \text{ mol } H_2 \rightarrow 1 \text{ mol ethane} \tag{5-18}$$

$$a = 1 \qquad b = 1 \qquad p = 1 \qquad q = 0$$

$$d' \frac{(1) - (1 + 1)}{1 + 1} = -\frac{1}{2} \qquad \frac{a + b}{a} = 2$$

$$N_T = (1 - y_0 x_A)N_T^0 \tag{5-19}$$

where at start $x_A = 0 \quad N_T = N_T^0$ and

at end $x_A = 1 \quad N_T = (1 - y_0)N_T^0$

If we write a materials balance equation for reactant B across the reactor, the number of moles of B, N_B, may be expressed as a function of x_A

$$N_B = N_B^0 - \frac{b}{a} x_A N_A^0 \tag{5-20}$$

$$= (1 - y_0) N_T^0 - \frac{b}{a} y_0 x_A N_T^0$$

$$= \left(1 - y_0 - \frac{b}{a} y_0 x_A\right) N_T^0 \tag{5-21}$$

In the case of ethylene hydrogenation:

$$N_B = (1 - y_0 - y_0 x_A) N_T^0 \tag{5-22}$$

$$= N_T^0 - y_0 N_T^0 (1 + x_A)$$

$$= N_T^0 - N_A^0 (1 + x_A) \tag{5-23}$$

Combining Eq. (5-19) with Eq. (5-23) gives:

$$\frac{N_B}{N_T} = \frac{N_T^0 - N_A^0(1 + x_A)}{N_T^0 (1 - y_0 x_A)} = \frac{1}{1 - y_0 x_A} - \frac{N_A^0(1 + x_A)}{N_T^0(1 - y_0 x_A)} \tag{5-24}$$

In Eq. (5-10) C_H may be expressed as:

$$C_H = \frac{N_B}{V} = \frac{p_{H_2}}{\dot{R}T} = \frac{P N_B}{\dot{R}TN_T}$$

$$= \frac{P}{\dot{R}T}\left[\frac{1}{1 - y_0 x_A} - \left(\frac{N_A^0}{N_T^0}\right)\frac{1 + x_A}{1 - y_0 x_A}\right] \tag{5-25}$$

where P is the total pressure. Now C_H in Eq. (5-10) may be replaced by its value from Eq. (5-25), taking in consideration that $(N_A^0/N_T^0) = y_0$

$$r_v = k\, C_H = k\frac{P}{\dot{R}T}\left[\frac{1}{1 - y_0 x_A} - y_0 \frac{1 + x_A}{1 - y_0 x_A}\right] \tag{5-26}$$

Substituting Eq. (5-26) into the design equation, Eq. (5-11)

$$\frac{dV}{Fy_0} = \frac{\dot{R}T}{kP}\left(\frac{1 - y_0\, x_A}{1 - y_0\,(1 + x_A)}\right) dx \tag{5-27}$$

$$\frac{kP}{\dot{R}TFy_0}\int_0^V dV = \int_0^{x_A} \frac{-1 + y_0\, x_A}{y_0 - 1 + y_0\, x_A}\, dx \tag{5-28}$$

Equation (5-28) can be integrated by using the following integration formula

$$\int_0^x \frac{a + bx}{\alpha + \beta x}\, dx = \frac{bx}{\beta} + \frac{(a\beta - \alpha b)}{\beta^2}\ln(\alpha + \beta x) \tag{5-29}$$

where $a = -1 \qquad b = y_0 \qquad \alpha = y_0 - 1 \qquad \beta = y_0$

$$\int_0^{x_A} \frac{-1 + y_0\, x_A}{y_0 - 1 + y_0\, x_A}\, dx = x_A + \ln \frac{y_0 - 1 + y_0\, x_A}{y_0 - 1}$$

Substituting this value into Eq. (5-28) and integrating dV gives

$$\frac{kPV}{\dot{R}TFy_0} = x_A + \ln \frac{y_0 - 1 + y_0\, x_A}{y_0 - 1}$$

$$V = \frac{\dot{R}TFy_0}{kP}\left[x_A + \ln \frac{y_0 - 1 + y_0\, x_A}{y_0 - 1}\right] \tag{5-30}$$

If an equal number of moles of ethylene and hydrogen is fed to the reactor, or if $y_0 = 0.5$, Eq. (5-30) reduces to

$$V = \frac{\dot{R}TF}{2kP}\left[x_A - \ln(1 - x_A)\right] \tag{5-31}$$

Let us assume some values for x_A and calculate the value of the bracket in Eq. (5-31)

$x =$	0	0.5	0.9	0.99	0.999	1.0
$x - \ln(1 - x) =$	0	1.193	3.2025	5.595	7.9068	∞

These numbers show that with an equimolar mixture of reactants, complete conversion of ethylene cannot be attained in a finite-sized reactor. But with a slight excess of hydrogen, e.g., with $y_0 = 0.49$ instead of $y_0 = 0.5$, the value of the bracket in Eq. (5-30) drops to 4.1065 for $x_A = 1$.

Let us now calculate the design of an actual laboratory reactor. We can use Eq. (5-30) with $y_0 = 0.49$. Other quantities in Eq. (5-30) are:

- $F = 2.0 \times 10^{-8}$ kmol/s of total feed
- $\dot{R} = 0.08314 \text{ m}^3 \cdot \text{bar/(kmol} \cdot \text{K)}$ gas constant
- $R = 8.314 \text{ kJ/(kmol} \cdot \text{K)}$ gas constant
- $T = 67°\text{C} + 273.2 = 340.2 \text{ K}$
- $k = 5.96 \times 10^6 \exp(-55{,}731/RT)$ $\text{kmol/(s} \cdot \text{m}^3)$ determined by Winkoop and Wilhelm,[1] at $T = 340.2$ K, $k = 0.0165$
- $x_A = 1.0$ desired
- $P = 1.0$ bar assumed.

$$V = \frac{(0.08314)(2 \times 10^{-8})(340.2)}{(2)(1.0)\,(0.0165)}[4.106] = 0.00007038 \text{ m}^3$$

$$= 70.38 \text{ cm}^3$$

If a 1-cm-inside diameter reactor tube is used, the reactor length Z will be $(70 \text{ cm}^3/\pi\ 0.5^2) = 89.1$ cm.

This whole calculation is only of academic value, since experimental reactors are not designed by this type of calculation and commercial-size reactors cannot be operated completely isothermally.

It is of interest to note that this isothermal reactor design example was computed analytically. In case a complex reacting system is involved or even in case the single reaction is reversible and the rate equation becomes messy, it may become necessary to resort to numerical integration using a digital computer.

5.2
ADIABATIC GAS REACTORS

Let us review the conditions of adiabaticity.

Definition

An *adiabatic* reactor is one which exchanges no heat with the surroundings. Consequently, if an exothermic reaction is run in an adiabatic fixed-bed reactor, the temperature of the gas stream will increase from the inlet toward the outlet. If, on the other hand, an endothermic reaction is run in the same reactor, the temperature of the gas stream will drop along the reactor length.

Most industrial fixed-bed gas reactors are designed as adiabatic reactors. A good insulation around the reactor vessel usually provides complete isolation and adiabaticity.

One-Dimensional Plug-Flow Model

The simplest model of an adiabatic gas reactor is the *one-dimensional plug-flow model.* A reactor must meet the following conditions in order to conform to this model:

- There should be no heat exchange between reactor and surroundings (condition of adiabaticity).
- The flow pattern through the fixed catalyst bed should be such that linear velocities of the reacting stream are the same at any point of the bed.
- There should be no axial dispersion.
- There should be no radial dispersion.

The first condition can be met by an efficient insulation around the reactor. The second condition can be met by using appropriate flow distributors at the inlet of the catalyst bed. Without such flow distributors the flow pattern would be somewhat parabolic, with lower velocities near the wall and higher velocities a few particle diameters from the wall (Fig. 4-2). The third condition (no axial dispersion) is easy to meet for fixed-bed gas reactors. Axial dispersion is fundamentally local backmixing of reactants and products in the axial, or longitudinal, direction in the small interstices of the packed bed, which is due to molecular diffusion, convection, and turbulence. Axial dispersion has been shown to be negligible in fixed-bed gas reactors (see Sec. 4.3). The fourth condition (no radial dispersion) can be met if the flow pattern through the bed already meets the second condition. If the velocity of flow in the axial direction is constant through the entire cross section and if the reactor vessel is well insulated (first condition), there can be no radial dispersion to speak of in gas reactors. Thus the one-dimensional adiabatic reactor model may be actualized without great difficulties.

Development of Design Equations for Adiabatic Gas Reactors

Basically, the design of adiabatic fixed-bed gas reactors according to the one-dimensional model consists in the simultaneous solution of three types of equations. The first type is the rate equation or a system of rate equations, similar to Eq. (5-1) or Eq. (5-2). The second type is the design equation proper, typified by Eq. (5-7)

$$F\, y_0\, dx = r_v dV = r_v\, A_c\, dz \tag{5-7}$$

just as in the case of isothermal reactors. The third type of equation is developed from an *energy balance.* In case of an exothermic process, this balance equates the amount of heat generated by the reaction with the heat absorbed by all reaction gases in order to increase their temperature. In the case of an endothermic process, the amount of heat absorbed by the reaction is equated to the heat supplied by all reaction gases from their decrease in temperature. This balance can be written as:

$$F\, y_0\, dx(-\Delta H) = \Sigma m_i\, C_{pi}\, dT \tag{5-32}$$

where $(-\Delta H)$ = the heat of reaction of the entire reacting system

m_i = the molar flow of each reacting species (this includes both reactants and products), kmol/s

C_{pi} = the molar heat capacity of each reacting species, kJ/(kmol · K)

The design equation Eq. (5-7) is sometimes written in a variety of forms. The difference stems from the basis of the rate equation. In Eqs. (5-1), (5-2), and (5-7) we used a rate expression that is based on moles reacted per second and per volume of fixed bed. This volume includes both the catalyst volume and the void space. This preference is based on the fact that in the United States catalysts are sold by volume. In the literature one often comes across various bases for expressing rate equations:

- Unit weight of catalyst bed
- Unit void volume of catalyst bed
- Unit surface area of the catalyst

When catalyst weight is used as a basis, then Eq. (5-7) can be modified to

$$Fy_0 dx = r_w\, \rho_B\, A_c\, dz \tag{5-33}$$

where r_w is the reaction rate in moles converted per unit time per unit weight of catalyst and ρ_B is the bulk density of the catalyst in kilograms per cubic meter.

When void volume of the catalyst is used as a basis, Eq. (5-7) can be modified to

$$F\, y_0\, dx = r_{v'}\, \varepsilon\, A_c\, dz \tag{5-34}$$

where $r_{v'}$ is the reaction rate in moles converted per unit time per unit void space of catalyst and ε is the fractional void space in the catalyst bed.

When the surface area of the catalyst bed is used as a basis, Eq. (5-7) can be modified to:

$$F\, y_0\, dx = r_s\, S_g\, \rho_B\, A_c\, dz \tag{5-35}$$

where r_s is the reaction rate in moles converted per unit time per unit surface area of catalyst and S_g is the catalyst surface area in unit surface area per unit weight. Catalyst surface area is almost always given in square meters per gram. Consequently, in order to make the system of units in Eq. (5-35) a consistent one, we must convert S_g into units consistent with the system employed, as follows:

F (kmol/s) $\quad r_s$ [kmol/(s · m^2)] $\quad S_g$ (m^2/kg) $\quad \rho_B$ (kg/m^3) $\quad A_c$ (m^2) $\quad z$(m)

Thus, it makes no difference on what basis the reaction rate is expressed as long as this basis is known and the proper units are used. In practice, the actual process design work for the reactor consists in finding the various kinetic and thermal data needed for Eqs. (5-1), (5-32), and any one of Eqs. (5-7), (5-33), (5-34), and (5-35), as the case may be, and in solving the three simultaneous equations. Details and complications will be seen in the treatment of examples that follows.

The Problem of Designing Fixed-Bed Gas Reactors for Exothermic Reactions[2]

Moderately exothermic gas reactions are usually run in ordinary fixed-bed reactors. The limitation to an adiabatic reactor is set by the limiting outlet temperature t_{max}, attainment of which may mark the beginning of some undesirable event such as a side reaction, poor selectivity, or excessive catalyst fouling (Fig. 5-2). If the limiting temperature is reached

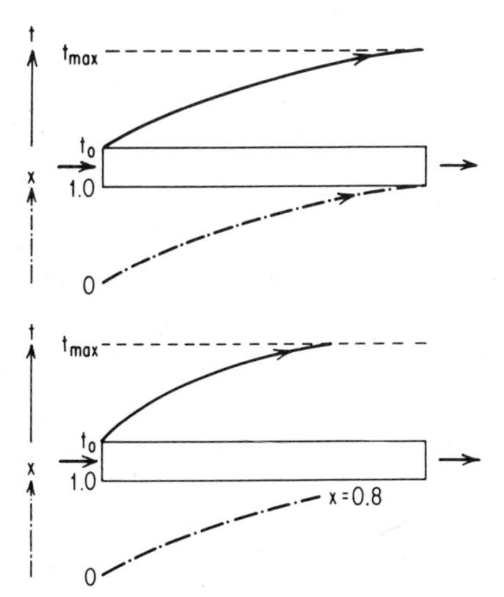

FIG. 5-2 Running exothermic reactions in adiabatic reactors.

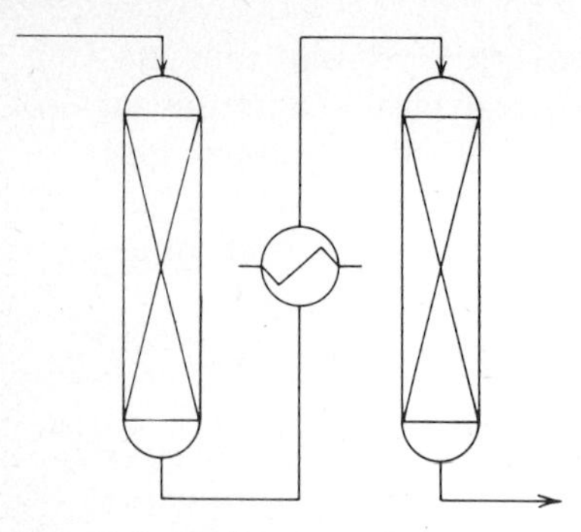

FIG. 5-3 Indirect cooling between two catalyst beds.

before the desirable fractional conversion x, then one of several methods may be applied to extend x to the desired value without exceeding t_{max}.

One such method, illustrated in Fig. 5-3, consists of (1) subdividing the catalyst volume into two or more beds so as to allow each bed to reach only t_{max} and (2) cooling the reactant gases between consecutive beds back to the inlet temperature t_0 of the first bed by using *indirect heat exchangers*. The temperature vs. conversion diagram would then look like Fig. 5-4, or after optimization like Fig. 5-5.

If the reaction temperature is too high for the use of indirect heat exchangers, a second method can be employed in which one of the reactants is injected cold into the reaction stream between consecutive beds, thus cooling them to t_0 (Fig. 5-6). This *direct cooling*, or *quenching*, method has the added advantage of pushing the reaction in the desired direction by replenishing one of the depleted reactants.

A third method is the old German technique of *stepwise quenching* (Fig. 5-7). Although this method does work, it has the disadvantage that it is somewhat sloppy and is difficult to design for.

A fourth method consists of *adding an inert gas* or an excess of one of the reactants *to the reactor feed*. The inert gas or the excess reactant acts as a heat sink by absorbing a large part of the exothermic heat and thus reduces the temperature increase for a given conversion. This method has a serious disadvantage over the other methods in that it requires an increase in the size of the reactor in order to accommodate the inert gases or the excess reactant.

In a variant of Method 4, one adds an inert liquid with a boiling point at the prevailing pressure that is close to the reaction temperature. The exothermic heat causes the inert liquid to vaporize, thus absorbing considerable heat to meet latent heat requirements. As Satterfield and Way have pointed out, in some cases with this method the reaction rate would be slower than it is in purely gas-phase methods.[3,4] The disadvantage, therefore, would be the requirement of large, costly reactors.

If no one of the methods offers a satisfactory solution to the problem of handling exothermic heat, consideration must be given to running the gas reaction in one of the following:

- A fluidized-bed reactor
- A gas-liquid-phase reactor with an inert liquid
- A NINAF gas reactor

The gas-liquid-phase reactors will be discussed in later chapters. The NINAF reactor will be discussed later in this chapter.

Example of Adiabatic Fixed-Bed Gas Reactor Design: Design of a Toluene Hydrodealkylation Reactor

Toluene can be hydrodealkylated to benzene and methane in the presence of certain catalysts[5–7] according to the equation:

$$C_6H_5\text{—}CH_3 + H_2 \longrightarrow C_6H_6 + CH_4 \qquad (5\text{-}36)$$

We will try to design a plant that will hydrodealkylate 66,000 metric tons of toluene per year to pure benzene using a fictitious catalytic process. It is necessary to resort to this assumption because there are no published or publishable data that can be used for any of the existing commercial hydrodealkylation processes. The author believes that it is perfectly all right to carry out a design procedure by using assumed data as long as these data are in the appropriate range of values. The purpose of this book is to *teach* design methods and this purpose will be met even if the calculations result in a reactor that should not be built. Anyone who actually wants to design a toluene hydrodealkylation reactor should either obtain a license from one of the commercial processes or develop a new process. In both cases reliable values will be obtained for all the parameters, which usually are not published. By using the general method of

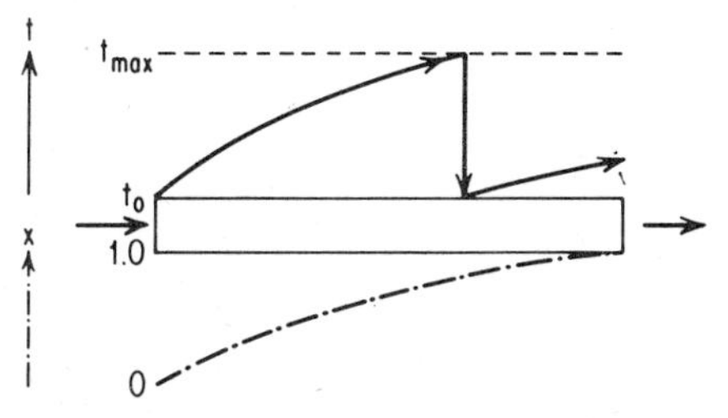

FIG. 5-4 Partition of an adiabatic reactor into two beds by cutting the first bed at t_{max}.

this book and the acquired data, it should be possible to make a reliable design that can be incorporated into an actual reactor.

Side reactions to the process of Eq. (5-36), such as the formation of biphenyl, are too slow to have any influence on reactor design, and therefore they will be ignored. The rate equation is:

$$r_v = -\frac{dC_A}{d\theta} = k\,C_A\,C_B^{0.5} = A\exp(-E/R_GT)C_AC_B^{0.5} \qquad (5\text{-}37)$$

where C_A = concentration of toluene, kmol/m^3

C_B = concentration of hydrogen, kmol/m^3

k = reaction rate constant for tolulene hydrodealkylation

A = frequency factor

E = activation energy = 148,114 kJ/kmol

ΔH = −49,974 kJ/kmol toluene converted

θ = residence time, s

The published value for the activation energy E is 35.4 kcal/(g · mol) but no published value for the frequency factor A is available. This value depends on the particular catalyst and will be assumed to be $A = 5.73 \times 10^6$. The reaction temperature at reactor inlet is assumed to be T_0 = 600°C + 273.2 = 873.2 K. The reactor pressure can be 35 to 70 atm abs. It will be assumed to be about 50 atm abs, or 50 bars. The hydrogen/aromatics ratio can be assumed to be 5.0 from general experience in hydrogenating aromatics.

For the energy balance equation, Eq. (5-32), the molar heat capacities of toluene, hydrogen, benzene, and methane between 600°C and 635°C are needed. Published c_p data[8] have been assumed to be linear between 800 and 1000 K and linear equations developed expressing c_p as a function of temperature.[8] The c_p of hydrogen is constant over this temper-

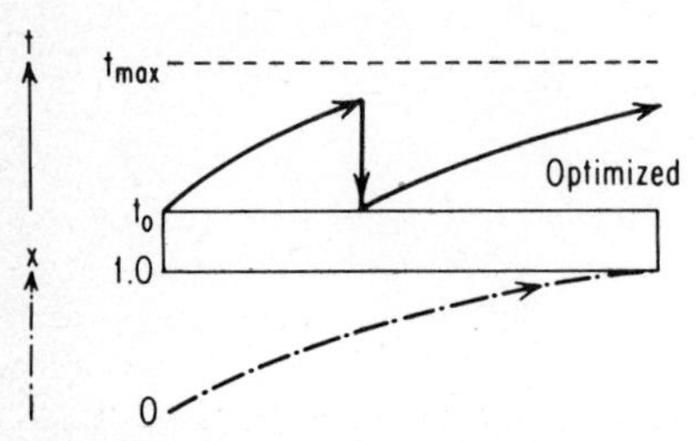

FIG. 5-5 Partition of an adiabatic reactor into two beds by optimizing the cutting point of the first bed.

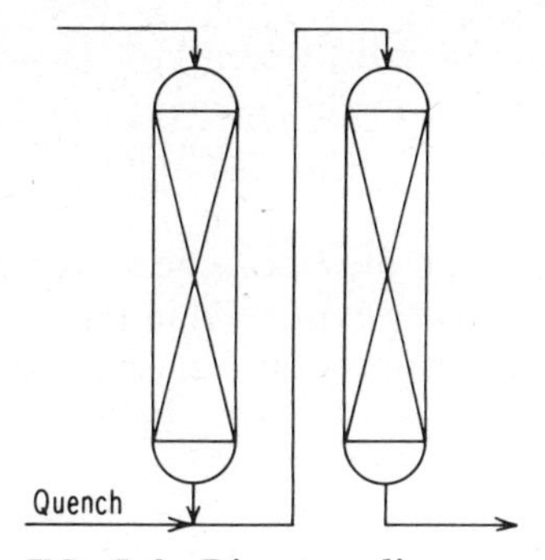

FIG. 5-6 Direct cooling, or quenching, between two catalyst beds.

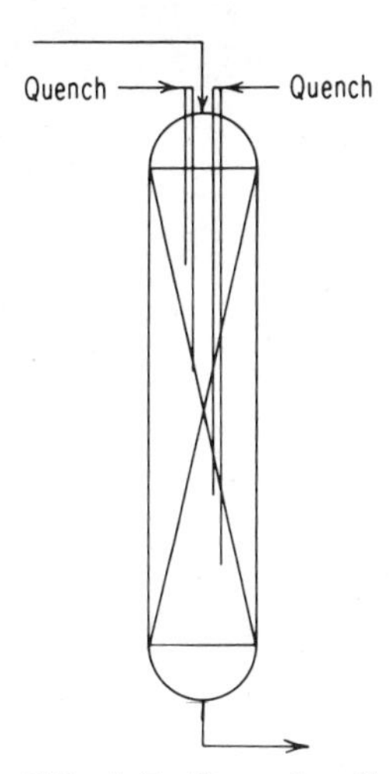

FIG. 5-7 Stepwise direct cooling in a catalyst bed.

ature interval. The following c_p data have the dimensions of kilojoules per kilomoles per kelvin.

Hydrogen: $C_p = 20.786$
Methane: $C_p = 0.04414T + 27.87$
Benzene: $C_p = 0.1067T + 103.18$
Toluene: $C_p = 0.03535T + 124.85$

The economics of any hydrogen-consuming hydrocarbon process depends upon the way the spent hydrogen is purified and reused. In this problem, it will be assumed that the spent hydrogen is purified according to Fig. 5-8[5,9] and that the purity of the combined hydrogen stream at the inlet to the hydrodealkylation unit is 90%, the balance being methane.

The toluene hydrodealkylation process provides a good example for exothermic heat removal by quenching the reaction gases with a "hydrogen gas," which in this case contains 90% hydrogen and 10% methane. Of course the first bed operates with only the inlet feedstock and the inlet hydrogen gas. However, the second and subsequent beds operate with a mixture of the effluent from the previous bed plus the quench. The design equations that will be developed in the following are applicable to any bed.

The system of equations, Eqs. (5-7), (5-32), and (5-37), can be solved simultaneously if the concentrations in Eq. (5-37) are expressed in terms of fractional conversion x. Let us do this. At any conversion x, the moles of each reactant or product are:

Toluene	$Fy_0\ (1 - x)$
Benzene	$Fy_0\ x$
Hydrogen	$Fy_0\ (5 - x) + 0.9$ quench
Methane	$Fy_0\ (5/9 + x) + 0.1$ quench
Total moles	$Fy_0\ (1 + 5 + 5/9) +$ quench, or $6.5555\ Fy_0 +$ quench

The mol fractions of each component are:

Toluene: $y_1 = Fy_0\ (1 - x)/(6.5555\ Fy_0 + \text{quench}) \qquad (=y_A)$
Benzene: $y_2 = Fy_0\ x/(6.5555\ Fy_0 + \text{quench})$
Hydrogen: $y_3 = (Fy_0\ (5 - x) + 0.9\ \text{quench})/(6.5555\ Fy_0 + \text{quench}) \qquad (=y_B)$
Methane: $y_4 = (Fy_0\ (5/9 + x) + 0.1\ \text{quench})/(6.5555\ Fy_0 + \text{quench})$

Concentration terms can be written as:

$$C = \frac{N}{V} = \frac{Np}{NR_G^*T} = \frac{p}{R_G^*T}$$

since $p = yP$

$$C = yP/R_G^*T$$

where
p = partial pressure, bars
C = molar concentration, kmol/m^3
R_G^* = gas constant = 0.0831417 bar · m^3/(kmol · K)
T = absolute temperature, K
y = mole fraction of individual reactants and products
P = total pressure, bars

$$C_A = \frac{P\ Fy_0(1 - x)}{R_G^*\ T(6.5555\ Fy_0 + \text{quench})}$$

$$C_B = \frac{P\ (Fy_0\ (5 - x) + 0.9\ \text{quench})}{R_G^*\ T(6.5555\ Fy_0 + \text{quench})}$$

Let us substitute these C_A and C_B terms into Eq. (5-37):

$$r_v = \frac{dC_A}{d\theta} = A \exp(-E/R_GT)[P/R_G^*T(6.5555\ Fy_0 + \text{quench})]^{1.5} \cdot Fy_0\,(1 - x) \cdot [Fy_0\,(5 - x) + 0.9\ \text{quench}]^{0.5}$$

which can be combined with Eq. (5-7) and rearranged:

$$\frac{dx}{dz} = A_c\,A \exp(-E/R_GT)\ [P/R_G^*T(6.5555\ Fy_0 + \text{quench})]^{1.5}\ (1 - x) \cdot [Fy_0\,(5 - x) + 0.9\ \text{quench}]^{0.5} \quad (5\text{-}38)$$

Let us now calculate the quench at the end of each bed (except the last bed, of course):

$$\text{Quench} = \frac{\Sigma m_1 C_{pi}\,(T - T_0)}{(C_{pi})_{\text{quench}}\,(T - 298.2)} \quad (5\text{-}39)$$

$$(C_{pi})_{\text{quench}} = (0.9)(20.786) + (0.1)(66.413) = 25.349\ \text{kJ/(kmol} \cdot \text{K)}$$

The pressure term P in Eq. (5-38) must be corrected at each step of the numerical computation according to the pressure drop per unit reactor length, which is calculated by means of the Ergun equation [Eq. (4-1)]. This calculation is quite involved.

In the Ergun equation, G is the mass flow rate in kilograms per second per square meter.

$$G = (92.141\ Fy_0/A_c) + (2.016)(5)Fy_0/A_c + (16.043)(5/9)Fy_0/A_c + [(0.9)(2.016) + (0.1)(16.043)]\text{quench}/A_c$$

$$G = (111.1338\ Fy_0 + 3.4187\ \text{quench})/A_c$$

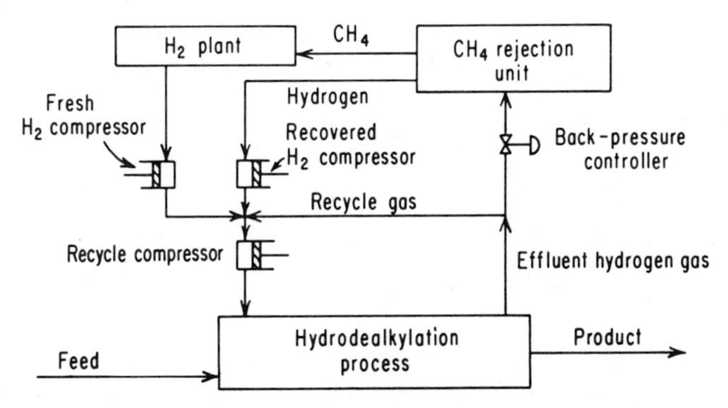

FIG. 5-8 Block diagram showing the recycle, purification, and makeup of effluent hydrogen gas from the hydrodealkylation plant.

The equation for u_m, the superficial fluid velocity based on the empty reactor, is:

$$u_m = \frac{(6.5555\ Fy_0 + \text{quench})}{A_c} \cdot \frac{(22.414\ T_0\ 1.01325)}{273.2 \qquad P}$$

$$u_m = 0.0831295\ (6.5555\ Fy_0 + \text{quench})\ T_0/A_c\ P$$

The effective diameter of catalyst particles, d_p, is defined by $d_p = 6\ A_cZ(1 - \varepsilon)/S_t$, where S_t is the total surface area of the catalyst load. On dividing both the numerator and the denominator of this expression by the number of catalyst particles in the entire catalyst load we obtain:

$$d_p = \frac{6(\text{particle volume})}{\text{particle surface area}} \tag{5-40}$$

If we use a catalyst shape such as a "square" cylinder, i.e., a cylinder having its diameter equal to its height, then with r_p = particle radius,

$$d_p = \frac{6(r_p^2\pi)(2r_p)}{(2\pi r_p)(2r_p) + 2r_p^2\pi} = 2\ r_p$$

Thus, if we set $2\ r_p = 3$ mm, then $d_p = 0.003$ m.

The viscosity μ of the reaction mixture can be computed from the individual viscosities μ_1, μ_2, μ_3, and μ_4 by using the elaborate relationship developed by C. R. Wilke.[10] This is necessary because hydrogen does not conform to simpler relationships. The equation is:

$$\mu = \frac{\mu_1}{1 + (y_2/y_1)\ \phi_{12} + (y_3/y_1)\ \phi_{13} + (y_4/y_1)\ \phi_{14}}$$
$$+ \frac{\mu_2}{1 + (y_1/y_2)\ \phi_{21} + (y_3/y_2)\ \phi_{23} + (y_4/y_2)\ \phi_{24}}$$
$$+ \frac{\mu_3}{1 + (y_1/y_3)\ \phi_{31} + (y_2/y_3)\ \phi_{32} + (y_4/y_3)\ \phi_{34}}$$
$$+ \frac{\mu_4}{1 + (y_1/y_4)\ \phi_{41} + (y_2/y_4)\ \phi_{42} + (y_3/y_4)\ \phi_{43}} \tag{5-41}$$

with

$$\phi_{ij} = \frac{[1 + (\mu_i/\mu_j)^{1/2}(M_j/M_i)^{1/4}0]^2}{(4/\sqrt{2})[1 + (M_i/M_j)]^{1/2}} \qquad i \neq j$$

The term ij can be 12, 13, 14, 21, 23, 24, 31, 32, 34, 41, 42, 43, and M_i and M_j are molecular weights of components. In the computer program, molecular weights will be designated MW1, MW2, MW3, and MW4, in order to differentiate them from m_1, m_2, m_3, and m_4, which are designated M1, M2, M3, and M4, respectively, and denote mass quantities.

Now Ergun's equation can be evaluated. The expression $(d_p/dz)g_c$ in it is designated DELPZ in the computer program.

Now, we can substitute the proper numerical values into Eqs. (5-32) and (5-38), and these equations will be ready for computer solutions. Let us calculate these numerical values:

$$Fy_0 = \frac{(66{,}000\ \text{t/yr})(1000\ \text{kg/t})}{(330\ \text{SD/yr})(24)(3600)(92.141\ \text{kg/kmol})} = \begin{array}{l}0.025122\ \text{kmol/s}\\ \text{toluene feed}\end{array}$$

For a plant of this kind 330 on-stream days, where SD stands for stream days/year, are assumed.

$$\text{Hydrogen feed} = 5\ Fy_0 = 0.12561\ \text{kmol/s}$$

$$\text{Methane feed} = 0.5555\ Fy_0 = 0.013955\ \text{kmol/s}$$

$$\text{Total feed} = 0.164687\ \text{kmol/s}$$

$$\text{Initial mole fraction of toluene } y_0 = 0.15254$$

The reactor cross-sectional area A_c is generally limited at its maximum by mechanical design considerations. The maximum for this process is not known. The internal diameter of 2 m assumed for this application seems to be a perfectly practical size.

In integrating Eq. (5-32), neither x nor T can be used as an independent variable. Both are dependent variables. This difficulty can be circumvented by dividing both sides of Eq. (5-32) by dz and rearranging to:

$$\frac{dT}{dz} = \frac{dx}{dz} \cdot \frac{Fy_0(-\Delta H)}{\Sigma m_i\, C_{pi}} \tag{5-42}$$

Equation (5-42) can be integrated with respect to dz, like Eq. (5-38).

This integration is implemented by means of a computer program, named RDMOT1, written in the Fortran IV language and run on an IBM 3032 machine. The entire source program and computer output are given in the following pages. Figure 5-9 is a block diagram of the computer program RDMOT1: it displays the general organization of the program. Figure 5-10 is a listing of definitions of computer symbols and terms used in the RDMOT1 program. Figure 5-11 is a listing of the RDMOT1 source program. At the end of the listing, the input data used in RDMOT1 are given. Figure 5-12 is a printout of two RDMOT1 run outputs, with $Fy_0 = 0.02512$ and $Fy_0 = 0.0345$, respectively.

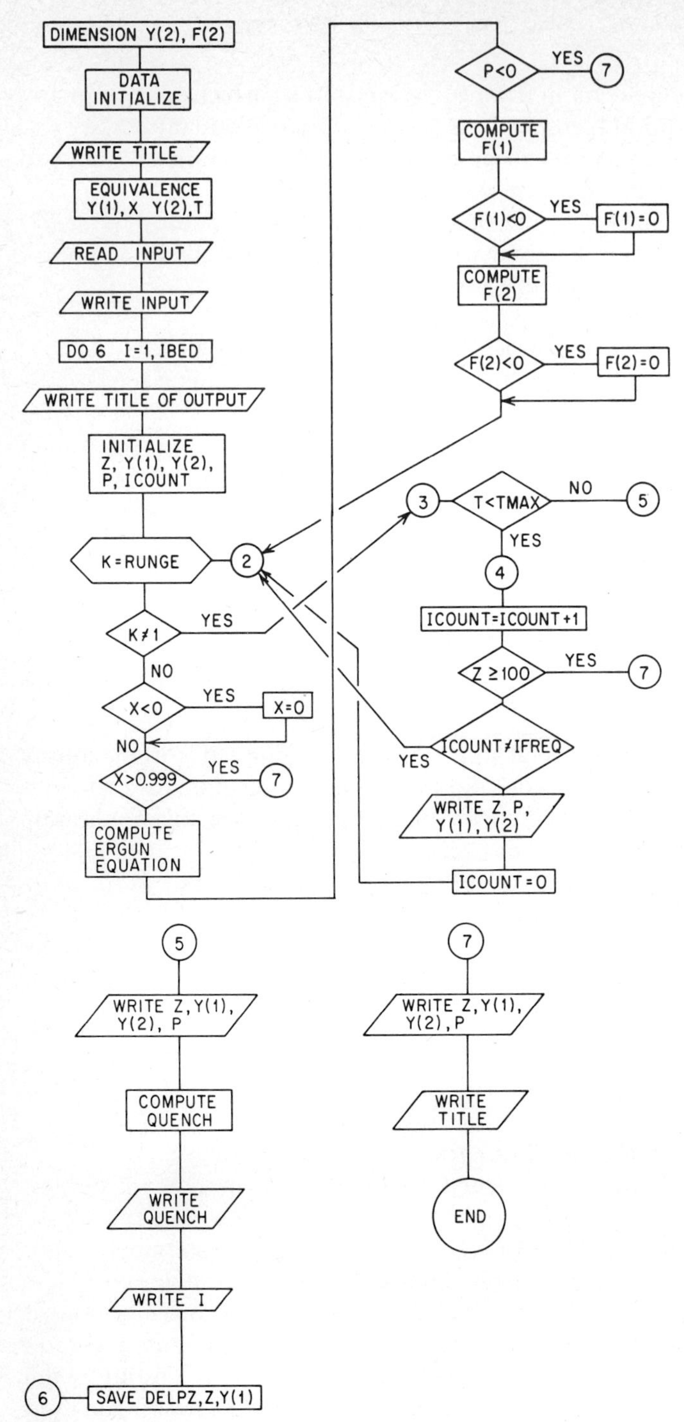

FIG. 5-9 Block diagram of the RDMOT1 program.

```
              DEFINITION OF SYMBOLS IN RDMOT1

A       FREQUENCY FACTOR
AC      CROSS-SECTIONAL AREA OF REACTOR, M**2
DELPZ   PRESSURE DROP PER UNIT LENGTH, BAR/M
DH      HEAT OF REACTION, KJ/KMOL
DP      CATALYST PARTICLE DIAMETER, M
E       ACTIVATION ENERGY, KJ/KMOL
EPS     VOID FRACTION IN BED, DIMENSIONLESS
F       DERIVATIVE IN FUNCTION RUNGE
FYO     TOLUENE FEED, KMOL/S
G       SUPERFICIAL MASS FLOW RATE, KG/S.M**2
H       STEP SIZE, M
I       SEQUENTIAL NUMBER OF BEDS, DIMENSIONLESS
IBED    NUMBER OF MAXIMUM BEDS, DIMENSIONLESS
ICOUNT  COUNTER OF STEPS FOR PRINTING FREQUENCY, DIMENSIONLESS
IFREQ   PRINTING FREQUENCY, DIMENSIONLESS
K       COUNTER OF PASSES IN FUNCTION RUNGE, DIMENSIONLESS
M       COUNTER IN FUNCTION RUNGE
MU      VISCOSITY OF REACTING GAS MIXTURE, PAS
MU1     VISCOSITY OF TOLUENE AT REACTION CONDITIONS, PAS
MU2     VISCOSITY OF BENZENE AT REACTION CONDITIONS, PAS
MU3     VISCOSITY OF HYDROGEN AT REACTION CONDITIONS, PAS
MU4     VISCOSITY OF METHANE AT REACTION CONDITIONS, PAS
MW1     MOLECULAR WEIGHT OF TOLUENE
MW2     MOLECULAR WEIGHT OF BENZENE
MW3     MOLECULAR WEIGHT OF HYDROGEN
MW4     MOLECULAR WEIGHT OF METHANE
M1      MOLAR FLOW OF TOLUENE, KMOL/S
M2      MOLAR FLOW OF BENZENE, KMOL/S
M3      MOLAR FLOW OF HYDROGEN,KMOL/S
M4      MOLAR FLOW OF METHANE, KMOL/S
P       PRESSURE, BAR
PAR     DUMMY VARIABLE IN COMPUTING F(1)
PHI..   DUMMY VARIABLES FOR VISCOSITY COMPUTATION
PHI(J)  VARIABLE IN FUNCTION RUNGE
QUENCH  HYDROGEN GAS INJECTED AT THE END OF THE BED, KMOL/S
RG      GAS CONSTANT = 8.316 KJ/KMOL.K
RSTAR   GAS CONSTANT = 0.08314 BAR*M**3/KMOL.K
SAVEP   DUMMY VARIABLE FOR RECYCLING P
SAVEX   DUMMY VARIABLE FOR RECYCLING X
SAVEZ   DUMMY VARIABLE FOR RECYCLING Z
SUM     DUMMY VARIABLE IN COMPUTING F(2)
S1 S2   S3  S4 DUMMY VARIABLES FOR VISCOSITY COMPUTATION
T       TEMPERATURE OF REACTION , K
TMAX    MAXIMUM TEMPERATURE ALLOWABLE BEFORE COOLING BED, K
TO      TEMPERATURE AT INLET, K
UM      SUPERFICIAL VELOCITY IN SABRI ERGUN EQUATION
X       CONVERSION OF TOLUENE, DIMENSIONLESS
XO      CONVERSION OF TOLUENE AT INLET, DIMENSIONLESS
Y(1)     = X
Y(2)     = T
Y1      MOL FRACTION OF TOLUENE, DIMENSIONLESS
Y2      MOL FRACTION OF BENZENE, DIMENSIONLESS
Y3      MOL FRACTION OF HYDROGEN, DIMENSIONLESS
Y4      MOL FRACTION OF METHANE, DIMENSIONLESS
Z       AXIAL COORDINATE, M
```

FIG. 5-10 Definition of symbols in the RDMOT1 computer program.

```
      DIMENSION Y(2),F(2)
      DATA IFREQ/10/
      DATA QUENCH,SAVEZ,SAVEX,SAVEP/0.0,0.0,0.0,0.0/
      INTEGER RUNGE
      REAL M1,M2,M3,M4,MU,MU1,MU2,MU3,MU4,MW1,MW2,MW3,MW4
      WRITE (6,150)
  150 FORMAT (1H1,20X,38HADIABATIC FIXED-BED GAS REACTOR DESIGN/1H0,20X,
     1 36HTOLUENE HYDRODEALKYLATION TO BENZENE)
C     ....READ AND PRINT DATA....
      EQUIVALENCE (Y(1),X),(Y(2),T)
      READ(5,100) X0,T0,TMAX,RG,P,DH,AC,H,E,FY0,RSTAR,A,IBED,MU1,MU2,
     1 MU3,MU4,EPS,DP,MW1,MW2,MW3,MW4
  100 FORMAT(7F10.3/2F10.3,2F10.5,E12.4,4X,I2/6F10.7/4F10.6)
      WRITE (6,200) X0,T0,TMAX,FY0,RG,RSTAR,P,H,DH,AC,E,A,MU1,MU2,MU3,
     1    MU4,EPS,DP,MW1,MW2,MW3,MW4,IBED
  200 FORMAT(1H0,5X,3HX0=,F6.4,5X,4HT0= ,F6.1,2H K,8X,6HTMAX= ,F6.1,
     12H K/1H ,5X,5HFY0= ,F7.5,7H KMOL/S,15X,5HRG  =,F9.3,10H KJ/KMOL.K/
     21H ,5X,6HRSTAR=,F8.5,16H BAR.M**3/KMOL.K,4X,2HP=,F5.1,8H BAR ABS,
     35X,2HH=,F5.3/1H ,5X,3HDH=,F8.1,8H KJ/KMOL,15X,3HAC=,F5.3,5H M**2/
     4 1H ,5X,2HE=,F9.1,8H KJ/KMOL,15X,2HA=,E15.7/1H ,5X,4HMU1=,F9.7,
     5   5H MU2=,F9.7,  7X,4HMU3=, F9.7,2X,4HMU4=, F9.7,4H PAS/1H ,5X,
     6 5HEPS= ,F5.3,4X,5HDP = ,F7.5,2H M/1H ,5X,5HMW1= ,F7.3,2X,5HMW2= ,
     7 F7.3,8X,5HMW3= ,F7.3,4X,5HMW4= ,F7.3/1H ,5X,5HIBED=,I9)
      DO 6 I=1,IBED
      WRITE (6,151) I
  151 FORMAT (1H1,35X,10HFIXED BED ,I2)
      WRITE(6,201)
  201 FORMAT (5X, 17HREACTOR LENGTH, M, 4X,10HCONVERSION,4X,
     113HTEMPERATURE,K,4X,12HPRESSURE,BAR)
C
C     ....INITIALIZE Z, Y(1), Y(2), P AND ICOUNT....
      Z = 0.0 + SAVEZ
      Y(1) = X0 + SAVEX
      Y(2) = T0
      P = P - (SAVEP*H)
      ICOUNT = 0
C     ....CALL ON THE FOURTH-ORDER RUNGE-KUTTA FUNCTION....
    2 K=RUNGE(2,Y,F,Z,H)
C     IF  K=1 , COMPUTE DERIVATIVE VALUES
      IF(K.NE.1) GO TO 3
C     ....MATERIAL BALANCE EQUATION....
      IF(X.LT.0.) X=0.
      IF (X.GE..999) GO TO 7

C     COMPUTE GAS MIX VISCOSITY MU ....
      Y1= FY0*(1.-X)/(6.5555*FY0 + QUENCH)
      Y2= FY0*X/(6.5555*FY0 + QUENCH)
      Y3= (FY0*(5.-X) + 0.9*QUENCH)/(6.5555*FY0 + QUENCH)
      Y4= (FY0*(0.5555 + X) + 0.1*QUENCH)/(6.5555*FY0 + QUENCH)
      PHI12= (1.+(SQRT(MU1/MU2))*((MW2/MW1)**0.25))**2/
     1       (2.8284*(1.+(MW1/MW2))**0.5)
      PHI13= (1.+(SQRT(MU1/MU3))*((MW3/MW1)**0.25))**2/
     1       (2.8284*(1.+(MW1/MW3))**0.5)
      PHI14= (1.+(SQRT(MU1/MU4))*((MW4/MW1)**0.25))**2/
     1       (2.8284*(1.+(MW1/MW4))**0.5)
      PHI21= (1.+(SQRT(MU2/MU1))*((MW1/MW2)**0.25))**2/
     1       (2.8284*(1.+(MW2/MW1))**0.5)
      PHI23= (1.+(SQRT(MU2/MU3))*((MW3/MW2)**0.25))**2/
     1       (2.8284*(1.+(MW2/MW3))**0.5)
      PHI24= (1.+(SQRT(MU2/MU4))*((MW4/MW2)**0.25))**2/
     1       (2.8284*(1.+(MW2/MW4))**0.5)
      PHI31= (1.+(SQRT(MU3/MU1))*((MW1/MW3)**0.25))**2/
     1       (2.8284*(1.+(MW3/MW1))**0.5)
      PHI32= (1.+(SQRT(MU3/MU2))*((MW2/MW3)**0.25))**2/
     1       (2.8284*(1.+(MW3/MW2))**0.5)
      PHI34= (1.+(SQRT(MU3/MU4))*((MW4/MW3)**0.25))**2/
     1       (2.8284*(1.+(MW3/MW4))**0.5)
      PHI41= (1.+(SQRT(MU4/MU1))*((MW1/MW4)**0.25))**2/
     1       (2.8284*(1.+(MW4/MW1))**0.5)
```

FIG. 5-11 The RDMOT1 computer program for the design of an adiabatic fixed-bed reactor for the hydrodealkylation of toluene to benzene.

```
      PHI42= (1.+(SQRT(MU4/MU2))*((MW2/MW4)**0.25))**2/
     1       (2.8284*(1.+(MW4/MW2))**0.5)
      PHI43= (1.+(SQRT(MU4/MU3))*((MW3/MW4)**0.25))**2/
     1       (2.8284*(1.+(MW4/MW3))**0.5)
      S1=0.0
      S2=0.0
      S3=0.0
      S4=0.0
      IF(Y1.GT.0.)S1=MU1/(1.+(Y2/Y1)*PHI12 + (Y3/Y1)*PHI13 +
     1                (Y4/Y1)*PHI14)
      IF(Y2.GT.0.)S2=MU2/(1.+(Y1/Y2)*PHI21 + (Y3/Y2)*PHI23 +
     1                (Y4/Y2)*PHI24)
      IF(Y3.GT.0.)S3=MU3/(1.+(Y1/Y3)*PHI31 + (Y2/Y3)*PHI32 +
     1                (Y4/Y3)*PHI34)
      IF(Y4.GT.0.)S4=MU4/(1.+(Y1/Y4)*PHI41 + (Y2/Y4)*PHI42 +
     1                (Y3/Y4)*PHI43)
      MU= S1 + S2 + S3 + S4
C     COMPUTE THE SABRI ERGUN EQUATION FOR PRESSURE DROP....
      UM= 0.08313*((6.5555*FY0) + QUENCH)*T0/(AC*P)
      G = ((111.13*FY0) + (3.4187*QUENCH))/AC
      DELPZ= (1.5E-03 *((1.-EPS)**2)*MU*UM/((EPS**3)*(DP**2)))+
     1      (1.75E-05 *( 1.-EPS)*G*UM/((EPS**3)*(DP)))
      P = P - (DELPZ*H)
      IF(P.LT.0.) GO TO 7
      PAR= (P/(RSTAR*T*(6.5555*FY0 + QUENCH)))**1.5
      F(1)= AC*A*EXP(-E/(RG*T))*PAR*(1.-X)*
     1      ((FY0*(5.-X) + 0.9*QUENCH)**0.5)
      IF (F(1).LT.0.) F(1)=0.0
C
C     ....ENERGY BALANCE EQUATION....
      M1=FY0*(1.0-X)
      M2=FY0*X
      M3=FY0*(5.0-X) + (0.9*QUENCH)
      M4=FY0*(0.5555+X) + (0.1*QUENCH)
      SUM=M1*(124.85+(0.03535*T)) +
     1    M2*(103.18+(0.1067*T)) +
     2    M3*(20.786) +
     3    M4*(27.87+(0.04414*T))
      F(2)=F(1)*FY0*DH/SUM
      IF (F(2).LT.0.) F(2)=0.0
      GO TO 2
C
C     ....IF T EXCEEDS TMAX, TERMINATE INTEGRATION....
    3 IF(Y(2).LE.TMAX) GO TO 4
      GO TO 5
    4 ICOUNT = ICOUNT + 1
      IF (Z.GE.100.0) GO TO 7

      IF (ICOUNT.NE.IFREQ) GO TO 2
      WRITE (6,202) Z,Y(1),Y(2),P
  202 FORMAT (1H , 7X,F8.3,13X,F5.3,10X,F6.1,11X,F6.2)
      ICOUNT = 0
      GO TO 2
    5 WRITE (6,202) Z,Y(1),Y(2),P
      SAVEQ = QUENCH
      QUENCH=SUM*(T-T0)/(25.349*(T0-298.2))
      WRITE (6,203) QUENCH
  203 FORMAT(1H0,5X,11HEND OF BED.,4X,9HQUENCH = ,F10.5,7H KMOL/S)
      QUENCH = QUENCH + SAVEQ
      SAVEP = DELPZ
      SAVEZ = Z
      WRITE(6,999) I
  999 FORMAT(1H ,5X, 7HBED NO=,I3)
    6 SAVEX = Y(1)
    7 WRITE(6,202) Z,Y(1),Y(2),P
      WRITE(6,204)
  204 FORMAT(1H ,5X,15HEND OF REACTOR.)
      STOP
      END
```

FIG. 5-11 **The RDMOT1 computer program for the design of an adiabatic fixed-bed reactor for the hydrodealkylation of toluene to benzene (*continued*).**

```
C
      FUNCTION RUNGE (N,Y,F,Z,H)
      INTEGER RUNGE
      DIMENSION PHI(50),SAVEY(50),Y(N),F(N)
      DATA M/0/
C
      M = M + 1
      GO TO (1,2,3,4,5), M
C                 PASS 1
    1 RUNGE = 1
      RETURN
C                 PASS 2
    2 DO 22 J=1,N
      SAVEY(J)=Y(J)
      PHI(J)=F(J)
   22 Y(J)=SAVEY(J) +0.5 * H * F(J)
      Z = Z + 0.5 * H
      RUNGE = 1
      RETURN
C                 PASS 3
    3 DO 33  J=1,N
      PHI(J) = PHI(J) + 2.0 * F(J)
   33 Y(J) = SAVEY(J) + 0.5 * H * F(J)
      RUNGE = 1
      RETURN
C                 PASS 4
    4 DO 44 J=1,N
      PHI(J) = PHI(J) + 2.0 * F(J)
   44 Y(J) = SAVEY(J) + H * F(J)
      Z = Z + 0.5 * H
      RUNGE = 1
      RETURN
C                 PASS 5
    5 DO 55 J = 1,N
   55 Y(J) = SAVEY(J) + (PHI(J) + F(J))* H/6.0
      M=0
      RUNGE = 0
      RETURN
      END
```

INPUT DATA; CASE 1: FY0 = 0.02512

```
     0.0       873.2      908.2        8.314     50.      49974.0        3.142
     0.05 148114.0      0.02512     0.08314   5.73    E+06       6
0.00002    0.0000224 0.0000182 0.000026   0.38        0.003
92.141     78.114      2.016      16.043
```

INPUT DATA; CASE 2: FY0 = 0.03390

```
     0.0       873.2      908.2        8.314     50.      49974.0        3.142
     0.05 148114.0      0.03390     0.08314   5.73    E+06       6
0.00002    0.0000224 0.0000182 0.000026   0.38        0.003
92.141     78.114      2.016      16.043
```

FIG. 5-11 The RDMOT1 computer program for the design of an adiabatic fixed-bed reactor for the hydrodealkylation of toluene to benzene (*continued*).

```
ADIABATIC FIXED-BED GAS REACTOR DESIGN

TOLUENE HYDRODEALKYLATION TO BENZENE

X0=0.0000        T0=  873.2 K            TMAX=  908.2 K
FY0=  .02512 KMOL/S                      RG  =      8.314 KJ/KMOL.K
RSTAR=  .08314 BAR.M**3/KMOL.K           P= 50.0 BAR ABS       H= .050
DH= 49974.0 KJ/KMOL                      AC=3.142 M**2
E= 148114.0 KJ/KMOL                      A=   .5730000E+07
MU1= .0000200 MU2= .0000224              MU3= .0000182  MU4= .0000260 PAS
EPS=  .380      DP =  .00300 M
MW1=  92.141  MW2=  78.114               MW3=   2.016     MW4=  16.043
IBED=         6
```

FIXED BED 1

REACTOR LENGTH, M	CONVERSION	TEMPERATURE,K	PRESSURE,BAR
.500	.040	879.8	49.99
1.000	.083	887.0	49.97
1.500	.131	894.9	49.96
2.000	.185	903.5	49.95
2.300	.220	909.0	49.94

```
END OF BED.     QUENCH =       .01966 KMOL/S
BED NO=  1
```

FIXED BED 2

REACTOR LENGTH, M	CONVERSION	TEMPERATURE,K	PRESSURE,BAR
2.800	.247	877.1	49.92
3.300	.274	881.2	49.91
3.800	.304	885.5	49.89
4.300	.334	889.9	49.88
4.800	.366	894.4	49.86
5.300	.399	899.2	49.85
5.800	.433	904.0	49.83
6.250	.465	908.4	49.82

```
END OF BED.     QUENCH =       .02190 KMOL/S
BED NO=  2
```

FIXED BED 3

REACTOR LENGTH, M	CONVERSION	TEMPERATURE,K	PRESSURE,BAR
6.750	.481	875.3	49.80
7.250	.497	877.4	49.79
7.750	.513	879.5	49.77
8.250	.530	881.6	49.75
8.750	.546	883.7	49.73
9.250	.563	885.9	49.72
9.750	.579	888.0	49.70
10.250	.596	890.1	49.68
10.750	.613	892.3	49.66
11.250	.629	894.4	49.65
11.750	.646	896.5	49.63
12.250	.662	898.5	49.61
12.750	.679	900.6	49.59
13.250	.695	902.6	49.58
13.750	.711	904.6	49.56
14.250	.727	906.5	49.54
14.700	.741	908.2	49.53

```
END OF BED.     QUENCH =       .02460 KMOL/S
BED NO=  3
```

FIG. 5-12 Printouts of two RDMOT1 computer runs.

FIXED BED 4

REACTOR LENGTH, M	CONVERSION	TEMPERATURE,K	PRESSURE,BAR
15.200	.747	874.0	49.51
15.700	.754	874.7	49.49
16.200	.760	875.5	49.47
16.700	.767	876.2	49.45
17.200	.773	877.0	49.43
17.700	.779	877.7	49.41
18.200	.785	878.4	49.39
18.700	.792	879.1	49.37
19.200	.798	879.8	49.35
19.700	.803	880.5	49.33
.			
.			
.			
.			
45.700	.972	899.5	48.27
46.200	.973	899.7	48.25
46.700	.974	899.8	48.23
47.200	.975	899.9	48.21
47.700	.976	900.0	48.19
48.200	.977	900.1	48.17
48.700	.978	900.2	48.15
49.200	.979	900.3	48.13
49.700	.980	900.4	48.11
50.200	.981	900.5	48.09
50.700	.982	900.6	48.07
51.200	.983	900.7	48.05
51.700	.983	900.8	48.03
52.200	.984	900.8	48.01
.			
.			
.			
.			
78.700	.998	902.4	46.90
79.200	.998	902.4	46.88
79.700	.999	902.4	46.86
80.200	.999	902.5	46.84
80.700	.999	902.5	46.81
81.200	.999	902.5	46.79
81.700	.999	902.5	46.77
82.200	.999	902.5	46.75
82.700	.999	902.5	46.73
83.200	.999	902.5	46.71
83.700	.999	902.5	46.69
84.200	.999	902.5	46.67
84.425	.999	902.5	46.66

END OF REACTOR.

FIG. 5-12 **Printouts of two RDMOT1 computer runs (*continued*).**

ADIABATIC FIXED-BED GAS REACTOR DESIGN

TOLUENE HYDRODEALKYLATION TO BENZENE

```
X0=0.0000      T0=  873.2 K               TMAX=   908.2 K
FY0=  .03390 KMOL/S                       RG  =      8.314 KJ/KMOL.K
RSTAR=  .08314 BAR.M**3/KMOL.K            P= 50.0 BAR ABS      H= .050
DH= 49974.0 KJ/KMOL                       AC=3.142 M**2
E= 148114.0 KJ/KMOL                       A=    .5730000E+07
MU1= .0000200 MU2= .0000224               MU3= .0000182  MU4= .0000260 PAS
EPS=  .380     DP =  .00300 M
MW1=  92.141  MW2=  78.114                MW3=    2.016    MW4=  16.043
IBED=        6
```

FIXED BED 1

REACTOR LENGTH, M	CONVERSION	TEMPERATURE,K	PRESSURE,BAR
.500	.029	878.0	49.98
1.000	.060	883.2	49.96
1.500	.093	888.7	49.93
2.000	.130	894.6	49.91
2.500	.169	900.8	49.89
3.000	.211	907.5	49.87
3.050	.215	908.2	49.87

END OF BED.   QUENCH =   .02590 KMOL/S
BED NO= 1

FIXED BED 2

REACTOR LENGTH, M	CONVERSION	TEMPERATURE,K	PRESSURE,BAR
3.550	.235	876.1	49.84
4.050	.255	879.1	49.82
4.550	.276	882.3	49.79
5.050	.298	885.4	49.76
5.550	.321	888.7	49.74
6.050	.344	892.1	49.71
6.550	.368	895.5	49.69
7.050	.393	899.1	49.66
7.550	.418	902.7	49.64
8.050	.445	906.3	49.61
8.350	.461	908.6	49.60

END OF BED.   QUENCH =   .02960 KMOL/S
BED NO= 2

FIXED BED 3

REACTOR LENGTH, M	CONVERSION	TEMPERATURE,K	PRESSURE,BAR
8.850	.472	874.7	49.57
9.350	.484	876.3	49.54
9.850	.496	877.9	49.51
10.350	.508	879.4	49.48
10.850	.520	881.0	49.45
11.350	.532	882.6	49.42
11.850	.545	884.2	49.39
12.350	.557	885.8	49.37
12.850	.569	887.4	49.34
13.350	.582	889.0	49.31
13.850	.594	890.6	49.28
14.350	.607	892.1	49.25
14.850	.619	893.7	49.22
15.350	.631	895.3	49.19
15.850	.644	896.8	49.16
16.350	.656	898.4	49.13
16.850	.668	899.9	49.10

FIG. 5-12 **Printouts of two RDMOT1 computer runs (*continued*).**

```
        17.350              .680            901.4              49.07
        17.850              .692            902.9              49.04
        18.350              .704            904.4              49.02
        18.850              .716            905.8              48.99
        19.350              .727            907.3              48.96
        19.700              .735            908.2              48.94

END OF BED.     QUENCH =        .03316 KMOL/S
BED NO=  3



                              FIXED BED  4
REACTOR LENGTH, M       CONVERSION      TEMPERATURE,K        PRESSURE,BAR
        20.200              .740            873.8              48.90
        20.700              .745            874.4              48.87
        21.200              .750            874.9              48.83
        21.700              .755            875.5              48.80
        22.200              .760            876.0              48.77
        22.700              .764            876.6              48.73
        23.200              .769            877.1              48.70
        23.700              .774            877.7              48.67
        24.200              .778            878.2              48.63
        24.700              .783            878.7              48.60
           .
           .
           .
           .
        53.200              .949            897.6              46.62
        53.700              .951            897.8              46.59
        54.200              .952            897.9              46.55
        54.700              .954            898.1              46.52
        55.200              .955            898.2              46.48
        55.700              .956            898.4              46.45
        56.200              .957            898.5              46.41
        56.700              .959            898.7              46.38
        57.200              .960            898.8              46.34
        57.700              .961            898.9              46.30
        58.200              .962            899.0              46.27
        58.700              .963            899.2              46.23
           .
           .
           .
           .
        93.200              .995            902.7              43.70
        93.700              .995            902.7              43.66
        94.200              .995            902.7              43.62
        94.700              .996            902.7              43.59
        95.200              .996            902.8              43.55
        95.700              .996            902.8              43.51
        96.200              .996            902.8              43.47
        96.700              .996            902.8              43.43
        97.200              .996            902.8              43.40
        97.700              .996            902.8              43.36
        98.200              .996            902.8              43.32
        98.700              .996            902.8              43.28
        99.200              .997            902.9              43.24
        99.700              .997            902.9              43.21
       100.050              .997            902.9              43.18
END OF REACTOR.
```

FIG. 5-12 Printouts of two RDMOT1 computer runs (*continued*).

Most aspects of RDMOT1 are self-explanatory. However, the following comments and the diagram of Fig. 5-9 should be helpful.

- RDMOT1 is an application of the fourth-order Runge-Kutta program explained in Sec. 2.5 for solving initial-value ODEs. It uses the FUNCTION RUNGE.
- The step size H is not varied inside the program. It is read in along with other input data. The program can be tested with various H values until one is found below which the results stay constant. For this purpose it suffices to test only a single bed.
- RDMOT1 is designed for a multibed reactor with intermediate gas quench. The program stops the integration of the ODEs when the reaction temperature T exceeds the maximum temperature T_{max}, computes the amount of H_2 gas required to quench the reaction gases from T_{max} to the inlet temperature T_0, adds this H_2 gas to the reaction stream, and proceeds with the calculation of the next bed. The program can be run with any number of beds; however, by setting IBED=6 we make it stop after the sixth bed, if it has not stopped for some other reason before. The computation also stops when the conversion approaches completion. At the end, the reaction slows down considerably and x approaches unity asymptotically. For this reason the program is stopped when $x = 0.999$. The program can also be stopped when the pressure P falls to zero or to any desired level.
- If RDMOT1 is used for a different reaction, it can be easily adapted to use a liquid quench, a gas-liquid quench, or indirect intermediate cooling.
- The program prints the results after every IFREQ calculation. It counts the steps by adding 1 to ICOUNT. When ICOUNT=IFREQ, it prints and starts all over again.

The results of the RDMOT1 program are given in Table 5-1. They show that most of the conversion occurs in the front part of the reactor and that it approaches unity asymptotically. Only four beds were calculated and the calculations were stopped at $x = 0.999$.

These results show that the conversion reaches 0.741 at the end of the third bed and that the fourth bed becomes unreasonably tall and slow. In such a case, it is more economical to build only three reactors and to distill and fractionate the product of the third reactor to obtain pure benzene overhead and toluene at the bottom. This toluene must be recycled to the inlet of the first reactor. The first three reactors may

TABLE 5-1
Results of the RDMOT1 Program

NBED	Bed length, m		Conversion		$\Delta T/\Delta Z$, K m	ΔP	$\Sigma\Delta P$	QUENCH, kmol/s
	Z	ΣZ	X	ΣX				
1	2.3	2.3	0.22	0.22	15.56	0.06	0.06	0.01966
2	3.95	6.25	0.245	0.465	8.91	0.12	0.18	0.0219
3	8.45	14.70	0.276	0.741	4.098	0.29	0.47	0.0246
4	43.00	57.70	0.258	0.999	0.658	1.75	2.22	—

be grouped as shown in Fig. 5-13 and the fractionation setup may be designed as shown in Fig. 5-14. The selection of the total reactor length versus the extent of the fractionation must be based on sound economics—a subject that will not be discussed here.

Our problem was to convert 66,000 t/yr or 0.02512 kmol/s of toluene to benzene. However, the just designed reactor system will only convert 74.1% of this quantity. In order to increase the production of the plant to the full amount, we can either increase the reactor cross-sectional area A_c by $1/x$, which corresponds to a reactor diameter $D_T = 2.323$ m, run the 2.0-m-diameter reactor with a feed of 0.0339 kmol/s of toluene, or select a combination of larger diameter and faster flow. First it must be

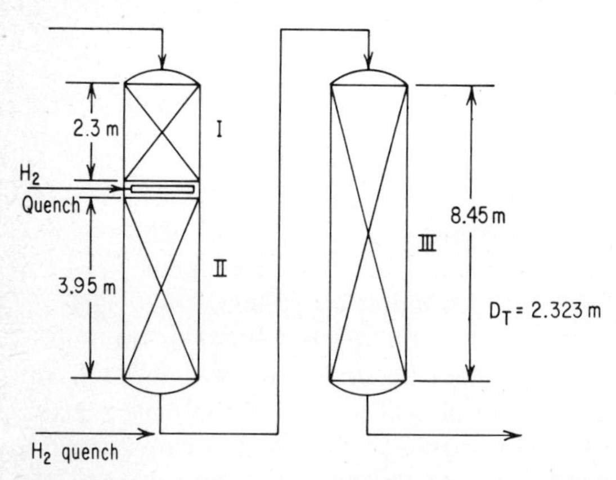

FIG. 5-13 **Configuration of three consecutive adiabatic fixed beds for toluene hydrodealkylation with intermediate hydrogen quench.**

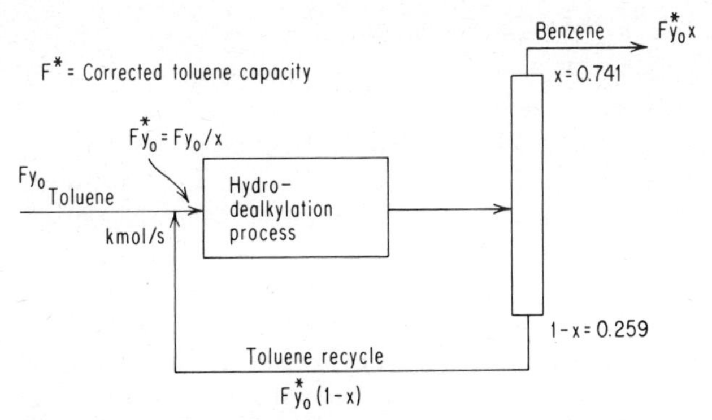

FIG. 5-14 Block diagram showing product distillation and toluene recycle in toluene hydrodealkylation.

ascertained that the choice of larger reactor diameter is really available. At high temperatures and pressures certain reactor designs set a practical limit to the reactor diameter.

A computer run with a diameter of $D_T = 2$ m and a high feed flow of 0.0339 kmol/s of toluene is shown in the third and fourth sheets of Fig. 5-12. We can see that the catalyst required in both design cases is about the same as summarized by the following results:

$$D_T = 2.323 \text{ m} \quad A_c = 4.240 \text{ m}^2 \quad Z = 14.70 \text{ m}$$
$$V = 62.228 \text{ m}^3 \quad x = 0.741$$
$$D_T = 2.000 \text{ m} \quad A_c = 3.142 \text{ m}^2 \quad Z = 19.70 \text{ m}$$
$$V = 61.89 \text{ m}^3 \quad x = 0.735$$

The choice will be decided by reactor metallurgy and of course by economics.

5.3 NONISOTHERMAL, NONADIABATIC FIXED-BED (NINAF) GAS REACTORS

NINAF gas reactors have been defined in Sec. 4.2 as packed tubular reactors which are sidewall-cooled or sidewall-heated and usually are bundled up like heat-exchanger tubes. The ratio of sidewall surface area to the catalyst volume becomes an important design parameter with NINAF reactors. Another important design consideration is that sidewall cooling creates a radial variation of temperature and concentrations in the reactor that considerably complicates calculations.

Existing Models of the NINAF Gas Reactor

Over the years, several NINAF gas reactor models have been developed: a *simplified model,* a *semirigorous model,* and a *rigorous model.* Discussions of simplified and semirigorous models, which were developed by a number of workers, were included in J. M. Smith's 1956 textbook[11] but were not substantially updated in his 1970 second edition.[12] The simplified model is too inaccurate to be of any practical use, especially because NINAF reactors are extremely temperature-sensitive.

The semirigorous model assumes that: (1) the thermal conductivity is constant in the whole catalyst bed, and (2) there is no difference in temperature between the solid catalyst and the bulk gas flow. These assumptions have resulted in the concept of a *two-dimensional reactor model* in which the catalyst particles and the bulk gas flow are replaced by a hypothetical solid in which conduction is the only mechanism of heat transfer. The thermal conductivity of the solid is called the *effective thermal conductivity.* The main objection to this model is simply that it is too far from reality. The fact of the matter is that the overall thermal conductivity of the catalyst bed plus the gas does change in the radial direction and that the temperature difference between catalyst and bulk gas does increase with increasing exothermicity of the chemical reaction. Precisely because a NINAF reactor would be selected only because of the high exothermicity of the reactions, the assumption that catalyst temperatures and bulk gas temperatures are equal just does not make sense.

Another objection to the semirigorous model is that, philosophically, the term *semi-rigorous* is self-contradictory. Something can be either rigorous or not but it cannot be *semi*rigorous.

Carberry has described a steady-state NINAF gas reactor model[13,14] which appears to be the closest yet to reality. On the basis of experimental evidence[15] that axial dispersion is not significant in gas reactors, this model rightly neglects this factor. However, the model takes full account of the radial dispersion of mass and heat. The bulk gas flow and the catalyst pellets are not assumed to be at the same temperature. Because the thermal conductivity of the solid catalyst is usually very high, no temperature gradient is assumed in any catalyst particle, although various particles are expected to be at different temperatures. Heat transfer between the catalyst and the bulk gas is assumed to occur across the exterior surface of the catalyst particle. The isothermal catalyst particle temperature is assumed to represent the reaction temperature at any point of the bed. We will henceforth refer to this model as the *rigorous NINAF model.*

Because NINAF gas reactors for exothermic reactions are extremely temperature-sensitive, it would be both unsafe and uneconomical to use anything but the most rigorous model to design them. In past decades various difficulties discouraged the use of such rigorous models, but today the proper computer software is widely available and there can be no more excuse for not using a really rigorous model.

Development of Design Equations for a NINAF Gas Reactor for a First-Order Reaction

Let us now consider an elongated tubular packed reactor of bed height or axial coordinate z and internal diameter D_T, fully packed with a heterogeneous catalyst of particle diameter d_p and jacketed on the sidewall in order to maintain a desired temperature along the wall of the long reactor shell, as shown on Fig. 5-15. Let us subdivide this reactor into five radial increments ΔR and into a number of axial increments Δz. In this way, we will have five *annular shells,* each one subdivided into a number of *annular sections,* commonly called "onion rings." One such onion ring is shown in detail in Fig. 5-15. The values of both the radial increment ΔR and the axial increment Δz are constant. It is possible to vary the step size during the course of integration as needed, but this refinement and complication was not deemed necessary in this book.

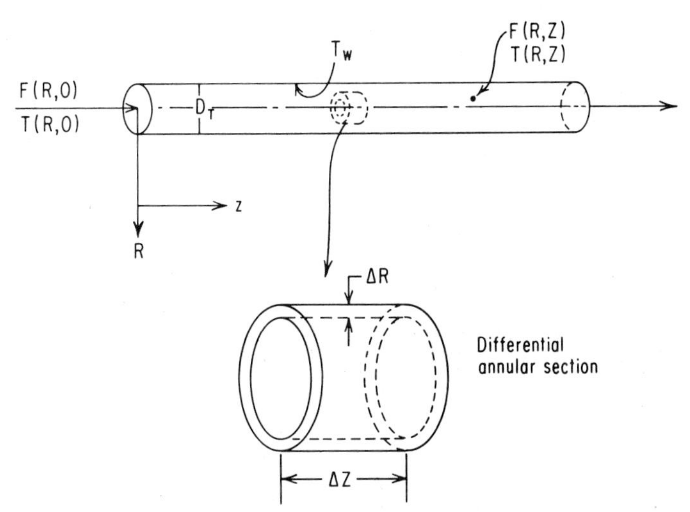

FIG. 5-15 Schematic representation of the NINAF gas reactor with details of a differential annular section.

The concentration of the key reactant at the inlet of the reactor is C_0. The absolute temperature of the reaction mixture is T_0. The inlet temperature is assumed to be somewhat above that maintained in the jacket.

A mass balance around any particular annular section leads to the development of the design equation. At steady state we can write:

$$\begin{pmatrix}\text{Molar}\\ \text{inflow}\\ \text{axially}\end{pmatrix} - \begin{pmatrix}\text{molar}\\ \text{outflow}\\ \text{axially}\end{pmatrix} + \begin{pmatrix}\text{molar}\\ \text{inflow}\\ \text{radially}\end{pmatrix} - \begin{pmatrix}\text{molar}\\ \text{outflow}\\ \text{radially}\end{pmatrix} - \begin{pmatrix}\text{molar}\\ \text{disappearance}\\ \text{by reaction}\end{pmatrix} = 0 \qquad (5\text{-}43)$$

The cross-sectional area of the onion ring in the Z direction is $2\pi r\Delta r$. With it, the above balance equation can be expressed mathemetically as follows, using Fick's law, i.e., molar flow $= D_r(2\pi r\Delta r)dC/dr$.

$$(2\pi r\Delta r)u(C|_z - C|_{z+\Delta z}) + \left(-D_r 2\pi r\Delta z \left.\frac{\partial C}{\partial r}\right|_r\right) - \left(-D_r 2\pi(r+\Delta r)\Delta z \left.\frac{\partial C}{\partial r}\right|_{r+\Delta r}\right) - (2\pi r\Delta r\Delta z)\,\mathcal{R} = 0 \qquad (5\text{-}44)$$

where u = fluid velocity in bed, m/s

C = molar concentration, kmol/m^3

D_r = radial mass diffusivity, m^2/s

$C|_z$ = molar concentration at axial distance z from the inlet

$\mathcal{R}$ = reaction rate function based on unit catalyst bed volume, kmol of reactant converted /(m$^3\cdot$ s)

Equation (5-44), divided by $2\pi r\Delta r\Delta zu$ and rearranged, gives:

$$\frac{C|_{z+\Delta z} - C|_z}{\Delta z} = \frac{D_r}{u}\left[\frac{(r+\Delta r)(\partial C/\partial r)|_{r+\Delta r} - r(\partial C/\partial r)|_r}{r\Delta r}\right] - \frac{\mathcal{R}}{u} \qquad (5\text{-}45)$$

At limiting conditions $z \to 0$, $r \to 0$, and Eq. (5-45) can be written:

$$(\partial C/\partial z) = (D_r/ur)\partial(r\partial C/\partial r)\partial r - \mathcal{R}/u \qquad (5\text{-}46)$$

A heat balance around any particular annular section leads to the development of the heat balance equation:

(Heat inflow axially) − (heat outflow axially)

+ (heat inflow radially) − (heat outflow radially)

+ (heat generated by reaction) = 0 (5-47)

$$(2\pi r\Delta r)u\rho c_p(T|_z - T|_{z+\Delta z}) + \left(-K_r 2\pi r\Delta z \left.\frac{\partial T}{\partial r}\right|_r\right)\rho\, c_p$$

$$-\left(-K_r 2\pi(r+\Delta r)\Delta z \left.\frac{\partial T}{\partial r}\right|_{r+\Delta r}\right)\rho c_p + (2\pi r\Delta r\Delta z)(-\Delta H)\mathfrak{R} = 0 \quad (5\text{-}48)$$

where c_p = specific heat of gas, kJ/kg (includes all gases)
ρ = specific gravity of gas, kg/m^3 (includes all reacting gases)
K_r = radial thermal diffusivity in packed bed, m^2/s

When divided by $2\pi r\Delta r\Delta z\, c_p u\rho$ and rearranged, Eq. (5-48) gives:

$$\frac{T|_z - T|_{z+\Delta z}}{z} + \left[\left.\frac{-K_r(\partial T/\partial r)}{u\Delta r}\right|_r - \left.\frac{-K_r(r + \Delta r)(\partial T/\partial r)}{u\, r\Delta r}\right|_{r+\Delta r}\right] + \frac{-\Delta H}{c_p u\rho} = 0 \quad (5\text{-}49)$$

$$[T|_{z+\Delta z} - T|_z]/\Delta z = (K_r/u)\cdot[(r + \Delta r)(\partial T/\partial r)|_{r+\Delta r} - r(\partial T/\partial r)|_r]/r\Delta r + (-\Delta \mathrm{H})\mathfrak{R}/c_p u\rho \quad (5\text{-}50)$$

When $\Delta z \rightarrow 0$ and $\Delta r = 0$,

$$[T|_{z+z} - T|_z]/\Delta z \rightarrow \partial T/\partial z$$

$$[(r + \Delta r)(\partial T/\partial r)|_{r+\Delta r} - r(\partial T/\partial r)|_r]/r\Delta r \rightarrow (1/r)\cdot \partial(r\partial T/\partial r)/\partial r$$

The derivative of a product can be expressed as follows:

$$\partial(r\partial T/\partial r)/\partial r = r\partial^2 T/\partial r^2 + (\partial T/\partial r)(\partial r/\partial r)$$

Thus Eq. (5-50) becomes:

$$(\partial T/\partial z) = (K_r/u)[(\partial^2 T/\partial r^2) + (\partial T/r\partial r)] + (-\Delta H)\mathfrak{R}/c_p u\rho \quad (5\text{-}51)$$

Equations (5-46) and (5-51) are the two PDEs that describe the NINAF reactor. Together with the proper rate equations and auxiliary condition expressions, they can be conveniently solved by the computer technique developed in Chap. 2 for PDEs. However, it is more desirable to transform Eqs. (5-46) and (5-51) into forms that contain dimensionless variables, not because the mathematical solution will be any easier—it will not—but because the resulting equations contain a number of dimensionless groups which are more generally applicable and thereby make designing considerably easier.

Let us use the following dimensionless variables:

$C_r = C/C_0$ reduced concentration of key reactant

$C_0 =$ molar concentration of key reactant at inlet, kmol/m^3

$T_r = T/T_0$ reduced gas temperature

$T_0 =$ absolute temperature of reactant at inlet, K

$Z = z/d_p$ reduced axial coordinate

$d_p =$ catalyst particle diameter (for catalyst particles of cylindrical shapes, d_p represents the diameter of the sphere having the same surface as the cylinder)

$R = r/d_p$ reduced radial coordinate

With these dimensionless variables Eq. (5-46) becomes:

$$\frac{\partial(C_r\, C_0)}{\partial(Z\, d_p)} = \frac{D_r}{uRd_p} \cdot \{\partial[Rd_p\partial(C_rC_0)/\partial(Rd_p)]/\partial(Rd_p)\} - \mathfrak{R}/u$$

$$\frac{\partial C_r}{\partial Z} = \frac{D_r}{uRd_p} \cdot [\partial(R\partial C_r/\partial R)/\partial R] - d_p\mathfrak{R}/C_0u$$

Again, the derivative of a product can be written as

$$[\partial(R\partial C_r/\partial R)]/\partial R = R \cdot \partial(\partial C_r/\partial R)/\partial R + (\partial C_r/\partial R)$$
$$= (R\partial^2 C_r/\partial R^2) + (\partial C_r/\partial R)$$

Thus, considering that d_pu/D_r is called the *radial Péclet number for mass* (Pe_m), we obtain (see Chap. 4)

$$\frac{\partial C_r}{\partial Z} = \frac{1}{\mathrm{Pe}_m}\left[\frac{\partial^2 C_r}{\partial R^2} + \frac{1}{R}\cdot\frac{\partial C_r}{\partial R}\right] - \frac{d_p\mathfrak{R}}{C_0u} \tag{5-52}$$

Similarly, Eq. (5-51) becomes, upon substitution with dimensionless variables,

$$\frac{\partial T_r}{\partial Z} = \frac{1}{\mathrm{Pe}_h}\cdot\left[\frac{\partial^2 T_r}{\partial R^2} + \frac{1}{R}\cdot\frac{\partial T_r}{\partial R}\right] + \frac{-\Delta H\, d_p\mathfrak{R}}{c_p\, u\rho T_0} \tag{5-53}$$

where K_r/ud_p has been replaced by the dimensionless group called *radial Péclet number for heat*, which is designated by the symbol Pe_h.

In Eqs. (5-52) and (5-53) the left-hand terms represent the *axial gradients*, the middle terms the *radial gradients*, and the right-hand terms the *species generation terms*, which include the apparent reaction rate $\mathfrak{R}$.

Finally, we need the auxiliary values of the PDEs (5-52) and (5-53), in order to integrate them. The auxiliary values are:

$$\text{Bed inlet} \qquad Z = 1 \qquad C_r(R, 0) = 1 \qquad T_r(R, 0) = 1 \tag{5-54}$$

$$\text{Centerline} \qquad \frac{\partial C_r(0,Z)}{\partial R} = 0 \qquad \frac{T_r(0,Z)}{\partial R} = 0 \tag{5-55}$$

$$\text{Reactor wall} \qquad \frac{\partial C_r(R_T, Z)}{\partial R} = 0 \tag{5-56}$$

$$\frac{\partial T_r(R_T, Z)}{\partial R} = (\text{Bi})_w(T_w - T_r(R_T, Z)) \tag{5-57}$$

The boundary conditions, Eq. (5-54), mean that at the reactor inlet both reduced concentration and reduced temperature are unity. The boundary condition, Eq. (5-55), states that at centerline or reactor axis, the reduced concentrations and reduced temperatures do not change with radial coordinates. The boundary condition, Eq. (5-56), states that no mass transfer can take place through the reactor wall. The boundary condition, Eq. (5-57), states that the heat flux at the wall, as expressed by the modified version of the Fourier law, is equal to the product of the wall heat transfer coefficient h_w by the temperature driving force between reduced bulk gas temperature T_r and the reduced inside wall temperature T_w. The reactor wall expression can be rearranged as:

$$\frac{-\partial T_r}{\partial R(T_r - T_w)} = \frac{h_w\, d_p}{2\rho c_p K_r} = \text{Biot}_{\text{wall}} = \text{Bi}_w \tag{5-58}$$

The Bi_w numbers were discussed in Chap. 4.

The calculation of h_w presents some difficulties. Reliable data are not available. Froment[16] gives a plot of $h_w\, d_p/\lambda_g$ vs. Re with a number of scattered lines obtained by various workers. Obviously the heat transfer coefficient at the wall is one of the most important data and one should be determined carefully if it turns out that a new process might be run in NINAF reactors. However, if such information cannot be obtained, a conservative way to design a NINAF reactor would be to use a rather lower h_w value corresponding to a given Reynolds number. If it turns out that more heat transfer is obtained at the wall during the startup tests of the reactors than the selected h_w value would provide, there is nothing to fear since the reactors would then be more stable than intended.

The system of Eqs.. (5-52), (5-53), and (4-1), the kinetic equation of the type (5-1), (3-45), (4-14), (4-12), (4-11), (4-17), and (3-59), and auxiliary conditions given by Eqs. (5-54), (5-55), (5-56), and (5-57) adequately describe a single first-order reaction occurring in a NINAF reactor.

However, it must be modified to handle a system of several first-order reactions by replacing the $(-\Delta H R_1)$ expression in Eq. (5-53) by $\Sigma(-\Delta H_i R_i)$ in order to take account of all heat developed by all reactions taking place in the reactor. In the case of two consecutive reactions

$$R_i = \eta_1 k_1 C_s \qquad R_2 = \eta_2 k_2 C_B \tag{5-59}$$

where C_B is the concentration of the product of reaction 1 on the catalyst surface. The value of C_B can be calculated for a "macromicropore model," according to Carberry.[17]

In solving this system of equations, we must use the computer program developed in Chap. 2 to solve PDEs. However, we cannot start at the inlet of the reactor and apply the PDE technique to compute T_r and C_r step by step for each Z, because at the inlet of the reactor we start with bulk gas conditions C_r and T_r and have to calculate catalyst surface conditions C_{rs} and T_{rs} using Eqs. (4-26) and (4-28), which relate bulk conditions to catalyst surface conditions. Such calculations can only be done by iteration, as will be seen in great detail in the example of the oxidation of naphthalene to phthalic anhydride, which will be discussed next.

Example of NINAF Reactor Design: Air Oxidation of Naphthalene to Phthalic Anhydride

This example was chosen because it has been widely discussed by Carberry[13,14] and others[18,19] and sufficient published data are available to design a reactor. When this oxidation reaction is conducted in an excess of oxygen, the reaction system may be summarized by the following simplified equations:

$$\underset{\text{Naphthalene}}{C_{10}H_8} + 4.5O_2 \xrightarrow{k_1} \underset{\substack{\text{Phthalic}\\ \text{anhydride}}}{C_6H_4(CO)_2O} + 2CO_2 + 2H_2O \tag{5-60}$$

$$C_6H_4(CO)_2O + 7.5O_2 \xrightarrow{k_2} 8CO_2 + 2H_2O \tag{5-60a}$$

Here, k_1 and k_2 are the rate constants of the two consecutive reactions. Input data for designing a NINAF reactor for this reaction system are given in Table 5-2. Kinetic studies reported by DeMaria[18] for a catalyst with small fluidizable particles suggest that all reactions are pseudo-first-order in naphthalene and phthalic anhydride and zero-order in oxygen. Oxygen is always present in vast stoichiometric excess. The oxygen/naphthalene ratio was selected slightly outside the explosive region. The excess of air constitutes both an excess of reactant and an inert diluent and hence forms a beneficial heat sink. On the other hand, it also constitutes a factor for increasing the number of reactor tubes, since the reactor diameter cannot be enlarged without badly affecting heat transfer.

The sources of the data used in this example are indicated in Table 5-2. Some data were recalculated. For most of the data the correctness of information given in the literature was relied on.

The computer program RDMOT2 developed to solve this type of problem is explained in detail in the following, with the assistance of Figs. 5-16 to 5-20.

First, all the input data are read in and also printed in order to define the problem. In the unlikely event that the temperature would run away, TRMAX$=2.0T_0$ is also read in as a limit. A fixed step size is read in. Next, dependent variable Y and its derivatives F are dimensioned in the form of two-dimensional arrays. There are two types of PDEs and each has six I values. An equivalence statement establishes correspondence between C_r, T_r, and their Y equivalents. Some information such as the highest I value, NR, and the frequency of printing, IFREQ, is supplied in form of data statements. Next Z, Y(I,1), Y(I,2), and ICOUNT are initialized. A DO loop assigns I values from 1 to 6 to all the Y's. Then nine quantities, ρ, c_p, Re, Pr, Sc, k_g, h, Bi_m, and Δr are calculated.

Now, dummy variables CSI and TSI are initialized in order to compute the catalyst-surface concentration CS(I) and catalyst-surface temperature TS(I). As a starting point, CSI is assumed to be the same as the concentration on the axis and inlet of the reactor, namely CSI$=$CS(1). This statement calls on the function CS(I) which is set up as one of the several separate functions. On Fig. 5-17, the sequence of computation which gives CS(I) is shown by an arrow diagram. We will come back to this sequence of computation.

The FUNCTION RUNGE is called. This function is set up to process a one-dimensional array of differential equations. Since there is one material balance ODE and one heat balance ODE, each with six I values, N = 12. The FUNCTION RUNGE works exactly as discussed in the adiabatic reactor examples. A DO loop assigns values between 1 and 6 to I. For I = 1 or on the reactor axis, special ODEs apply. For I = 2, 3, 4, 5, the regular ODEs apply and for I = 6 or at the reactor wall, the ODEs include the boundary conditions.

The calculation of I-dependent quantities, such as the temperature-corrected RHOC, Sc, K_g, HTC, and Bi_m, also have to be located inside the DO loop in which the value of I is defined.

Following the FUNCTION RUNGE a temperature limit is set: if the bulk temperature exceeds 2.0 times the inlet temperature, the integration is terminated and the program writes its final statements and stops. Otherwise, it continues. Here, the axis points are taken as the temper-

TABLE 5-2
Input Data for the Computer Program RDMOT2 to Design a NINAF Reactor for the Oxidation of Naphthalene to Phthalic Anhydride

Text symbol	Computer symbol	Value	Dimensions	Data source (ref. no.)
a	A	1200.	m^{-1}	
A_1	A1	5.809×10^{13}	s^{-1}	Calculated from 14
A_2	A2	2.222×10^{5}	s^{-1}	14
Bi_w	BIW	Note 1	Dimensionless	
c_p	CP	30.334	kJ/(mol·K)	14
$\mathcal{D}$	D	10^{-5}	m^2/s	14
D_{1m}	D1M	$2.05\ 10^{-5}$	m^2/s	14
D_B/D_A	DBDA	0.93	Dimensionless	14
d_p	DP	0.001	m	14
D_T	DT	0.05	m	20
E_1	E1	158990.	kJ/kmol	14
E_2	E2	83680.	kJ/kmol	14
H	H	0.1	Dimensionless	
k_1	K1	7.0	s^{-1}	14
k_2	K2	0.035	s^{-1}	14
M_1	MW1	128.174		
M_2	MW2	28.860		
Pe_m	PEM	10.0	Dimensionless	14
Pe_h	PEH	7.0	Dimensionless	14
R_G	RG	8.316	kJ/(kmol·K)	
T_0	TO	643.2	K	14
T_{rmax}	TRMAX	2.0	Dimensionless	

ature sensing points, since the peak is expected to show up there.

Each time that a certain number of integration steps are compiled, the results are printed. The number of integration steps between each printing is designated as IFREQ.

Various quantities needed for the calculation of the ODEs are computed as separate functions. The relationships between these functions is shown in Fig. 5-17. There are some problems in these relationships which require a detailed explanation. Thus, starting with the bulk gas

TABLE 5-2

Input Data for the Computer Program RDMOT2 to Design a NINAF Reactor for the Oxidation of Naphthalene to Phthalic Anhydride (*Continued*)

Text symbol	Computer symbol	Value	Dimensions	Data source (ref. no.)
T_w	TW	0.983	Dimensionless	
u	U	8.0	m/s	
y_0	YO	Note 2	Dimensionless	
μ	VIS	0.0000305	kg/m·s	14
λ_G	LG	3.853×10^{-5}	kJ/(s·m·K)	14
ΔH_1	DH1	-1.8×10^6	kJ/kmol	Note 3
ΔH_2	DH2	-1.82×10^6	kJ/kmol	Note 3

NOTE 1: Heat transfer across the reactor walls of NINAF reactors is reported[20] to be in the order of 200 to 400 Btu/(h·ft^2·°F), which corresponds to 1.1356 – 2.2712 kJ/(s·m^2·K). The author selected the upper range and calculated

$$\text{Bi}_w = \frac{h_w\, d_p}{\rho c_p\, K_r} \quad \text{but} \quad K_r = d_p u/\text{Pe}_h$$

$$\text{Bi}_w = h_w\, \text{Pe}_h/\rho c_p u = (2.27)(7.)/(0.56094)(1.0246)(8.) = 3.456$$

Too low a Bi_w would make the NINAF reactor approach an adiabatic reactor. This is exactly what would happen if the above calculated Bi_w figure were used. We have used $\text{Bi}_w = 92.0$ to demonstrate a strong wall effect. Heat transfer in the process side is reported to be[20] 32 Btu/(h·ft^2·°F) or 0.1817 kJ/s·m^2·K), which is 6.46 times lower than the value calculated by formula. We prefer to use the experimental data.

NOTE 2: One must be very careful in selecting the naphthalene mole fraction in air because of the explosivity of air-naphthalene mixtures:

Lower explosive limit: 0.9 mol % naphthalene in air

Upper explosive limit: 5.9 mol % naphthalene in air

Thus $y_0 = 0.0075$ (¾% naphthalene) is probably the highest safe concentration. However, it is also known that some industrial reactors are being operated even in the explosive range.[20]

NOTE 3: Literature data on ΔH_1 and ΔH_2 are spread over an order of magnitude. Data of Coleman and Pilcher,[21] G. C. Parks et al.,[22] L. M. Elkin,[20] and a private source were compared and the following data were adopted: $-\Delta H_1 = 0.18 \times 10^7$ kJ/kmol and $-\Delta H_2 = 0.182 \times 10^7$ kJ/kmol.

concentration CR(I) and bulk gas temperature TR(I), it is not possible to calculate the catalyst surface concentration CS(I) and temperature TS(I) explicitly from the differential equations. The reason is that the terms η_1, k_1, R_1, and $\Sigma\Delta H{\cdot}R$, all of which depend on temperature and concentration, must be evaluated as functions of CS(I) and TS(I). This means that CS(I) and TS(I) appear implicitly in the system of equations and must therefore be computed by iteration. Thus, CS(I) and TS(I) are assumed; η_1, k_1, R_1, and $\Sigma\Delta H{\cdot}R$ are computed based on these as-

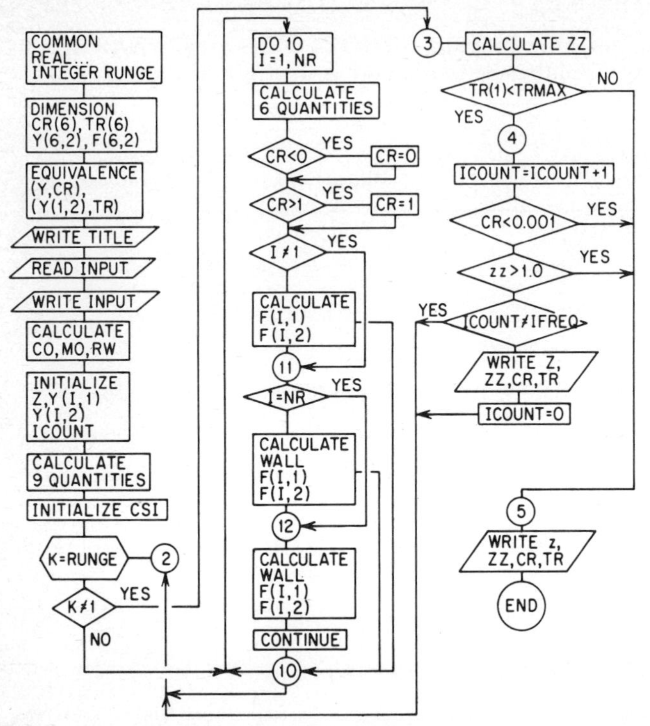

FIG. 5-16 Block diagram of the RDMOT2 computer program.

sumed values; new values of CS(I) and TS(I) are computed from the set of equations; and the entire calculation is then repeated until convergence on CS(I) and TS(I) is obtained. Specifically, the call to $R1$(I) in calculating F(I,1) initiates the iterative calculation of the catalyst surface concentration and temperature:

R1 ⟵ EFF1 ⟵ PHI1 ⟵ K1 ⟵ TSI ⟵ DHR

CS

The initial values of C_s and T_s are set equal to the bulk fluid concentrations and temperature, respectively, and are designated as the dummy variables CSI and TSI. Now CSI and TSI are computed by the equations:

$$\mathrm{CSI} = C_0\, C_r/(1 + (\eta_1\, k_1/k_g\, a))$$

$$\text{TSI} = T_0\, T_r + (\sum(-\Delta Hj\, R_j)/ha)$$

The number of iterations is set at NITER = 3.

The function DHR stands for $\Sigma(-\Delta H_j\, R_j)$, where j is the number of reactions. In the calculation of the function DHR, R_1 in the expression $(-\Delta H_1)R_1 + (-\Delta H_2)R_2$ is computed locally to avoid a recursive call to the function CS [CSI is used instead of CS(I)]. A recursive call is forbidden and by the use of intermediate dummy variables the computer is, so to speak, "cheated" and induced to do what it would not do otherwise.

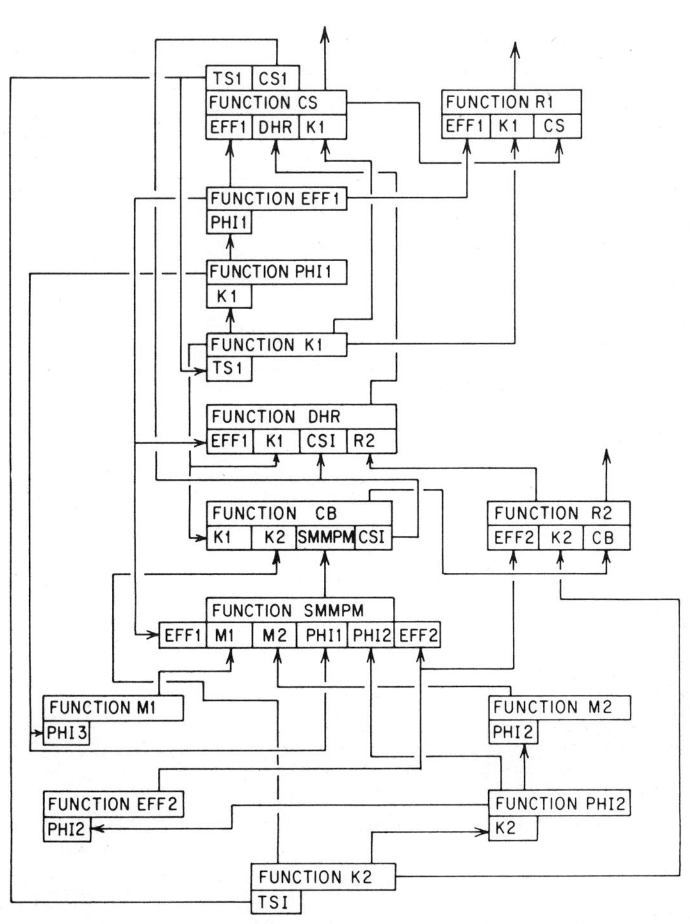

FIG. 5-17 Arrow diagram of calculation sequence of various functions in the RDMOT2 program.

```
A      CATALYST MASS-TRANSFER SURFACE AREA /UNIT VOLUME, 1/M
A1     FREQUENCY FACTOR FOR REACTION 1
A2     FREQUENCY FACTOR FOR REACTION 2
BIM    BIOT NUMBER FOR MASS, DIMENSIONLESS
BIW    BIOT NUMBER FOR REACTOR WALL, DIMENSIONLESS
CB     REDUCED CONCENTRATION OF PHTHALIC ANHYDRIDE, DIMENSIONLESS
CP     HEAT CAPACITY OF GAS ,KJ/KG
CR     REDUCED CONCENTRATION OF NAPHTHALENE,DIMENSIONLESS
CRS    REDUCED CONCENTRATION OF NAPHTHALENE ON CATALYST SURFACE
CSI    DUMMY VARIABLE = CS(I)
C0     NAPHTHALENE CONCENTRATION AT REACTOR INLET,KMOL/M**3
D      INTRAPHASE DIFFUSIVITY, M**2/S
DBDA   DB/DA ;DB=DIFFUSIVITY OF THE PRODUCT, M**2/S ;
              DA=DIFFUSIVITY OF THE REACTANT, M**2/S
DELTAR RADIAL INCREMENT
DH1    HEAT OF REACTION 1, KJ/KMOL
DH2    HEAT OF REACTION 2, KJ/KMOL
DP     CATALYST PARTICLE DIAMETER, M
DR     RADIAL MASS DIFFUSIVITY, M**2/S
D1M    MOLECULAR DIFFUSIVITY IN MULTICOMPONENT MIXTURE, M**2/S
EFF1   EFFECTIVENESS FACTOR OF REACTION 1 , DIMENSIONLESS
EFF2   EFFECTIVENESS FACTOR OF REACTION 2 , DIMENSIONLESS
E1     ACTIVATION ENERGY FOR REACTION 1 , KJ/KMOL
E2     ACTIVATION ENERGY FOR REACTION 2 , KJ/KMOL
F      DERIVATIVE DY/DZ
H      STEPSIZE IN INTEGRATION
HTC    INTERPHASE HEAT TRANSFER COEFFICIENT, KJ/S.K.M**2
ICOUNT COUNTER FOR PRINTING FREQUENCY
IFREQ  PRINTING FREQUENCY, DIMENSIONLESS
KG     INTERPHASE MASS-TRANSFER COEFFICIENT, M/S
KR     RADIAL HEAT DIFFUSIVITY, M**2/S
K1     RATE CONSTANT OF REACTION 1
K2     RATE CONSTANT OF REACTION 2
LG     THERMAL CONDUCTIVITY OF GAS, KJ/S.M.K
MW1    MOLECULAR WEIGHT OF NAPHTHALENE
MW2    MOLECULAR WEIGHT OF AIR
N      NUMBER OF ORDINARY DIFFERENTIAL EQUATIONS
NITER  ITERATION COUNTER IN FUNCTION CS(I)
NR     THE LAST (WALL) TERM OF I=2,3,...,NR IN RADIAL INCREMENTATION
PEH    PECLET NUMBER FOR HEAT TRANSFER, DIMENSIONLESS=(DP*U/KR)
PEM    PECLET NUMBER FOR MASS TRANSFER, DIMENSIONLESS=(DP*U/DR)
PHI    DUMMY VARIABLE OF FUNCTION RUNGE, EFF1(I),EFF2(I)
PR     PRANDTL NUMBER, DIMENSIONLESS = (CP*VIS/LG)
R      REDUCED RADIAL COORDINATE, DIMENSIONLESS
RE     REYNOLDS NUMBER, DIMENSIONLESS=12.189*DP*M0*U/(VIS*T0*TR(I))
RG     GAS CONSTANT = 8.316 KJ/KMOL.K
RHO    FLUID DENSITY AT INLET, KG/M**3
RHOC   FLUID DENSITY AT ANY POINT, KG/M**3
RW     DIMENSIONLESS RADIUS OF REACTOR
R1     EFFECTIVE RATE OF REACTION 1
R2     EFFECTIVE RATE OF REACTION 2
SAVEY  DUMMY VARIABLE OF FUNCTION RUNGE TO SAVE Y
TR     REDUCED GAS TEMPERATURE, DIMENSIONLESS = T/T0
TRMAX  MAXIMUM ALLOWABLE REDUCED TEMPERATURE, DIMENSIONLESS
TSI    DUMMY VARIABLE = TS(I)
TW     WALL TEMPERATURE, DIMENSIONLESS
T0     ABSOLUTE TEMPERATURE OF REACTANTS AT INLET, K
U      FLUID VELOCITY IN BED, M/S
VIS    VISCOSITY OF FLUID, KG/M.S (=PAS)
Y      DEPENDENT VARIABLE IN INTEGRATION
Y0     MOL FRACTION OF NAPHTHALENE AT INLET, DIMENSIONLESS
Z      REDUCED AXIAL COORDINATE, DIMENSIONLESS
ZZ     AXIAL COORDINATE, M.
```

FIG. 5-18 Definition of symbols in the RDMOT2 computer program.

```
C      PROCESS DESIGN OF NINAF GAS REACTOR
C                        FOR
C      AIR-OXIDATION OF NAPHTHALENE TO PHTHALIC ANHYDRIDE
C
       COMMON A,A1,A2,BIM,CO,D,DBDA,DH1,DH2,DP,E1,E2,HTC,KG,RG,TO,
     1        CSI,TSI,CR,TR
       REAL MO,LG,KG,MW1,MW2
       INTEGER RUNGE
       DIMENSION CR(6), TR(6)
       DIMENSION Y(6,2),F(6,2)
       EQUIVALENCE (Y,CR),(Y(1,2),TR)
       WRITE(6,150)
   150 FORMAT(1H1,21X,27HDESIGN OF NINAF GAS REACTOR/1H0,11X,
     150HAIR OXIDATION OF NAPHTHALENE TO PHTHALIC ANHYDRIDE)
C      ....READ AND PRINT DATA ....
       READ(5,100) PEM,PEH,DP,CP,U,TO,TRMAX,E1,E2,A1,A2,DH1,DH2,VIS,BIW,
     1 LG,D1M,D,A,YO,RG,DBDA,DT,H,TW,MW1,MW2
   100 FORMAT(7F10.4/3E20.6/3E20.6/3E20.6/2E20.6,2F10.4/7F10.4)
       DATA NR/6/
       DATA IFREQ/250/
       WRITE(6,200) TO,U,TRMAX,A,YO,CP,MW1,MW2,PEM,E1,A1,DT,H,PEH,E2,A2,
     1 DBDA,TW,DP,BIW,VIS,DH1,LG,RG,DH2,D,D1M
   200 FORMAT(1H0,2X,4HTO= ,F5.1,7H K    U=,F6.3,12H M/S   TRMAX=,F6.3,8X,
     1 2HA=,F7.1,4H 1/M/1H ,2X,4HYO= ,E9.3,4H CP=,F6.3,8H KJ/KMOL,2X,
     2 4HMW1=,F7.3,4X,4HMW2=,F6.3,5H PEM=,F6.3/1H ,2X,4HE1= ,E9.3,
     3 4H A1=,E10.4,4H DT=,F6.3,2H M,9X,2HH=,F5.3,7H    PEH=,F6.3/1H ,2X,
     4 4HE2= ,E9.3,4H A2=,E10.4,
     5 6H DBDA=,F5.3,10X,3HTW=,F5.3,5H   DP=,F5.3,2H M/1H ,2X,4HBIW=,
     6 E9.3,15X,4HVIS=,E9.3,4H PAS,3X,4HDH1=,E9.3,8H KJ/KMOL/1H ,2X,
     7 4HLG= ,E9.3,9H KJ/S.M.K,6X,3HRG=,F5.3,12H KJ/KMOL.K   ,4HDH2=,
     8 E9.3,8H KJ/KMOL/1H ,2X,4HD=   ,E9.3,7H M**2/S,8X,4HD1M=,E9.3,
     9 7H M**2/S)
C      ....CALCULATE CO, MO, RW ....
       CO=12.189*YO/TO
       MO=(YO*MW1) + ((1.-YO)*MW2)
       RW=DT/(2.*DP)
C      ....INITIALIZE Z,Y(I,1),Y(I,2), AND ICOUNT ....
       Z = 0.0
       DO 1 I=1,NR
       Y(I,1) = 1.0
     1 Y(I,2) = 1.0
       ICOUNT=0
C      ....CALCULATE RHO, CP, RE, PR, SC, KG, HTC, BIM, DELTAR ....
       RHO=273.16*MO/(22.414*TO)
       CP=CP/MO
       RE=12.1888*DP*MO*U/(VIS*TO)
       PR=CP*VIS/LG
       FACTOR=1.15*U/SQRT(RE)
       SC=VIS/(RHO*D1M)
       KG=FACTOR*(SC)**(-2./3.)
C      HTC=FACTOR*RHO*CP*(PR)**(-2./3.)
       HTC = 0.182
       BIM=KG/(D*A)
       DELTAR = RW/5.0
C      ....INITIALIZE CSI, TSI VIA FUNCTION CS(I)....
       CSI = CS(1)
C      ....CALL ON THE FOURTH-ORDER RUNGE-KUTTA FUNCTION....
     2 K=RUNGE  (12,Y,F,Z,H)
C      IF K=1 COMPUTE DERIVATIVE VALUES
       IF(K.NE.1) GO TO 3
       DO 10 I = 1,NR
C      ....CALCULATE RHOC, RE, SC, KG, HTC, AND BIM ....
       RHOC = RHO/TR(I)
       RE=12.1888*DP*MO*U/(VIS*TO*TR(I))
       SC=VIS/(RHOC*D1M)
       KG=FACTOR*(SC)**(-2./3.)
       HTC=FACTOR*RHOC*CP*(PR)**(-2./3.)
       BIM=KG/(D*A)
```

FIG. 5-19 **The RDMOT2 computer program for the design of a NINAF reactor for the oxidation of naphthalene to phthalic anhydride.**

```
      IF(CR(I).LT.0.)CR(I)=0.
      IF(CR(I).GT.1.)CR(I)=1.
      IF(I.NE.1)GO TO 11
      F(I,1)=(4./PEM)*(CR(I+1)-CR(I))/(DELTAR**2)-(DP*R1(I)/(CO*U))
      F(I,2)=(4./PEH)*(TR(I+1)-TR(I))/(DELTAR**2)
     1       +DHR(I)*DP/(CP*U*RHOC*TO)
      GO TO 10
   11 IF(I.EQ.NR) GO TO 12
      WALL=(TR(I+1)-TR(I-1))/(2.*DELTAR)
      F(I,1)=(1./PEM)*((CR(I+1)-2.*CR(I)+CR(I-1))/(DELTAR**2)+
     1       (1./((I-1)*DELTAR))*(CR(I+1)-CR(I-1))/(2.*DELTAR))
     2       -(DP*R1(I)/(CO*U))
      F(I,2)=(1./PEH)*((TR(I+1)-2.*TR(I)+TR(I-1))/(DELTAR**2)+
     1       (1./((I-1)*DELTAR))*WALL)
     2       +(DHR(I)*DP/(CP*U*RHOC*TO))
      GO TO 10
   12 WALL=BIW*(TW-TR(NR))
      F(I,1)=(2./PEM)*(CR(I-1)-CR(I))/(DELTAR**2)
     1       -(DP*R1(I)/(CO*U))
      F(I,2)=(2./PEH)*((TR(I-1)-TR(I))/(DELTAR**2)+
     1       (1./((I-1)*DELTAR))*WALL)
     2       +(DHR(I)*DP/(CP*U*RHOC*TO))
   10 CONTINUE
      GO TO 2
    3 ZZ = Z * DP
C
C     ....IF TR EXCEEDS TRMAX, TERMINATE INTEGRATION....
      IF(TR(1).LE.TRMAX) GO TO 4
      GO TO 5
    4 ICOUNT = ICOUNT + 1
      IF(CR(1).LE.0.001) GO TO 5
      IF(ZZ.GE.1.5) GO TO 5
      IF(ICOUNT.NE.IFREQ) GO TO 2
C
C     ....PRINT SOLUTION ....
C
      WRITE (6,202) Z, ZZ
      WRITE (6,203) (CR(I),I=1,NR)
      WRITE (6,204) (TR(I),I=1,NR)
  202 FORMAT(1H0,2X,4HZ = ,E10.3,3X,5HZZ = ,E10.3/1H ,6X,
     1 11H     R=0    ,11H     R=1    ,11H     R=2    ,
     2 11H     R=3    ,11H     R=4    ,11H     R=5    )
  203 FORMAT (1H ,6HCR(I)=,6E11.3)
  204 FORMAT (1H ,6HTR(I)=,6E11.3)
      ICOUNT = 0
      GO TO 2
C
C     THE CALL TO R1(I) IN CALCULATING F(I,1) INITIATES THE ITERATIVE
C     CALCULATION OF THE CATALYST SURFACE CONCENTRATION AND TEMPERATURE,
C     CSI AND TSI
C
    5 WRITE(6,202) Z, ZZ
      WRITE(6,203) (CR(I),I=1,NR)
      WRITE(6,204) (TR(I),I=1,NR)
      STOP
      END
C
```

FIG. 5-19 **The RDMOT2 computer program for the design of a NINAF reactor for the oxidation of naphthalene to phthalic anhydride (*continued*).**

```
      FUNCTION RUNGE (N,Y,F,Z,H)
      INTEGER RUNGE
      DIMENSION PHI(50),SAVEY(50),Y(N),F(N)
      DATA M/0/
C
      M = M + 1
      GO TO (1,2,3,4,5), M
C                   PASS 1
    1 RUNGE = 1
      RETURN
C                   PASS 2
    2 DO 22 J=1,N
      SAVEY(J)=Y(J)
      PHI(J)=F(J)
   22 Y(J)=SAVEY(J) +0.5 * H * F(J)
      Z = Z + 0.5 * H
      RUNGE = 1
      RETURN
C                   PASS 3
    3 DO 33  J=1,N
      PHI(J)  = PHI(J)  + 2.0 * F(J)
   33 Y(J)  = SAVEY(J)  + 0.5 * H * F(J)
      RUNGE = 1
      RETURN
C                   PASS 4
    4 DO 44 J=1,N
      PHI(J)  = PHI(J)  + 2.0 * F(J)
   44 Y(J)  = SAVEY(J)  + H * F(J)
      Z = Z + 0.5 * H
      RUNGE = 1
      RETURN
C                   PASS 5
    5 DO 55 J = 1,N
   55 Y(J)  = SAVEY(J)  + (PHI(J)  + F(J))* H/6.0
      M=0
      RUNGE = 0
      RETURN
      END
```

```
C
      FUNCTION R1(I)
C
      REAL K1
C     THE FOLLOWING STATEMENT WILL ITERATIVELY CALCULATE CSI AND TSI,
C     VIA THE CALL TO CS(I)
      CSI=CS(I)
      R1 = EFF1(I)*K1(I)*CSI
      RETURN
      END
```

```
C
      FUNCTION R2(I)
C
      REAL K2
      R2 = EFF2(I)*K2(I)*CB(I)
      RETURN
      END
```

FIG. 5-19 **The RDMOT2 computer program for the design of a NINAF reactor for the oxidation of naphthalene to phthalic anhydride (*continued*).**

```
C
      FUNCTION EFF1(I)
C
      PHI = PHI1(I)
      EFF1 = TANH(PHI)/PHI
      RETURN
      END
```

```
C
      FUNCTION EFF2(I)
C
      PHI = PHI2(I)
      EFF2 = TANH(PHI)/PHI
      RETURN
      END
```

```
C
      FUNCTION PHI1(I)
C
      REAL K1
      COMMON A,A1,A2,BIM,CO,D,DBDA,DH1,DH2,DP,E1,E2,HTC,KG,RG,TO,
     1       CSI,TSI,CR,TR
      DIMENSION CR(6), TR(6)
      PHI1 = DP/6.*SQRT(K1(I)/D)
C     SET PHI1 TO A MINIMUM VALUE TO AVOID A NUMERICAL PROBLEM IN
C     COMPUTING EFF1,  SMMPM
      IF(PHI1.LT.1.0E-10) PHI1 = 1.0E-10
      RETURN
      END
```

```
C
      FUNCTION PHI2(I)
C
      REAL K2
      COMMON A,A1,A2,BIM,CO,D,DBDA,DH1,DH2,DP,E1,E2,HTC,KG,RG,TO,
     1       CSI,TSI,CR,TR
      DIMENSION CR(6), TR(6)
      PHI2 = DP/6.*SQRT(K2(I)/D)
      IF(PHI2.LT.1.0E-10) PHI2 = 1.0E-10
      RETURN
      END
```

```
C
      REAL FUNCTION K1(I)
C
C     NOTE - K1 IS NOW  BASED ON THE CATALYST SURFACE TEMPERATURE, TSI
C
      COMMON A,A1,A2,BIM,CO,D,DBDA,DH1,DH2,DP,E1,E2,HTC,KG,RG,TO,
     1       CSI,TSI,CR,TR
      DIMENSION CR(6), TR(6)
      K1 = A1*EXP(-E1/(RG*TSI))
      RETURN
      END
```

FIG. 5-19 **The RDMOT2 computer program for the design of a NINAF reactor for the oxidation of naphthalene to phthalic anhydride (*continued*).**

```
C
      REAL FUNCTION K2(I)
C
C     NOTE - K2 IS NOW BASED ON THE CATALYST SURFACE TEMPERATURE,  TSI
C
      COMMON A,A1,A2,BIM,CO,D,DBDA,DH1,DH2,DP,E1,E2,HTC,KG,RG,TO,
     1       CSI,TSI,CR,TR
      DIMENSION CR(6), TR(6)
      K2 = A2*EXP(-E2/(RG*TSI))
      RETURN
      END
```

```
C
      FUNCTION CS(I)
C
C     CS IS THE CATALYST SURFACE CONCENTRATION OF KEY REACTANT
C     COMPUTED VIA  MASS AND HEAT TRANSFER COEFFICIENTS
C     CSI AND TSI  ARE CALCULATED ITERATIVELY VIA EQUATIONS
C          CSI = CO*CR/(1.0+(EFF1*K1/(KG*A)))                    (A)
C          TSI = TO*TR+DHR/(HTC*A)                               (B)
C
      COMMON A,A1,A2,BIM,CO,D,DBDA,DH1,DH2,DP,E1,E2,HTC,KG,RG,TO,
     1       CSI,TSI,CR,TR
      DIMENSION CR(6), TR(6)
      REAL K1,KG
C     SET THE NUMBER OF ITERATIONS, NITER
      NITER = 3
C     SET THE INITIAL VALUES OF CSI AND TSI TO THE BULK GAS
C     CONCENTRATION AND TEMPERATURE,
      CSI = CO*CR(I)
      TSI = TO*TR(I)
C     COMPUTE CSI AND TSI VIA EQUATIONS A AND B
C
      DO 1 L=1,NITER
      CSI = CO*CR(I)/(1.+(EFF1(I)*K1(I)/(KG*A)))
    1 TSI = TO*TR(I)+(DHR(I)/(HTC*A))
      CS = CSI
      RETURN
      END
```

```
C
      FUNCTION CB(I)
C
C     CB IS THE CATALYST SURFACE CONCENTRATION OF THE PRODUCT OF
C     REACTION  1
C
      COMMON A,A1,A2,BIM,CO,D,DBDA,DH1,DH2,DP,E1,E2,HTC,KG,RG,TO,
     1       CSI,TSI,CR,TR
      DIMENSION CR(6), TR(6)
      REAL K1, K2
      RK1K2 = K1(I)/K2(I)
      S = SMMPM(I)
C     NOTE - CB IS NOW BASED  ON CSI
      CSCO = CSI/CO
      CB = CO*((S-DBDA)/(S-1.))*(RK1K2/(RK1K2*DBDA-1.))*((CSCO**S)-CSCO)
      IF(CB.LT.0.) CB=0.
      RETURN
      END
```

FIG. 5-19 **The RDMOT2 computer program for the design of a NINAF reactor for the oxidation of naphthalene to phthalic anhydride (*continued*).**

```
C
      FUNCTION SMMPM(I)
C
C     SMMPM IS THE FACTOR S FOR THE MACRO-MICRO PORE MODEL
C
      COMMON A,A1,A2,BIM,CO,D,DBDA,DH1,DH2,DP,E1,E2,HTC,KG,RG,TO,
     1       CSI,TSI,CR,TR
      DIMENSION CR(6), TR(6)
      REAL MM1,MM2
      SMMPM=DBDA*MM1(I)*(PHI2(I)**2)*EFF2(I)/
     1           (MM2(I)*(PHI1(I)**2)*EFF1(I))
      RETURN
      END




C
      REAL FUNCTION MM1(I)
C
C     MM1 IS A FACTOR USED IN THE CALCULATION OF S FOR THE MACRO-MICRO
C          PORE MODEL
      COMMON A,A1,A2,BIM,CO,D,DBDA,DH1,DH2,DP,E1,E2,HTC,KG,RG,TO,
     1       CSI,TSI,CR,TR
      DIMENSION CR(6), TR(6)
      PHI = PHI1(I)
      MM1= 1. + (PHI*TANH(PHI)/BIM)
      RETURN
      END




C
      REAL FUNCTION MM2(I)
C
C     MM2 IS A FACTOR USED IN THE CALCULATION OF S FOR THE MACRO-MICRO
C          PORE MODEL
      COMMON A,A1,A2,BIM,CO,D,DBDA,DH1,DH2,DP,E1,E2,HTC,KG,RG,TO,
     1       CSI,TSI,CR,TR
      DIMENSION CR(6), TR(6)
      PHI = PHI2(I)
      MM2= 1.+ (PHI*TANH(PHI)/BIM)
      RETURN
      END




C
      FUNCTION DHR(I)
C
C     DHR IS THE SUM OF THE PRODUCTS OF THE HEATS OF REACTION AND
C         RATES OF REACTION
      COMMON A,A1,A2,BIM,CO,D,DBDA,DH1,DH2,DP,E1,E2,HTC,KG,RG,TO,
     1       CSI,TSI,CR,TR
      DIMENSION CR(6), TR(6)
       REAL K1
C      COMPUTE R1 IN DH1*R1 + DH2*R2 LOCALLY TO AVOID  A RECURSIVE CALL
C      TO FUNCTION CS (CSI IS USED IN PLACE OF CS(I) )
       R1I = EFF1(I)*K1(I)*CSI
       DHR = DH1*R1I + DH2*R2(I)
       RETURN
       END
```

FIG. 5-19 The RDMOT2 computer program for the design of a NINAF reactor for the oxidation of naphthalene to phthalic anhydride (*continued*).

```
1                       DESIGN OF NINAF GAS REACTOR
0             AIR OXIDATION OF NAPHTHALENE TO PHTHALIC ANHYDRIDE
0  T0= 643.2 K    U= 8.000 M/S  TRMAX= 2.000            A= 1200.0 1/M
   Y0= 0.250E-02 CP=30.334 KJ/KMOL  MW1=128.174         MW2=28.860 PEM=10.000
   E1= 0.159E+06 A1=0.5809E+14 DT= 0.050 M              H=0.100    PEH= 7.000
   E2= 0.837E+05 A2=0.2222E+06 DBDA=0.930               TW=0.983  DP=0.001 M
   BIW=0.920E+02               VIS=0.290E-04 PAS     DH1=0.180E+07 KJ/KMOL
   LG= 0.385E-04 KJ/S.M.K      RG=8.316 KJ/KMOL.K   DH2=0.182E+07 KJ/KMOL
   D=  0.100E-04 M**2/S        D1M=0.205E-04 M**2/S
0  Z =   0.250E+02   ZZ =   0.250E-01
              R=0          R=1          R=2          R=3          R=4          R=5
 CR(I) =  0.976E+00  0.976E+00  0.976E+00  0.976E+00  0.977E+00  0.986E+00
 TR(I)=   0.101E+01  0.101E+01  0.101E+01  0.101E+01  0.100E+01  0.983E+00
0  Z =   0.500E+02   ZZ =   0.500E-01
              R=0          R=1          R=2          R=3          R=4          R=5
 CR(I) =  0.947E+00  0.947E+00  0.947E+00  0.948E+00  0.953E+00  0.970E+00
 TR(I)=   0.101E+01  0.101E+01  0.101E+01  0.101E+01  0.101E+01  0.983E+00
0  Z =   0.750E+02   ZZ =   0.750E-01
              R=0          R=1          R=2          R=3          R=4          R=5
 CR(I) =  0.913E+00  0.913E+00  0.914E+00  0.917E+00  0.929E+00  0.953E+00
 TR(I)=   0.102E+01  0.102E+01  0.102E+01  0.102E+01  0.101E+01  0.983E+00
0  Z =   0.100E+03   ZZ =   0.100E+00
              R=0          R=1          R=2          R=3          R=4          R=5
 CR(I) =  0.871E+00  0.871E+00  0.873E+00  0.880E+00  0.902E+00  0.934E+00
 TR(I)=   0.103E+01  0.103E+01  0.103E+01  0.102E+01  0.101E+01  0.983E+00
0  Z =   0.125E+03   ZZ =   0.125E+00
              R=0          R=1          R=2          R=3          R=4          R=5
 CR(I) =  0.817E+00  0.817E+00  0.821E+00  0.836E+00  0.873E+00  0.915E+00
 TR(I)=   0.104E+01  0.104E+01  0.104E+01  0.103E+01  0.102E+01  0.983E+00
0  Z =   0.150E+03   ZZ =   0.150E+00
              R=0          R=1          R=2          R=3          R=4          R=5
 CR(I) =  0.740E+00  0.742E+00  0.752E+00  0.782E+00  0.841E+00  0.893E+00
 TR(I)=   0.106E+01  0.106E+01  0.106E+01  0.105E+01  0.102E+01  0.983E+00
0  Z =   0.175E+03   ZZ =   0.175E+00
              R=0          R=1          R=2          R=3          R=4          R=5
 CR(I) =  0.617E+00  0.623E+00  0.649E+00  0.711E+00  0.804E+00  0.869E+00
 TR(I)=   0.109E+01  0.109E+01  0.108E+01  0.106E+01  0.103E+01  0.983E+00
0  Z =   0.200E+03   ZZ =   0.200E+00
              R=0          R=1          R=2          R=3          R=4          R=5
 CR(I) =  0.411E+00  0.425E+00  0.480E+00  0.607E+00  0.759E+00  0.843E+00
 TR(I)=   0.114E+01  0.114E+01  0.112E+01  0.108E+01  0.103E+01  0.983E+00
0  Z =   0.225E+03   ZZ =   0.225E+00
              R=0          R=1          R=2          R=3          R=4          R=5
 CR(I) =  0.206E+00  0.219E+00  0.275E+00  0.447E+00  0.701E+00  0.812E+00
 TR(I) =  0.120E+01  0.119E+01  0.117E+01  0.112E+01  0.105E+01  0.983E+00
0  Z =   0.250E+03   ZZ =   0.250E+00
              R=0          R=1          R=2          R=3          R=4          R=5
 CR(I) =  0.913E-01  0.995E-01  0.137E+00  0.269E+00  0.621E+00  0.775E+00
 TR(I)=   0.123E+01  0.122E+01  0.121E+01  0.117E+01  0.106E+01  0.983E+00
0  Z =   0.275E+03   ZZ =   0.275E+00
              R=0          R=1          R=2          R=3          R=4          R=5
 CR(I) =  0.392E-01  0.439E-01  0.660E-01  0.153E+00  0.515E+00  0.729E+00
 TR(I)=   0.124E+01  0.124E+01  0.123E+01  0.119E+01  0.108E+01  0.983E+00
0  Z =   0.300E+03   ZZ =   0.300E+00
              R=0          R=1          R=2          R=3          R=4          R=5
 CR(I) =  0.168E-01  0.194E-01  0.326E-01  0.920E-01  0.386E+00  0.669E+00
 TR(I) =  0.125E+01  0.125E+01  0.124E+01  0.121E+01  0.111E+01  0.984E+00
0  Z =   0.325E+03   ZZ =   0.325E+00
              R=0          R=1          R=2          R=3          R=4          R=5
 CR(I) =  0.727E-02  0.881E-02  0.170E-01  0.576E-01  0.262E+00  0.598E+00
 TR(I) =  0.125E+01  0.125E+01  0.124E+01  0.121E+01  0.114E+01  0.984E+00
0  Z =   0.350E+03   ZZ =   0.350E+00
              R=0          R=1          R=2          R=3          R=4          R=5
 CR(I) =  0.323E-02  0.416E-02  0.944E-02  0.367E-01  0.174E+00  0.522E+00
 TR(I) =  0.125E+01  0.125E+01  0.124E+01  0.121E+01  0.115E+01  0.984E+00
0  Z =   0.374E+03   ZZ =   0.374E+00
              R=0          R=1          R=2          R=3          R=4          R=5
 CR(I) =  0.149E-02  0.207E-02  0.553E-02  0.241E-01  0.122E+00  0.447E+00
 TR(I) =  0.125E+01  0.125E+01  0.124E+01  0.121E+01  0.115E+01  0.984E+00
0  Z =   0.388E+03   ZZ =   0.388E+00
              R=0          R=1          R=2          R=3          R=4          R=5
 CR(I) =  0.998E-03  0.146E-02  0.424E-02  0.195E-01  0.104E+00  0.410E+00
 TR(I) =  0.125E+01  0.125E+01  0.124E+01  0.121E+01  0.115E+01  0.984E+00
```

FIG. 5-20 Printout of RDMOT2 computer run.

The computation of C_B, the concentration of the product of reaction 1 (phthalic anhydride) on the catalyst surface, was carried out according to the *macromicropore model*[17] by the expression:

$$C_B = C_0 \frac{s' - (D_B/D_A)}{s' - 1} \frac{k_1/k_2}{(k_1/k_2)(D_B/D_A) - 1} \left[\left(\frac{C}{C_0}\right)^{s'} - \frac{C}{C_0} \right] + C_{B0}(C/C_0)^{s'}$$

where
$$s' = \frac{D_B m_1 \varphi_2 \tanh \varphi_2}{D_A m_2 \varphi_1 \tanh \varphi_1} = \frac{D_B\ m_1\ \varphi_2^2\ \eta_2}{D_A\ m_2\ \varphi_1^2\ \eta_1}$$

$$m_1 = 1 + [(\varphi_1 \tanh \varphi_1)/\mathrm{Bi}_m]$$

$$m_2 = 1 + [(\varphi_2 \tanh \varphi_2)/\mathrm{Bi}_m]$$

D_A and D_B = micropore (Knudsen) diffusivities of naphthalene and phthalic anhydride, respectively

C_{B0} = initial concentration of phthalic anhydride at reactor

φ_1 and φ_2 = Thiele moduli for macropores

η_1 and η_2 = macropore effectiveness factors

The derivation of this kinetic relationship will not be treated in this book. It can be found in part in a paper by Carberry.[17] In our example $C_{B0} = 0$. Other quantities were taken from Carberry's paper.

In this example we will calculate the design of a single reactor tube. A number of these tubes will have to be grouped together into a heat-exchanger bundle in order to meet a desired production capacity.

The feed to the reactor is determined by the mole fraction y_0 of naphthalene in air and by the fluid velocity u in the bed. Naphthalene contents of 0.25 to 1.0% in air have been used, corresponding to y_0 values of 0.0025 to 0.01. At higher concentrations the mixture becomes explosive and the excess of oxygen is depleted.

Various quantities must be calculated by the computer before the call for CS(I).

$$C_0 = (y_0/22.414)(273.2/T_0) = 12.189\ y_0/T_0$$

The average molecular weight of the reacting mixture is:

$$M_0 = y_0 M_1 + (1 - y_0) M_2$$

The dimensionless reactor radius is $R_w = D_T/2d_p$. The gas density ρ is calculated at the inlet and, later, in the bed by

$$\rho_0 = 273.2\ M_0/(22.414\ T_0) = 12.189\ M_0/T_0 \qquad \rho = \rho_0/T_r(I)$$

The various dimensionless groups must now be calculated:

$$\mathrm{Re} = (M_0/22.414)(273.2/T_0)(u/\mu) = 12.189\, M_0\, u/(T_0\mu)$$

$$\mathrm{Pr} = c_p\mu/\lambda_G$$

$$\mathrm{Sc} = \mu/\rho\, D_{1m}$$

$$k_g = 1.15\, u\mathrm{Re}^{-0.5}\, \mathrm{Sc}^{-2/3}$$

$$h = 1.15\, u\mathrm{Re}^{-0.5}\, \rho\, c_p\mathrm{Pr}^{-2/3}$$

$$\mathrm{Bi}_m = k_g/\mathcal{D}\mathrm{a}$$

$$\Delta r = R_w/5$$

Some of these calculations must be repeated inside the DO loop which calculates the derivatives $F(\mathrm{I},1)$ and $F(\mathrm{I},2)$ because the expressions contain the variable I.

Figure 5-18 lists definitions of symbols used in the source program RDMOT2. The complete RDMOT2 source program and its output printout are given in Figs. 5-19 and 5-20, respectively.

NOMENCLATURE

- A — Frequency factor
- A_c — Cross-sectional area of reactor bed, m^2
- C — Molar concentration of reactant or product, $kmol/m^3$
- C_A — Molar concentration of toluene, $kmol/m^3$
- C_B — Molar concentration of hydrogen, $kmol/m^3$, or molar concentration of phthalic anhydride, $kmol/m^3$
- C_{pi} — Molar heat capacity of each i reacting species, kJ/(kmol·K)
- E — Activation energy, kJ/kmol
- F — Molar flow, kmol/s
- k — Reaction rate constant
- m_i — Molar flow of each i reacting species, kmol/s
- N — Number of moles passing from the reactor per unit time
- p — Partial pressure of reactant or product, bars
- P — Total pressure, bars
- r_s — Reaction rate, mole converted per unit time per unit surface area of catalyst, $kmol/(s\cdot m^2)$
- r_v — Intrinsic reaction rate, $kmol/(s\cdot m^3)$
- r_{vp} — Reaction rate expressed as partial pressure converted per second per unit volume, $p/(s\cdot m^3)$

r_w Intrinsic reaction rate, moles converted per unit time per unit weight of catalyst, kmol/(s·kg)

$\dot{R}$ Gas constant = 8.314 kJ/(kmol·K)

R Gas constant = 0.08314 (m³·bar)/(kmol·K)

$\mathcal{R}$ Apparent reaction rate or global reaction rate, kmol/(m³·s)

S_g Catalyst surface area, or unit catalyst surface area per unit weight, m²/kg

t_{max} Maximum tolerable temperature in fixed bed

T Absolute temperature, K

V Volume of reactor bed, m³

x Conversion, dimensionless

y_0 Initial mole fraction of key reactant, dimensionless

z Reactor height, m

α,β Reaction order, dimensionless

ΔH Heat of reaction, kJ/kmol

ε Void fraction, dimensionless

η Intraphase effectiveness factor, dimensionless

ρ_B Bulk density of catalyst, kg/m³

Subscripts

A Ethylene

0 Inlet

T Total

REFERENCES

1. R. Winkoop and R. H. Wilhelm, "Kinetics of Tubular Flow Reactors—Hydrogenation of Ethylene on Cu–MgO Catalyst," *Chem. Eng. Prog.* **46:**300–310 (1950).
2. M. Orhan Tarhan and William E. Schiesser, "Computer-Aided Design of Nonisothermal Nonadiabatic Fixed-Bed (NINAF) Gas Reactors," paper presented at the 74th Am. Inst. Chem. Engrs. National Meeting, New Orleans, March 11–15, 1973.
3. Charles N. Satterfield and Peter F. Way, "The Role of the Liquid Phase in the Performance of a Trickle-Bed Reactor," *AIChE J.* **18:**305–311 (1972).
4. Peter F. Way, "The Performance of Trickle-Bed Reactors," Ph.D. thesis, MIT, Cambridge, 1971.

5. M. Orhan Tarhan and Louis H. Windsor, "Coke Ovens Yield High Quality Benzene," *Chem. Eng. Progr.* **62**(2):67–72 (1966).

6. Alvin H. Weiss and L. Friedman, "Development of Houdry Detol Process," *Ind. Eng. Chem. Process Design Develop.* **2:**163–168 (1963).

7. Alvin H. Weiss, J. B. Maerker, and R. Newirth, "Houdry Detol Process Shows Good Results at Crown Central Refinery," *Oil Gas J.* **60,** Jan. 22, 1962, pp. 64–71.

8. F. D. Rossini et al., *Selected Values of Physical and Thermodynamic Properties of Hydrocarbons and Related Compounds,* API Research Project 44, Carnegie Press, 1953.

9. M. Orhan Tarhan and Louis H. Windsor, "The Catalytic Route to Benzene from Coke-Oven Oil," *Chem. Eng.* 96–98 Mar. 28, 1966.

10. C. R. Wilke, "A Viscosity Equation for Gas Mixtures," *J. Chem. Phys.* **18**(4):517–519 (1950).

11. J. M. Smith, *Chemical Engineering Kinetics,* McGraw-Hill, New York, 1956.

12. J. M. Smith, *Chemical Engineering Kinetics,* 2d ed., McGraw-Hill, New York, 1970.

13. James J. Carberry, "Heat and Mass Diffusional Intrusions in Catalytic Reactor Behavior," *Catalysis Rev.* **3**(1):61–91 (1969).

14. James J. Carberry and Donald White, "On the Role of Transport Phenomena in Catalytic Reactor Behavior—Digital Simulation of Naphthalene Oxidation over V_2O_5," *Ind. Eng. Chem.* **61**(7):27–35 (1969).

15. James J. Carberry and M. Wendel, "Computer Model of the Fixed Bed Catalytic Reactor—The Adiabatic and Quasiadiabatic Cases," *AIChE J.* **9:**129–133 (1963).

16. Gilbert F. Froment, "Analysis and Design of Fixed-Bed Catalytic Reactors," in *Chemical Reactor Engineering,* Advances in Chemistry Series 109, American Chemical Society, 1972, pp. 1–34.

17. James J. Carberry, "Mass Diffusion and Isothermal Catalytic Selectivity," *Chem. Eng. Sci.* **17:**675–681 (1962).

18. F. DeMaria, J. E. Longfield, and G. Butler, "Catalytic Reactor Design," *Ind. Eng. Chem.* **53**(4):259–266 (1961).

19. K. R. Westerterp, "Maximum Allowable Temperature in Chemical Reactors," *Chem. Eng. Sci.* **17:**423–433 (1962).

20. L. M. Elkin, "Phthalic Anhydride," *Stanford Research Institute Report* No. 34, 1968, Chap. 7, p. 73.

21. D. J. Coleman and G. Pilcher, "Heats of Combustion of Biphenyl, Naphthalene, Anthracene, and Phenanthrene," *Trans. Faraday Soc.* **62**(4):821–827 (1966).

22. George S. Parks, John R. Morley, and Peter V. Peterson, Jr., "Heats of Combustion and Formation of Some Organic Compounds Containing Oxygen," *J. Chem. Phys.* **18:**152–153 (1950).

Chapter 6 GAS-LIQUID-PHASE FIXED-BED REACTORS—CLASSIFICATION AND TRANSPORT PHENOMENA OF TRICKLE-BED REACTORS

6.1 DEFINITIONS—CLASSIFICATION OF GAS-LIQUID-PHASE REACTORS

A gas-liquid-phase reactor is a reactor in which the gas and the liquid phases coexist during the catalytic reaction. It is possible to react:

- A gas with a liquid
- Two gases dissolved in a liquid
- Two liquids stirred by a gas

The two major types of gas-liquid phase reactors using heterogeneous catalysts are:

- Gas-liquid fixed-bed reactors
- Suspended-bed reactors

The latter class includes:

- Continuous stirred-tank reactors (CSTRs)
- Slurry reactors
- Ebullated-bed reactors
- Three-phase transport reactors (3PTR)

In this chapter we will study only gas-liquid fixed-bed reactors.

Before going into the process design of each major type of reactor, we must study their flow dynamics, heat transfer, and mass transfer behavior because transport phenomena play a much greater role in gas-liquid reactor types than in gas reactors. In most gas-liquid reactors, the main problem is the definition of the exact conditions in the respective gas-liquid systems. With the exception of gas-liquid fixed-bed reactors, once the exact conditions have been defined, the design equations are usually very simple and in most cases can be solved analytically unless the reaction kinetics presents some complexities.

In fixed-bed gas reactors it does not matter in what position or direction the reactor is and whether the gas flows upward or downward, although usually the flow is vertical. In gas-liquid fixed-bed reactors the direction of flow becomes very important and leads to a number of new reactor types: the gas and liquid streams may separately flow upward or downward; hence concurrent or countercurrent flow may occur. In addition to these varieties, some of the reactants may change phase during the reaction. Also one of the phases may be continuous and the other disperse, and this condition may be reversed. Thus a great variety of gas-liquid-phase fixed-bed reactors are possible.

Let us represent these various types of the theoretically possible fixed beds in Fig. 6-1 in the form of elongated rectangles. Let us divide the area of these rectangles proportionately to the molar flow per unit cross-sectional area, with the light areas representing the gas phase and the dark areas representing the liquid phase. Types I to IV have no appreciable net change of molar flow between the phases, although considerable mass transfer may occur between the gas and liquid phases. This means that there is no substantial diminution or increase of any phase through gas formation or condensation. All the other types V to X show a net change of molar flow between the gas and liquid phases.

Let us now examine each of these reactor types, consider their applications, and give examples, if such examples are known.

The downflow concurrent reactor (type I, Fig. 6-1) is the most commonly used of all gas-liquid fixed-bed reactors. It is commonly called the *trickle-bed reactor*. Here, both the gas and the liquid flow downward. The gas is the continuous phase and the liquid is the disperse phase. The hydrodesulfurization of petroleum oils and tar oils and many other reactions can be carried out in trickle-bed reactors. If the hydrocracking reaction becomes prominent at elevated temperatures, the same oils produce considerable gas at the expense of the liquid. Thus we have a trickle-bed reactor of type V. On the other hand, the hydrogenation of hydrocarbon oils at relatively low temperatures and high pressures depletes the gas phase, and consequently is performed in type VI trickle-bed reactors.

Trickle-bed reactors may also be countercurrent, as in type III, IX, and X reactors. In these reactor types, the continuous gas phase flows upwards, countercurrently to the downward flowing disperse liquid phase.[1] As we will see further below, countercurrent fixed-bed reactors are lim-

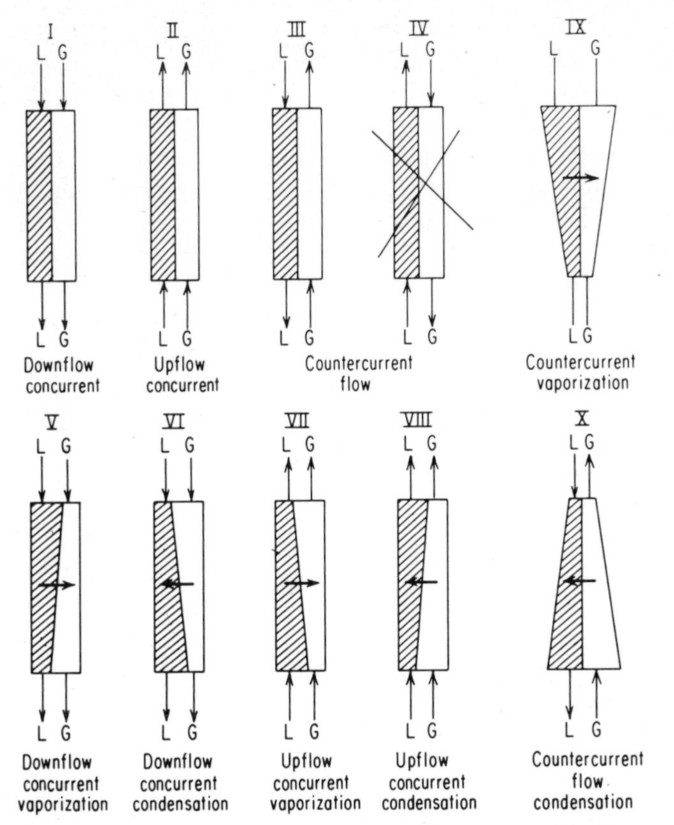

FIG. 6-1 Various kinds of gas-liquid-phase fixed-bed reactors.

ited in use to very low flows and are not common in the industry. The limitation is imposed by the occurrence of flooding. Actually, for given flow rates of gas and liquid, concurrent-flow fixed-bed reactors have the advantages of dissipating less power as fluid friction and of achieving higher values of gas absorption coefficient and gas-liquid interfacial area without flooding the column. On the other hand, the main advantage of the countercurrent fixed-bed reactors is their ability to attain considerably more than one equilibrium stage for gas-liquid contacting.[2]

The type IV reactor is not feasible.

In the *upflow concurrent reactors,* types II, VII, and VIII, both the continuous liquid phase and the disperse gas phase flow upward. The catalyst is fully submerged in the continuous liquid phase and the gas moves in the form of bubbles. For this reason these reactor types are sometimes called *fixed-bed bubble reactors.*

At very high flow rates of gas and liquid, it is possible to operate concurrent fixed-bed reactors with a dispersed liquid phase and a continuous gas phase. More will be said about such reactors later in this chapter.

Likewise, countercurrent gas-liquid reactors (types III, IX and X) may be conceivably operated in flooded condition by restricting the liquid outlet flow. Although the author cannot think of any reason for using such reactors in preference to upflow concurrent bubble reactors, this possibility is mentioned here simply for reasons of completeness. In the resulting types of reactors, which may be designated as types IIIF, IXF, and XF, the liquid phase would be the continuous phase and the gas phase the disperse phase.

Tarhan[3] has discussed a particular type of concurrent downflow reactor in which a cold liquid and a hot gas are mixed at the top of a reactor bed in the presence of a catalyst. The liquid is simultaneously evaporated and reacted. Thus, the reactor begins as a type V vaporizing reactor and ends up as a gas-phase reactor.

A type VIII reactor may conceivably be used in the alkylation of benzene with ethylene over a zeolite catalyst[4] since the reaction occurs in the liquid phase and the gas phase is consumed.

The remaining part of the present chapter covers only the transport phenomena of all gas-liquid fixed-bed reactor types in which the gas phase is the continuous phase, e.g., the trickle-bed reactors. The process design of these same reactors will be discussed in Chap. 7.

Fixed-bed reactors in which the liquid phase is the continuous phase, e.g., the fixed-bed bubble reactors (FBBR), will be discussed in Chap. 8, which covers both related transport phenomena and process design.

Finally the entire class of suspended-bed reactors, including both related transport phenomena and process design, will be discussed in Chap. 9.

6.2 TRANSPORT PHENOMENA IN TRICKLE-BED REACTORS

Two-phase flow through fixed beds of catalyst has not yet been sufficiently studied. Most of the knowledge on gas-liquid flow dynamics in packed beds is based on work done with absorption-desorption packings, such as Raschig rings,[2,5–15] spheres,[16,17] or glass beads.[18,19] Very few papers exist on the flow dynamics of beds packed with common porous catalyst shapes.[20,21] The reactor designer must have an accurate idea of the flow regime in the catalyst bed and must be able to calculate the pressure drop across the bed. This accurate idea should include knowledge of any axial or radial dispersion in the gas and liquid phases and the texture of the liquid flowing through the bed.

In order to understand the various flow regimes encountered in a gas-liquid-phase fixed-bed reactor, let us refer to Fig. 6-2, which shows an upflow concurrent reactor. Let us assume that the catalyst bed consists of commercial 3-mm extrusions of some catalyst. Let us establish a liquid upflow of 6 $m^3/(h \cdot m^2)$ through the bed (this corresponds to a linear hourly space velocity (LHSV) of about 1 for a 3-m-diameter by 6-m-high catalyst bed). At first, the liquid will flow upward without disturbing the packed bed. The catalyst particles will be completely wetted by the liquid. Now, let us start a modest gas upflow in addition to the liquid upflow and let us increase the gas flow stepwise at constant liquid flow rate. First, at low gas rates the gas flows through the packing in the form of bubbles at slightly higher velocity than the liquid phase. The liquid phase is the continuous phase and the gas phase is the dispersed phase. This flow regime is called *bubble flow,* and reactors operating with this regime can be called "*fixed-bed bubble reactors* (*FBBR*). As the gas rate is increased at constant liquid rate, one of two things can happen: (1) If the catalyst bed is not limited on top by a hold-down screen or by a *bed limiter,* at some point the packing will start to become fluidized, beginning from the top of the bed. (2) If the catalyst is fixed by a bed limiter, then new flow regimes may be observed without losing the fixed-bed concept. The first one of these regimes is termed *slug flow*[22] or *pulsing flow.*[23] This regime is characterized by a periodic fluctuation of the density of the composite fluid (gas-liquid mixture) flowing through the bed between the gas density and the liquid density. This alternate variation between mostly gas flow and mostly liquid flow constitutes a sort of pulsing. The frequency of the pulsing increases both with increasing liquid rate and with increasing gas rate. With still further increase of gas flow rate, the density difference between the alternate slugs disappear entirely, producing a third flow regime, *spray flow.* This is a regime in which the gas

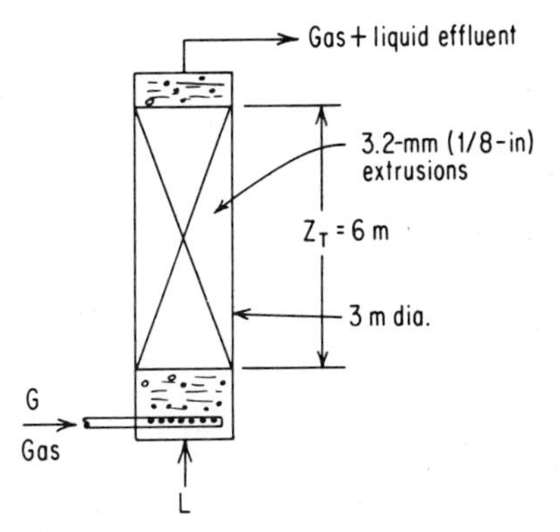

FIG. 6-2 Schematic representation of an upflow gas-liquid reactor.

phase is the continuous phase. The liquid phase becomes disperse and is carried through the column as a heavy mist in the gas stream. At this point the packing surface is covered by a thick layer of liquid, which becomes progressively thinner with increasing gas rate. Finally all the liquid is transported away as a mist or spray.

No unsteady flow regime has been used intentionally to design any reactor in the past. It was thought that unsteady flow would require extremely strong mechanical design and the kinetics under these conditions would be difficult to predict. However, recent experience with fluidized-bed reactors suggests that the unsteadiness of the pulsing flow does not have to be a disadvantage. It is perfectly possible to operate a fixed-bed reactor with an intense gas-liquid flow that pulses. With even faster flows, the spray regime might be used, as demonstrated in pilot stage by the upflow spray regime fixed-bed reactor of the Synthoil process,[24–28] a process developed by the U.S. Bureau of Mines to liquefy coal by hydrogenation in a fixed-bed reactor. Although the Synthoil process involves a coal slurry rather than a pure liquid, coal particles are almost completely dissolved by the time they reach the Synthoil reactor, and besides it may be argued that any flow regime that works with gas and slurry will most certainly work with gas and liquid. Incidentally, the Synthoil process turned out to be coal hydrogenation catalyzed by coal ash under turbulent hydrogen supply and has been abandoned for all practical purposes. The pulse flow and the spray flow may have some applications in the taming of exothermic reactions.

Turpin and Huntington[22] showed these three flow regimes in 1967 by plotting the ratios of gas-liquid velocities against gas mass velocity, as seen in Fig. 6-3. They state that the lines drawn on this figure "to separate the three flow regimes are actually transition regions rather than points

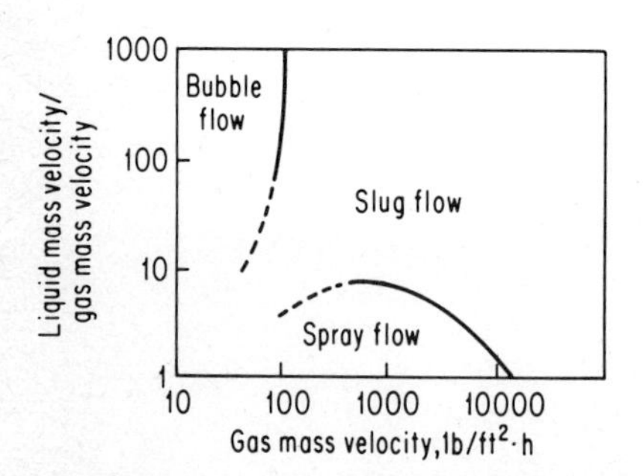

FIG. 6-3 Various flow regimes in vertical flow through gas-liquid-phase fixed beds. [1 lb/(ft^2 · h) = 0.001356 kg/(m^2 · s), 1 kg/(m^2 · s) = 737.3 lb/(ft^2 · h)] ***(From Turpin and Huntington[22] by permission from the American Institute of Chemical Engineers.)***

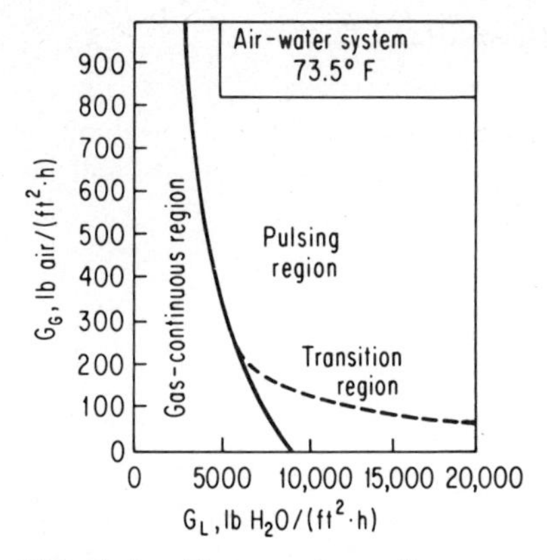

FIG. 6-4 Flow regimes for concurrent air-water flow through fixed beds. (*From Weekman and Myers*[23] *by permission from the American Institute of Chemical Engineers.*)

of abrupt change from one flow type to another." Their experiments were made with the practical air-water system. Other systems have yet to be investigated.

Another diagram has been prepared by Weekman and Myers[23] by plotting superficial velocities of gas versus liquid, as seen in Fig. 6-4.

The above experiment may be repeated with a downflow fixed-bed reactor. At the start the system behaves as a trickle-bed reactor in which the gas phase is the continuous phase and the liquid phase is the disperse phase. If the liquid flow rate is kept constant and the gas flow rate is increased, the flow regime goes over to spray flow without going through the pulsating regime, since at all times the gas phase remains as the disperse phase. However, if the gas flow is kept low and constant and the liquid flow is progressively increased, the packed bed may be brought to a pulsating flow regime, since the increasing liquid flow is bound to reach the flooding point.

The most common downflow concurrent regime is the *trickle flow* regime, in which moderate flow rates of liquid and gas are used and the gas phase is the continuous phase. Trickle flow is probably the best studied among gas-liquid systems, although it has not yet been studied quite sufficiently. The *texture* of the liquid phase appears to be a mixture of films, rivulets, and droplets flowing on the surface of the catalyst particles.[2,6,21,29]

Gas-liquid fixed-bed reactors may also be operated countercurrently either in trickle flow or in bubble flow. However, the range of flow rates for this regime is too narrow for catalyst-packed beds to be of any industrial importance.

Pressure Drop across Concurrent Trickle-Bed Reactors

At least two methods for computing the pressure drop across a concurrent trickle-bed reactor have been published. The one is by D. E. Sweeney[30] and the other is by Turpin and Huntington.[22] These methods will be discussed below.

Sweeney proposed a simple relationship:

$$\left(\frac{(\Delta P)_{LF}}{(\Delta p)_{LGT} + \rho_L}\right)^{1/3} + \left(\frac{(\Delta P)_{GF}}{(\Delta P)_{LGT} + \rho_G}\right)^{1/3} = 1 \qquad (6\text{-}1)$$

where (ΔP) = pressure drop per unit length, Pa/m

ρ = fluid density, kg/m^3

Subscripts G denotes gas-phase

L denotes liquid-phase

LG denotes two-phase

F denotes frictional

T denotes total

The single-phase pressure drop figures $(\Delta P)_G$ and $(\Delta P)_L$ can be calculated by the equation proposed by Ergun and Orning[31]:

$$g_c(\Delta P)_G = 4.935\,\frac{(1 - \varepsilon)^2}{\varepsilon^3}\,\mu\, a^2 u + \frac{\beta}{8}\,\frac{(1 - \varepsilon)}{\varepsilon^3}\,\rho_G\, u^2 a \qquad (6\text{-}2)$$

where ε = fractional void volume, dimensionless

μ = viscosity of fluid, $Pa \cdot s = kg/(m \cdot s)$

a = specific surface of solid particle, m^2/m^3

u = superficial velocity, based on empty reactor cylinder, m/s

ρ_G = gas density, kg/m^3

β = dimensionless constant

g_c = force-to-mass conversion factor = $1.0\ kg \cdot m/(N \cdot s^2)$

A list of β values was given by Ergun and Orhing. These values vary between 1.1 and 5.6 for gases and various materials. Equation (6-2) can also be used for $(\Delta P)_L$ if ρ_G is replaced by ρ_L. The same authors also discuss a simple method for determining the exact β coefficient for the fluids and the packing shapes used.

The method of Turpin and Huntington[22] is considerably more complicated. These workers proposed a correlation applicable to vertical high-pressure reactors operated in concurrent upflow or downflow regimes:

$$-(P_2 - P_1) = (\Delta P)_{GLF} + \frac{1}{A_c}(C_2\bar{A}_G Z + \rho_L \bar{A}_L Z + \tfrac{1}{2}C_3\bar{A}_G Z^2)$$

$$+ \frac{W_G}{g_c A_c}(W_{G2} - W_{G1}) + \frac{W_L}{g_c A_c}(u_{L1} - u_{L2}) \qquad (6\text{-}3)$$

where Z = height of packed section in reactor, m

P = pressure; P_1 = inlet pressure; P_2 = outlet pressure

W = weight flow rate

$\bar{A}$ = average area

u = linear velocity

C_1 = MW/RT, a constant

C_2 = C_1P_1

C_3 = C_1k_z

k_z = constant depending on variation of pressure with the longitudinal coordinate = $(P_1 - P_2)/Z$

Subscripts G = gas

L = liquid

The use of Eq. (6-3) requires the evaluation of the two-phase frictional pressure drop $(\Delta P)_{GLF}$, $\bar{A}_L$ (and thus $\bar{A}_G$), and the pressure loss due to the acceleration of the fluids. The pressure drop $(\Delta P)_{GLF}$ can be expressed in terms of a two-phase friction factor f_{GLF} which is defined as:

$$f_{GLF} = \frac{(\Delta P/Z)_{GLF}\, D_e g_c}{2\, \rho_{G0}\, \bar{u}_{GS}^2} \quad \text{dimensionless} \qquad (6\text{-}4)$$

where $\bar{u}_{GS}$ is the velocity which the gas would have if it were flowing in single-phase flow through the unpacked conduit (or reactor) at the entering density ρ_{G0}.

The factor f_{GLF} has been correlated with the gas-phase and liquid-phase Reynolds numbers separately for upflow and downflow. These correlations are:

$$\ln f_{GLF} = 8.0 - 1.12\, B - 0.0769\, B^2 + 0.0152\, B^3 \qquad (6\text{-}5)$$

where $B = \ln(\mathrm{Re}_G^{1.167}/\mathrm{Re}_L^{0.767})$ for upflow with

$$0.3 \le \frac{\mathrm{Re}_G^{1.167}}{\mathrm{Re}_L^{0.767}} \le 500$$

$$\ln f_{GLF} = 7.96 - 1.34\, B + 0.0021\, B^2 + 0.0078\, B^3$$

$$\text{for downflow with } 0.2 \leq \frac{\mathrm{Re}_G^{1.167}}{\mathrm{Re}_L^{0.767}} \leq 500 \tag{6-6}$$

An equivalent diameter D_e is defined by

$$D_e = 4\,R_H \tag{6-7}$$

where R_H is the hydraulic radius. To determine R_H the bed is assumed to consist of a number of parallel channels, the total volume of which is the volume of voids V_v in the bed and the total surface of which is the total surface area of the solids. With these assumptions, R_H is then the ratio of the total volume of voids to the total area of solids. Thus:

$$D_e = 4\,R_H = 4\,\frac{\text{total volume of voids}}{\text{total area of solids}} = \frac{4\,V_v}{S_p} \tag{6-8}$$

Since we can write:

$$\frac{\text{Total volume of voids}}{\text{Total volume of particles}} = \frac{V_v}{V_p} = \frac{\varepsilon}{1 - \varepsilon} \tag{6-9}$$

$V_v = V_p\,\varepsilon/(1 - \varepsilon)$ substituting this value of V_v in Eq. (6-8):

$$D_e = \frac{4\,V_p\,\varepsilon}{(1 - \varepsilon)S_p} \tag{6-10}$$

In order to determine $\bar{A}_L$ in Eq. (6-3), Turpin et al. determined what they call the *liquid saturation* or the fraction of the voids filled with liquid $\varepsilon_L/\varepsilon$. The mass velocity G, based on the total cross-sectional area of the unpacked reactor, was correlated with $\varepsilon_L/\varepsilon$ as follows:

$$\text{For upflow} \qquad \frac{\varepsilon_L}{\varepsilon} = -0.035 + 0.182(G_L/G_G)^{0.24} \tag{6-11}$$

$$\text{For downflow} \qquad \frac{\varepsilon_L}{\varepsilon} = -0.017 + 0.132(G_L/G_G)^{0.24} \tag{6-12}$$

with $1.0 \leq (G_L/G_G)^{0.24} \leq 6.0$ for both equations, which are said to be only $\pm 25\%$ accurate.

The pressure loss due to the acceleration of the liquid does not have to be considered for operating pressures below 3.4 atm gauge (3.36 bars gauge). Above this pressure, the acceleration terms can be calculated from inlet and outlet quantities.

A trial-and-error procedure must be used in the solution of Eq. (6-3). The frictional pressure drop $(\Delta P)_{GLF}$ can be obtained directly from Eq. (6-4) and Eq. (6-5) or (6-6). However, a trial-and-error solution is required to obtain the total pressure drop $-(P_2 - P_1)$. The procedure is to assume an average column pressure, which in effect fixes P_2. Then

$$k_z = \frac{P_1 - P_2}{Z}$$

This quantity is used in Eq. (6-3) and the procedure is repeated until the calculated average column pressure is sufficiently close to the assumed average column pressure.

Turpin's correlations were made with the well-known water-air system. For other gases, the viscosity was not expected to change appreciably, but for liquids other than water a viscosity correction factor $(\mu_w/\mu_L)^{0.9}$ was used. Here subscripts w and L denote water and other liquid, respectively. This factor is used to multiply the $\mathrm{Re}_G^{1.167}/\mathrm{Re}_L^{0.767}$ term in Eqs. (6-5) and (6-6).

Pressure drop in packed beds in countercurrent flow is determined by means of the generalized pressure drop correlation first established by Sherwood et al.,[32] which can be found in its improved present form in a brochure by the Norton Co.[33] Unless extremely large particles of catalyst are used, the design of countercurrent gas-liquid fixed-bed reactors does not make much sense, since with the usual sizes of catalysts the packing factor F would be very high and flooding would occur at quite low rates of gas and liquid flow. Thus, industrial-size countercurrent gas-liquid fixed-bed reactors are not practical.

Axial Dispersion and Holdup in Trickle-Bed Reactors

In contrast to fixed-bed gas reactors, axial dispersion in gas-liquid-phase fixed-bed reactors is not insignificant. In studies made with laboratory and pilot-plant reactors an appreciable amount of liquid holdup was measured in the porous catalyst bed. Even the gas flow appeared to have some axial dispersion. However, in large industrial trickle-bed reactors both the liquid and the gas flow were found to be plug flow.

The studies of Lapidus,[21] Schiesser and Lapidus,[16] Hochman and Effron,[19] Sater and Levenspiel,[34] and Glaser and Lichtenstein[20] are of great interest in this field. These workers used various tracers in gas and liquid phases to detect and measure the *residence time distribution* of the fluid in laboratory-scale packed beds. They did this by two methods:

1. The *step function input:* In this method the tracer is fed at full concentration during a sufficiently long period of time to reach a steady concentration in the effluent equal to that in the input. Then the tracer addition is suddenly discontinued and the decrease in tracer concentration in the effluent was measured (Fig. 6-5).

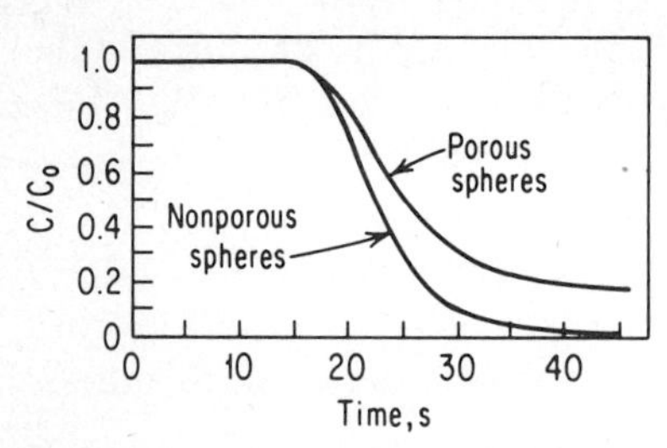

FIG. 6-5 Comparison of the step response for porous and nonporous packings. C = tracer concentration in effluent; C_0 = tracer concentration at inlet. *(From Schiesser and Lapidus,[16] by permission from the American Institute of Chemical Engineers.)*

2. The *pulse function input:* In this method the packing is brought into equilibrium with a tracer-free flow. Then suddenly, a tracer concentration is added to the inlet of the packing, maintained constant for a short time, and then again suddenly discontinued. Again the tracer concentration in the effluent is monitored (Fig. 6-6).

Figure 6-7 shows three types of time-of-contact curves[21] obtainable by a step function input. If there is absolutely no backmixing in the reactor, the response would be a steplike line labeled *A—plug flow.* If there is complete backmixing, as in a CSTR, curve *B* would be obtained. In real-life cases, type *C* curves are obtained. Lapidus[21] found that in concurrent flow over nonporous packing the time-of-contact or residence-time curve approached the plug-flow regime and that the effects of minor deviations from plug flow would not be important unless chemical conversions of 95% or greater were desired. By contrast, residence time experiments with porous packing produced distorted curves, the distortion being a consequence of mass transfer of tracer into and from the internal voids, or pores, of the packing. Pulse-type input curves are affected only to a minor degree by this mass transfer and thus produce results almost identical to those of a nonporous packing. Lapidus[21] and Schiesser and Lapidus[16] separated the contributions of pore diffusion and backmixing in bulk voids. As can be seen from the plot of Schiesser and Lapidus[16] in Fig. 6-8, diffusion of liquids into pores adds a long tail to the step response curve. Lapidus found that only 40 to 50% of the pore volume is filled with liquid. A corresponding fraction of the packing is thus unavailable for liquid-phase catalytic reaction, which indicates poor overall liquid-catalyst contacting. The reactor model which emerges from all this is one in which a reactant molecule enters a catalyst bed either in the gas phase or the liquid phase, moves along with the bulk flow to a particular catalyst particle, diffuses into a catalyst pore to an active site, becomes adsorbed at the site, and reacts with another adsorbed molecule or all by itself (depending upon the particular chemical reaction). The reaction product—another molecule—becomes desorbed and diffuses all the way back to the bulk flow. By that time the bulk flow may have moved, say, some 20 min downstream and the product molecule coming out of the pore joins fresh reactant molecules in the main bulk flow with this much delay. This is the essence of axial dispersion and its net effect is a decrease in overall conversion.

The task of expressing this axial dispersion in a manner useful for design purposes has been carried out by DeMaria and White,[7] Hochman and Effron,[19] Sater and Levenspiel,[34] and others. The axial dispersion term in the chemical reaction equation has been expressed as a *Péclet number,* as discussed in Sec. 4.3. The Péclet numbers proposed by various workers are listed below:

1. In the gas phase of a two-phase system:

Sater and Levenspiel[34] $$\text{Pe}_G = (ud_p/D_a)_G = 3.4\ \text{Re}_G^{-0.67}\ 10^{-0.0026\ \text{Re}_L} \quad (6\text{-}13)$$

DeMaria and White[7] $$\text{Pe}_G = 2.4\ \text{Re}_G^{-0.20} 10^{-0.002\ \text{Re}_L} \quad (6\text{-}14)$$

Hochman and Effron[19] $$\text{Pe}_G = 1.8\ \text{Re}_G^{-0.7}\ 10^{-0.005\ \text{Re}_L} \quad (6\text{-}15)$$

with $\sigma = \mp 40\%$

2. In the liquid phase of a two-phase system:

Sater and Levenspiel[34] $$\text{Pe}_L = 7.58\ 10^{-3}\ \text{Re}_L^{0.703} \quad (6\text{-}16)$$

Hochman and Effron[19] $$\text{Pe}_L = 0.034\ \text{Re}_L^{0.5}\ 10^{0.003\ \text{Re}_G} \quad (6\text{-}17)$$

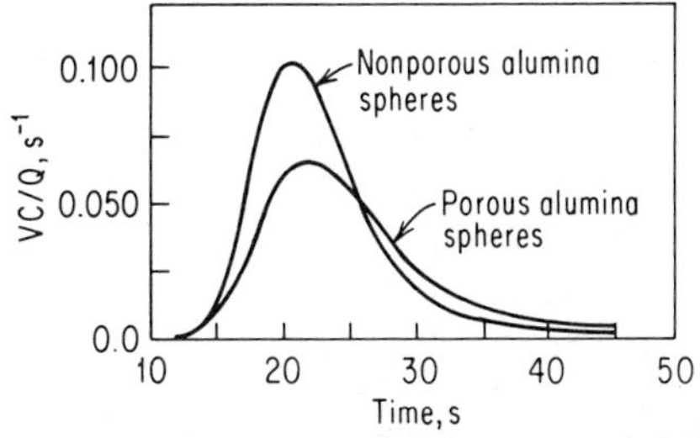

FIG. 6-6 Comparison of pulse response for porous and nonporous packing. C = tracer concentration in effluent; V = volumetric flow rate of liquid; Q = moles tracer injected in pulse input. (*From Schiesser and Lapidus,*[16] *by permission from the American Institute of Chemical Engineers.*)

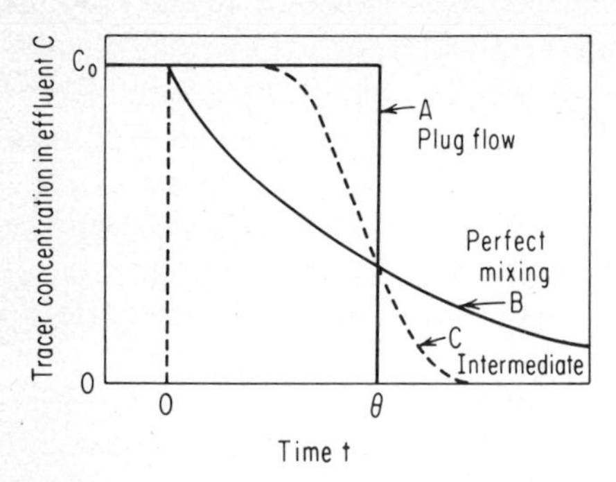

FIG. 6-7 Three types of experimental time-of-contact curves. ***(From Leon Lapidus, "Flow Distribution and Diffusion in Fixed-Bed Two-Phase Reactors, Ind. Eng. Chem.,*** **49:*1001* (*1957*),** ***by permission from the American Chemical Society.)***

where u = axial velocity, m/s

D_a = axial dispersion coefficient, m^2/s

d_p = nominal catalyst particle diameter (diameter of a sphere having the same surface area as the actual particle)

Subscripts L and G denote liquid phase and gas phase, respectively.

The fact that these workers came out with such a variety of results is quite disconcerting and confusing to the designer. It seems that everyone has been missing something important. Fortunately for the reactor designer, most design problems encountered involve industrial-size reactors, which are of the plug-flow type. In the case of laboratory or pilot-scale reactors, the designer can act conservatively without committing a significant economic sin. He can simply select the Péclet number correlation which gives the highest backmixing (the poorest yield), hence the smallest Pe. If the actual pilot plant then produces a higher yield, no one will complain.

Mears[35] has proposed a minimum reactor length z required for freedom from significant axial dispersion effects in trickle-bed reactors. For less than 90% conversion and first-order reactions, Mears' condition is expressed as:

$$\frac{Z}{d_s} > \frac{20\,\alpha}{\text{Bo}} \ln \frac{C_0}{C_f} \tag{6-18}$$

where α = reaction order

Z = length of reactor bed, m

d_s = equivalent spherical diameter of catalyst particle, m

$= (d_p\, l_p + d_p^2/2)^{0.5}$

d_p = diameter of catalyst particle, m

l_p = length of catalyst particle, m

Bo = Bodenstein number = $d_s\, u/D_{ae}$, dimensionless

u = superficial velocity, m/s

D_{ae} = axial eddy diffusivity, m^2/s

C = concentration of reactant, $kmol/m^3$

Subscripts: 0 = initial value; f = final value

The *Bodenstein number* is a Péclet number based on the particle diameter d_s instead of d_p. Mears used the correlations of Hochman and Effron[19] to calculate it.

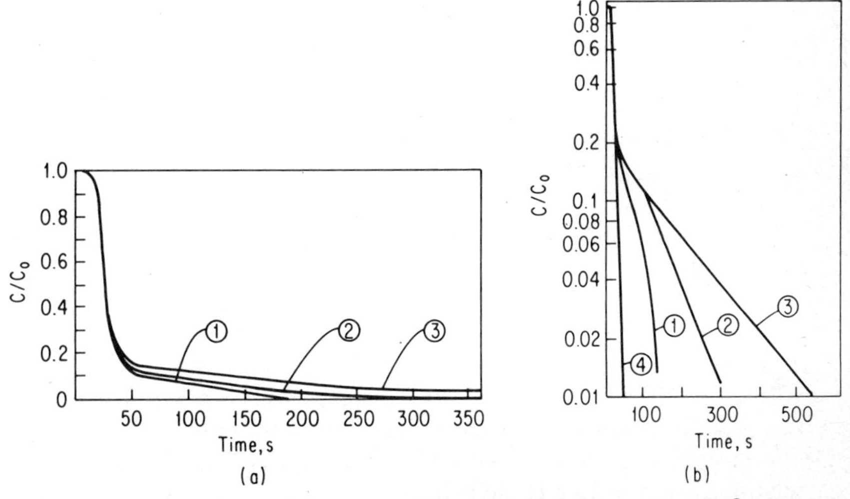

FIG. 6-8 Comparison of the step and integrated pulse responses for porous packing: (*a*) arithmetic plot and (*b*) semilogarithmic plot. Curve 1: integrated pulse response, porous spheres. Curve 2: saturation step response, porous spheres. Curve 3: elution step response, porous spheres. Curve 4: nonporous spheres (*From Schiesser and Lapidus,*[16] *by permission from the American Institute of Chemical Engineers.*)

The *holdup* of a trickle-bed reactor is important information that a reactor designer must have in order to calculate gas and liquid flow rates and also to estimate conversion rates.

Three kinds of liquid holdup in the catalyst bed can be defined[36]: the *total holdup* ε_L is the total liquid in the packing under operating conditions; the *static holdup* ε_s is the liquid in the packing which does not drain from the packing when the liquid supply to the column is discontinued; and the *operating holdup* ε_o is the difference between the total and static holdups. All three types of holdup are expressed as cubic meters of liquid per cubic meter of packed bed.[36,37] D. L. Ross[37] showed that holdup of any type is exponential with liquid superficial mass velocity G, that is, if holdup and G are plotted on double logarithmic paper, the data points fit a straight line. Holdup may be determined experimentally in either pilot reactors or existing commercial reactors. In case this is not possible, holdup may be estimated from the following correlation by Satterfield et al.[38]:

$$\epsilon_L = 9.9\left(\frac{G\,d}{\mu}\right)^{1/3}\left(\frac{d^3 g\,\rho^2}{\mu^2}\right)^{-1/3} \tag{6-19}$$

where G = superficial mass velocity, $kg/(s \cdot m^2)$

d = characteristic diameter of catalyst particle, m

μ = dynamic viscosity, $kg/(m \cdot s)$

g = gravitational constant, m/s^2

ρ = liquid density, kg/m^3

The dimensionless group (Gd/μ) is the Reynolds number and the group $d^3 g\rho^2/\mu^2$ is made up from the ratio of the Reynolds number squared to the Froude number $Fr = (G^2/\rho^2 dg)$ and is known as the Galileo number Ga.[39]

This equation neglects the additional dimensionless term $(ad)^{2/3}$ in Davidson's holdup correlation,[40] where a is the area per unit volume. Others have correlated experimental holdup data for trickle beds with the dimensionless groups proposed by Davidson and Satterfield. These correlations are listed in Table 6-1.

It appears that there is not much agreement on the correlation. All except Otake and Okada agree that Davidson's term plays no role. All except Satterfield agree on w and find twice the value found by the latter. In the absence of a higher certainty, the designer is advised to use Eq. (6-17).

The holdup affects many parameters in the trickle bed. As the holdup

TABLE 6-1
Correlation of Holdup Data for Trickle-Bed Reactors
$\varepsilon_L = k \cdot (Gd/\mu)^w \cdot (d^3 g\rho^2/\mu)^Y \cdot (ad)^z$

w	Y	z	Authors	References
0.676	−0.44	1.0	Otake and Okada	41
0.76	0	0	Hochman and Effron	19
0.75	−0.5	0	Mohunta and Laddha	42
0.333	−0.333	0	Satterfield	38

ε_L increases, and the volume fraction ε_p occupied by solid catalyst remains constant, the relationship

$$\varepsilon_L + \varepsilon_p + \varepsilon_G = 1 \tag{6-20}$$

indicates that ε_G has to decrease. The pressure drop will also be thereby affected.

Henry and Gilbert[39] base the local reaction rate constant on the volume of liquid, hence holdup, rather than on the bulk volume of catalyst when deriving kinetic relationships in their reactor element. Thus, holdup becomes part of their rate expression, as we will see further below. Ross[37] shows that the logarithm of conversion in trickle beds is inversely proportional to the residence time of the reactants in the holdup in the bed. Henry and Gilbert[39] report on a more complicated relationship between conversion and holdup. Satterfield[43] states that, all other things being equal, the reaction rate is proportional to liquid holdup.

Generally speaking, the liquid distribution over the catalyst bed can be very nonuniform at the low liquid space velocities occurring in 1-m-tall reactors as compared with full scale, 15- to 20-m-tall reactors. As liquid velocities increase, distribution uniformity improves, but does not become perfect even in full-scale reactors.[37,44]

Radial Dispersion in Trickle-Bed Reactors

Radial dispersion in trickle-bed reactors is less important than axial dispersion, from the viewpoint of the reactor. Most of the studies on radial dispersion in packed beds have been made with common tower packings, which are used for absorption-desorption purposes. Of course, with the large packings there is a large increase in the void volume near the wall and the ratio of this volume to the total packed volume is not negligible. In contrast, with catalyst particles of the order of magnitude $d_p = 0.003$

m, or 3 mm, the increase in void volume at the reactor wall is practically negligible.

Axial dispersion actually means a delay in part of the fluid stream reaching the end of the reactor bed, the practical result of which is a decrease in yield. The effect of radial dispersion is not a delay but a variation in the gas/liquid ratio $\varepsilon_G/\varepsilon_L$. The random packing of catalyst pellets causes a variation of this ratio from point to point, but the extent of the variation should not adversely affect the reaction kinetics.

Liquid distribution in packed columns and trickle-bed reactors has been made the subject of a model study by G. J. Jameson.[10] In this model "the liquid is assumed to spread from one packing piece to another at the common point of contact. By the use of a mechanistic approach a mathematical description of the flow process was synthesized." Then, "predictions from the model were compared with experimental results from the literature and they were found to agree quite well."

There is another type of radial dispersion which may become very significant and even dangerous. If the catalyst contains or forms fines mixed with regular particles at one particular point of the catalyst bed, or if the catalyst bed is stepped on while being filled into the tower and thus compressed and compacted, the flow of fluid will be curtailed through the dust-loaded or compacted region and will be diverted to the more open regions of the bed. If the reaction is an exothermic one, the compacted region might turn into a hot bed and trigger really serious trouble because low flow rates or longer residence times mean a poorer ability to remove the generated heat. If the reaction is endothermic, the compacted region would be cooled and practically excluded from the reactor capacity. All these considerations are really not under the direct control of the designer. However, the designer must be aware of such possibilities and prescribe proper and detailed procedures for charging the catalyst and for operating the catalyst bed. Also, the designer must provide for proper gas and liquid distribution to prevent radial dispersion. The persons who should be responsible for preventing radial dispersion are those supervising the filling of the reactor with catalyst. That job must be done with utmost care.

Heat Transfer in Trickle-Bed Reactors

Heat transfer relationships in trickle-bed reactors were first studied by Weekman and Meyers[17,45] in an air-water system. Actually most common trickle-bed processes are run in adiabatic reactors, with interbed heat exchange if necessary. For this reason, standard heat transfer information is fully adequate. Only in the case of strongly exothermic reactions did Weekman and Meyers suggest the use of sidewall-cooled reactors, in fact, gas-liquid-phase NINAF reactors. They developed experimental data for such reactors and found that a change from gas-continuous (trickle-bed) to pulsing flow results in very large improvements in radial two-phase heat transfer. In some cases this improvement reached 400%. The addition of a gas-phase flow to the liquid flow increases the effective thermal conductivity over that measured for single-phase liquid flow. Lumped heat transfer coefficients at the wall were quite high, e.g.,

$$h = 0.6241 \text{ kJ/(s} \cdot \text{m}^2 \cdot \text{K)}$$

observed at $G_L = 33.91 \text{ kg/(s} \cdot \text{m}^2)$

and $G_G = 0.610 \text{ kg/(s} \cdot \text{m}^2)$

The concept of the overall effective thermal conductivity K_e lumps all the conductivities in the gas, liquid, and catalyst phases in one parameter and assumes the temperatures in these three phases to be the same.

An *equivalent heat transfer coefficient* h_0 is defined as:

$$h_0 = \frac{Q}{2\pi r_0 z \, \Delta t_{lm}} \tag{6-21}$$

where Q = heat-transfer rate, kJ/s

r_0 = radius of the reactor tube, m

z = axial distance, m

Δt_{lm} = the log mean temperature difference

$$\frac{(t_w - t_0) - (t_w - t_b)}{\ln(t_w - t_0)/(t_w - t_b)}$$

t_w = wall temperature, °C

t_0 = inlet bulk temperature, °C

t_b = outlet mixing cup temperature, °C

Weekman and Meyers calculate h_0 as[17]:

$$h_0 = \frac{2.892}{r_0} K_e + \frac{0.183}{z} (G_L C_{pi} + G_G C^*_{pG}) \tag{6-22}$$

where K_e = overall effective thermal conductivity, kJ/(s · m · K)

G = mass velocity based on empty tube area, kg/(s · m²)

C_p = specific heat, kJ/(kg · K)

C^*_p = specific heat of saturated air, kJ/(kg · K)

Subscripts: G denotes gas

L denotes liquid

In SI units h_0 will have the dimensions of kilojoules per second per square meter per kelvin.

It was found that even at the highest gas rates and lowest liquid rates the air was saturated with water vapor. Thus where vaporization takes place, as in the air-water system, the correct heat balance can be achieved by using $C^*_{pG} = \Delta H_G/\Delta t_G$ instead of C_{pG} where ΔH_G = enthalpy increase of moist air and $\Delta t_G = t_0 - t_b$.

The transition from gas-continuous to pulse flow strongly influences heat transfer. Generally, both K_e and h_0 increase with increasing gas and liquid rates. The transition regime imposes certain bends and inflections on the K_e versus G_G curves.[17]

A *radial transport model* has been developed by assuming that the various heat-transfer mechanisms can be lumped into two terms.[46] According to this model, all the heat transferred by eddy diffusion in the radial direction would be included in one term and the molecular conduction in the stagnant bed would be included in the other term. This concept led to the development of the following relationship:

$$\frac{K_e}{\lambda_L} = \frac{(K_e)_o}{\lambda_L} + \gamma \mathrm{Re}_L \mathrm{Pr}_L + \beta(\lambda_G/\lambda_L)\mathrm{Re}_G \mathrm{Pr}_G \tag{6-23}$$

where λ_L = molecular conductivity of liquid, kJ/(s · m · K)

λ_G = molecular conductivity of gas, kJ/(s · m · K)

$(K_e)_o$ = contribution to overall effective thermal conductivity due to molecular conduction in stagnant bed, kJ/(s · m · K)

γ, β = radial fractions of liquid and gas mass velocity.

The constants $(K_e)_o$, γ, and β were determined from experimental data in the pulsing region and are given in Table 6-2 in both U.S. Customary System (USCS) and SI units.

TABLE 6-2
Values of $(K_e)_o$, γ, and β in USCS and SI Units

	Btu/(h · ft² · °F)	kJ/(s · m² · K)
$(K_e)_o$	7.71	4.37×10^{-3}
γ	1.74×10^{-3}	0.987×10^{-6}
β	0.172	0.976×10^{-4}

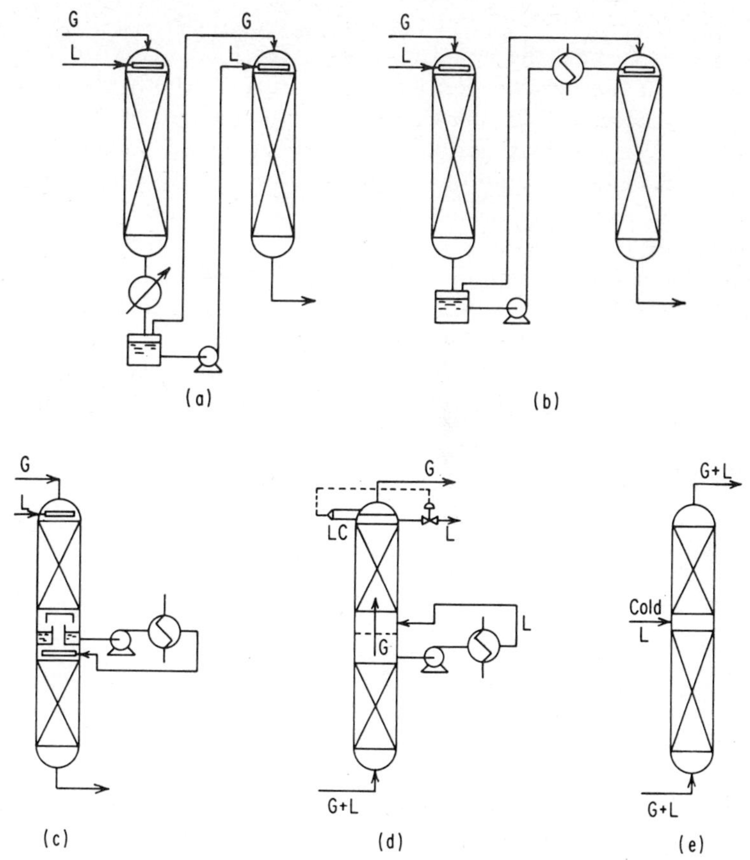

FIG. 6-9 Various ways of cooling an adiabatic gas-liquid reactor.

Trickle-bed NINAF reactors might be applicable to highly exothermic reactions. However, most industrial trickle-bed processes are not that exothermic and some sort of interbed cooling is sufficient to tame the heat evolved.

The interbed cooling or heating of gas-liquid fixed-bed reactors is considerably more complicated than that of adiabatic fixed-bed gas reactors. The mere addition of the liquid phase to a gas reactor creates a host of new problems. Some of the cooling methods of gas-liquid reactors are shown in Fig. 6-9. In Fig. 6-9*a* both phases are cooled in a joint indirect cooler, the cooled gas and liquid are separated, and the gas is further piped while the liquid is pumped up to the top of the second bed. Obviously gas and liquid cannot be pumped together. In Fig. 6-9*b* both phases are first separated and then only the liquid phase is cooled after being pumped up to the next bed. This scheme is based on the knowledge that cooling of liquids is more efficient and economical than cooling of gases. In fact, the liquid may be cooled low enough so that by mixing it with the gas the desired temperature for both phases is obtained. The scheme of Fig. 6-9*c* can be either concurrent or countercurrent. In any case, the liquid is downflow. Here again, the liquid phase is separated and cooled and redistributed on top of the next bed. In Fig. 6-9*d* we have an upflow concurrent reactor. Above the lower bed, gas bubbles continue to ascend and pass through the valve tray into the upper bed. The continuous liquid phase can be cooled by withdrawing liquid from the side and pumping it through a heat exchanger; the cooled liquid is returned to the reactor at the bottom of the upper bed just above the valve tray. Above the upper bed, the two phases separate and can be withdrawn separately. In Fig. 6-9*e* we have another upflow concurrent reactor, but here the interbed cooling is done by direct injection of additional cold liquid or cold gas. Probably, other methods of cooling liquid phase reactors are also available, e.g., Fig. 7-2.

Mass Transfer in Trickle-Bed Reactors

Extensive work has been done on mass transfer in trickle-bed reactors. The reader is especially directed to the publications of C. N. Satterfield[29,47] of MIT, J. J. Carberry[48] of the University of Notre Dame, and J. Hanika in Prague.[49–51]

The addition of the liquid phase to the simple gas-phase catalytic system introduces entirely new problems in reaction kinetics and mass transfer. Figure 6-10 represents the mass-transfer phenomena around a catalyst particle in a trickle-bed reactor. It is known that 40 to 50% of the pore volume is filled with liquid. For truly liquid-phase reactions, it can then be safely assumed that catalytic reactions will take place in the liquid phase or at liquid-covered surface sites. Consequently, a gaseous reactant molecule will have to be absorbed in a liquid droplet, diffuse inside the droplet through the pore to the catalyst site, become adsorbed on the site, and react there with an adsorbed liquid molecule. That liquid droplet comes there first by bulk transport as a droplet, after which part of it intrudes by capillary force into the catalyst pore. The reaction product will have to diffuse through the liquid out of the pore and if it stays in the liquid phase, it will move further with the outside part of the droplet, which might fall further below in the catalyst bed. If the reaction product is a gas, it will have to be desorbed from the liquid droplet once outside the pore.

Studies of Satterfield[29,43] and others suggest that the practical result of mass transfer in gas-liquid reactors is a lower value for the effectiveness factor η. The effectiveness factor of α-methylstyrene hydrogenation

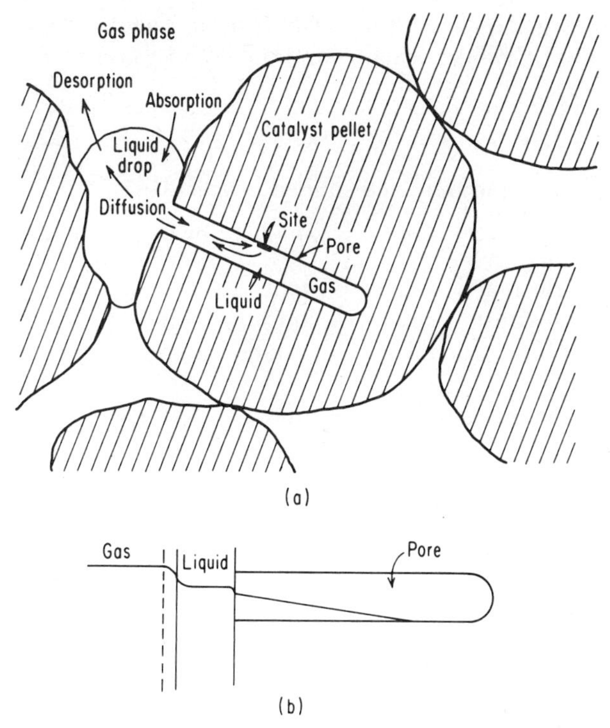

FIG. 6-10 Mass-transfer phenomena around a catalyst particle in a trickle-bed reactor.

over a Pt/alumina catalyst was found to be as low as 0.07 to 0.13 for 3.2 by 1.3 mm (⅛ in by $\frac{1}{20}$ in) pellets.[52] On the other hand, Cecil et al.[53] in trickle-bed hydrodesulfurization studies have found effectiveness factors as high as 0.8, i.e., of the same order of magnitude as effectiveness factors of gas reactions. If both gas-phase and liquid-phase reactions occur in a trickle bed, the overall effectiveness factor can be quite high, i.e., close to 1.0. However, in purely liquid-phase reactions η is expected to be typically low. Why Cecil's value is as high as it is is not quite clear.

Peter F. Way[54] in his Ph.D. thesis at MIT made a thorough review of the literature on trickle-bed reactors and discussed the mass transfer of gas-liquid reactions in trickle-bed reactors under certain limiting conditions such as isothermality, first-order kinetics, plug flow, volume constancy, and gas-liquid equilibrium. Way's experimental strategy is of interest: he first ran his heterogeneous catalytic reaction (isomerization of cyclopropane to propylene over a silica-alumina cracking catalyst) in the gas phase and made measurements. He then ran the same reaction over the same catalyst in the presence of a liquid which is a solvent for the feedstock, operating the reactor as a trickle bed, and again made measurements. The rates of the gas reaction and the liquid-gas reaction are expressed as follows:

$$\text{Gas-phase rate} = -k\,\eta\,C_s \qquad \text{kmol/(s} \cdot \text{m}^3) \tag{6-24}$$

where all the terms can be separately determined or calculated.

$$\text{Two-phase rate} = -k_{\ell\ell}\,\eta\,C_s \qquad \text{kmol/(s} \cdot \text{m}^3) \tag{6-25}$$

Two types of two-phase reaction rate constants are considered: $k_{\ell\ell}$, the two-phase reaction rate constant, based on concentration in the liquid phase; and $k_{\ell g}$, the two-phase reaction rate constant, based on concentration in the gas phase.

A factor for the external mass-transfer resistance is defined:

$$\gamma = \frac{C_s}{C_i}$$

where C_i is the concentration in the liquid at the gas-liquid interface. The relationships between the bulk gas concentration C, C_s, C_i, and C^* are diagrammatically represented in Fig. 6-11, C^* being the concentration in the gas phase that would be in equilibrium with the liquid at the catalyst interface C_s.

Vapor-liquid equilibrium is maintained at all points of the reactor:

$$y = Kx$$

where K is the vapor-liquid equilibrium constant. This is one of the original assumptions and means that C (bulk) is in equilibrium with C_i. It follows that:

$$C^* = \gamma\,C$$

If Arrhenius expressions are written for $k_{\ell\ell}$ and $k_{\ell g}$, their activation energies $E_{\ell\ell}$ and $E_{\ell g}$, respectively, would be related as follows:

$$E_{\ell\ell} = E_{\ell g} + E_k \tag{6-26}$$

where $E_k = 12{,}500$ kJ/kmol for the solvents Isopar 1 and Nujol.

We may obtain some insight into the nature of two-phase kinetics by comparing the rate expressions

Gas phase:
$$\ln\frac{C_1}{C_2} = \frac{k\,\eta\,V_c}{F} \tag{6-27}$$

Two-phase (liquid concentration units):

$$\ln\frac{C_1}{C_2} = \frac{k_{\ell\ell}\,\eta\,\gamma\,V_c}{[F_\ell + F(K\,v_L/V_G)]} \tag{6-28}$$

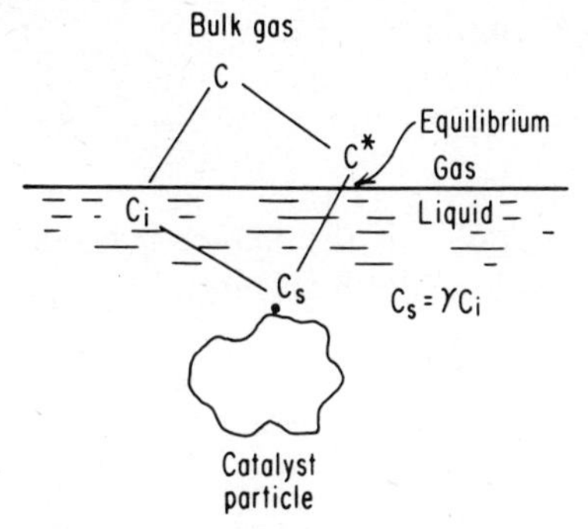

FIG. 6-11 Relationships among C, C_s, C_i, and C^* in mass transfer between bulk gas and catalyst surface across the gas-liquid interface.

Two-phase (gas concentration units):

$$\ln \frac{C_1}{C_2} = \frac{k_{\ell g}\, \eta\, \gamma\, V_c}{[(FV_G/Kv_L) + F]} \qquad (6\text{-}29)$$

where C_1, C_2 = molar concentrations of feed and product, kmol/m^3

V_c = volume of catalyst particle, m^3

F = feed rate of gas at reactor temperature and pressure, m^3/s

F_L = feed rate of liquid at reaction temperature and pressure, m^3/s

v_G = gas molar volume, m^3/kmol

v_L = liquid molar volume, m^3/kmol

The terms in the brackets can be considered as "effective" feed rates in the two-phase equations. The quantities γ and η can be evaluated and hence, the intrinsic rate constants can be calculated:

$$\gamma = 1 - \left\{\frac{1}{V_c}[F_L + F(Kv_L/v_G)] \ln(X_1/X_2)\right\}/[(6K_{LS}/d_p) + (F_L/2V_c) \ln(X_1/X_2)] \qquad (6\text{-}30)$$

where K_{LS} = overall mass-transfer coefficient from gas-liquid interface to the catalyst surface

d_p = diameter of pellet = length of pellet, m

x = mole fraction in liquid phase

For spheres and cylinders K_{LS} can be calculated as

$$K_{LS} = \frac{6\,D\,(1 - \varepsilon)}{\varepsilon_L d_p} \tag{6-31}$$

where D is the diffusivity in liquid phase and ε_L is the external liquid holdup. With the value of γ obtained from Eq. (6-30), $K_{\ell\ell}\eta\gamma$ and $K_{\ell_g}\eta\gamma$ can be calculated from the following relationships:

$$K_{\ell\ell}\gamma\eta = \frac{1}{V_o}\left[F_L\left(\frac{1 + \gamma}{2}\right) + F\left(\frac{Kv_L}{v_G}\right)\right]\ln\frac{x_1}{x_2} \tag{6-32}$$

$$K_{\ell_g}\gamma\eta = \frac{1}{V_c}\left[F_L\left(\frac{v_G}{Kv_L}\right)\left(\frac{1 + \gamma}{2}\right) + F\right]\ln\frac{y_1}{y_2} \tag{6-33}$$

where y is the mole fraction in the gas phase.

Finally, the value of η is obtained graphically by the method of Satterfield[29] after calculating ϕ for the two-phase system:

$$\phi = \frac{R^2}{D}\frac{(K_{\ell\ell}\eta)\tau}{\varepsilon} \tag{6-34}$$

where ϕ is the tortuosity factor.

The above formulas were all based on volume constancy during the reaction. In case the volume changes during the reaction, it is still possible to compute the rate of the reaction. In most cases the volume change in the liquid phase and concentration changes of the reactant in both phases can be neglected. With concentration being constant, the term $K_{\ell\ell}\eta\gamma$ can be readily calculated from the expression for $K_{\ell\ell}$:

$$F_L\,dC_L + FdC = -K_{\ell\ell}\eta\,C_s\,dV_c \tag{6-35}$$

where $C_s = \gamma\,C_i$ and

$$-K_{\ell\ell}\eta\gamma = \frac{1}{C_i}\left[F_L\frac{dC_L}{dV_c} + F\frac{dC}{dV_G}\right] \tag{6-36}$$

Also, in case the gas volume change can be measured, a simple rate equation can be used.[53]

In addition to the foregoing studies made in the United States, some very interesting work has been done by J. Hanika et al.[49–51] in Prague. These workers attempted a fundamental approach by using a vertical flat plate[49] as an oversimplified model. They distinguished among three flat models: plug flow, the linear velocity profile, and the parabolic velocity profile. The first was solved by the Fourier method. For laminar flow, the diffusion equation was solved by the finite difference method. It was found that the conversion is affected very little by the transverse velocity profile in the flowing liquid film and that the effect on conversion of diffusive mass transfer in the direction of flow is also very small. Basically, three regions were observed in the reactor during operations:

At $Sh > 10$, the diffusion region

At $10^{-1} < Sh < 10$, the transition region

At $Sh < 10^{-1}$, the kinetic region

This model was checked experimentally for catalytic hydrogenation of cyclohexene in methanol and 1-propanol as solvent in presence of a Pt black catalyst.[51]

A more realistic model of a vertical column of spheres was developed[50] by the same authors. This mathematical model is very similar to the experimental model of Satterfield et al.[38]

The foregoing information on mass-transfer relationships in trickle-bed reactors should enlighten the reader in general terms. In specific terms, mass transfer will have to be expressed by means of an effectiveness factor for the particular liquid-phase reaction. That effectiveness factor is used in the design equations. How this factor is calculated will be discussed in detail in the next chapter.

NOMENCLATURE

a	Catalyst particle surface-area/volume ratio, m^{-1}
$\bar{A}$	Average area, m^2 [Eq. (6-3)]
Bo	Bodenstein number = $d_s u/D_a$, dimensionless
C	Molar concentration of reactant, $kmol/m^3$
C^*	Concentration in the gas phase that would be in equilibrium with the liquid at the catalyst interface, $kmol/m^3$
C_1 C_2 C_3	Constants of Eq. (6-3)
C_i	Molar concentration in the liquid at the gas-liquid interface, $kmol/m^3$
C_p	Specific heat, $kJ/(kg \cdot K)$
C_p^*	Specific heat of saturated air, $kJ/(kg \cdot K)$
C_s	Molar concentration on the catalyst surface, $kmol/m^3$
d_p	Catalyst particle diameter, m
d_s	Equivalent spherical diameter of catalyst particle, m
D	Diffusivity in liquid phase, m^2/s
D_a	Axial dispersion coefficient for mass, m^2/s

D_{ae}	Axial eddy diffusivity, m^2/s
D_e	Equivalent diameter of reactor, m
E_K	Activation energy for the group Kv_L/v_G
$E_{\ell g}$	Activation energy of gas-liquid reaction based on gas-phase concentrations, kJ/kmol
$E_{\ell\ell}$	Activation energy of gas-liquid reaction based on liquid-phase concentrations, kJ/kmol
f	Frictional factor, dimensionless
F	Feed rate of gas at reaction temperature and pressure, m^3/s
Fr	Froude number, dimensionless
g	Gravitational constant, m/s^2
g_c	Force-to-mass conversion factor = 1.0 $kg/(N \cdot s^2)$
G_G	Mass flow rate in gas phase, $kg/(m^2 \cdot s)$
G_L	Mass flow rate in liquid phase, $kg/(m^2 \cdot s)$
Ga	Gallileo number, dimensionless
h_0	Equivalent heat transfer coefficient, $kJ/(s \cdot m^2 \cdot K)$
k	Gas-phase reaction rate constant
$k_{\ell g}$	Two-phase reaction rate constant based on concentration in the gas phase
$k_{\ell\ell}$	Two-phase reaction rate constant based on concentration in the liquid phase
k_z	Constant of Eq. (6-3), depending on variation of pressure with the longitudinal coordinate
K	Vapor-liquid equilibrium constant
K_e	Overall effective thermal conductivity, $kJ/(s \cdot m \cdot K)$
K_{LS}	Overall mass-transfer coefficient from gas-liquid interface to the catalyst surface
l_p	Length of catalyst particle, m
P	Pressure: P_1 = inlet pressure and P_2 = outlet pressure
Pe	Péclet number, dimensionless
Q	Heat transfer rate, kJ/s
r_0	Radius of reactor tube, m
R_H	Hydraulic radius of reactor, m

Re	Reynolds number, dimensionless
S_p	Total area of solids or catalysts, m^2
t	Temperature, °C
t_b	Outlet mixing cup temperature, °C
u	Superficial velocity based on empty reactor cylinder, m/s
v	Molar volume
V_c	Volume of single catalyst particle, m^3
V_p	Total volume of catalyst particles, m^3
V_v	Total volume of voids in the catalyst bed, m^3
W	Weight flow rate
x	Conversion, dimensionless
y	Mole fraction in gas phase, dimensionless
z	Axial coordinate, m
Z	Reactor length, m
α	Reaction order
β	Dimensionless constant in the equation of Ergun and Orning or Radial fraction of gas mass velocity
γ	External mass transfer resistance factor $= C_s/C_i$ or Radial fraction of liquid mass velocity
(ΔP)	Pressure drop per unit length, Pa/m
Δt_{lm}	Log mean temperature difference, °C
ε	Fractional void volume, dimensionless
ε_G	Gas-phase fraction, dimensionless
ε_L	Liquid-phase fraction or liquid holdup, dimensionless
ε_0	Operating holdup, dimensionless
ε_p	Catalyst-particle-phase fraction, dimensionless
ε_s	Static holdup, dimensionless
η	Effectiveness factor, dimensionless
λ_G	Molecular conductivity of gas, $kJ/(s \cdot m \cdot K)$
λ_L	Molecular conductivity of liquid, $kJ/(s \cdot m \cdot K)$
μ	Viscosity, $Pa \cdot s$
μ_w	Viscosity of water, $Pa \cdot s$

ρ	Fluid density, kg/m^3
σ	Standard deviation
τ	Empirical factor to correct for "tortuosity" and for nonuniformity of catalyst pore cross section

Subscripts

f	Final
F	Frictional
G	Gas phase
L	Liquid phase
LG	Two-phase
0	Initial or inlet
T	Total
w	Wall

REFERENCES

1. J. Klassen and R. S. Kirk, "Kinetics of the Liquid-Phase Oxidation of Ethanol," *AIChE J.* **1:**488–495 (1955). (Cited as example of countercurrent trickle-bed process.)
2. L. Philip Reiss, "Cocurrent Gas Liquid Contacting in Packed Columns," *Ind. Eng. Chem. Process Design Develop.* **6:**486–499 (1967).
3. M. Orhan Tarhan, Vaporizing and Pretreating Aromatic Hydrocarbons Feedstocks without Polymerization, U.S. Patent 3,448,039, 1969.
4. Paul B. Venuto and P. S. Landis, "Organic Catalysis over Crystalline Aluminosilicates," *Advan. Catalysis* **18:**259–371 (1968).
5. J. C. Charpentier, C. Post, and P. LeGoff, "Écoulement ruisselant de liquide dans une colonne à garnissage. Determination des vitesses et des débits relatifs des films, des filets et des gouttes," *Chim. Ind.—Genie Chim.* **100**(5):653–665 (1968).
6. J. C. Charpentier, C. Post, W. Van Swaaij, and P. LeGoff, "Étude de la rétention de liquide dans une colonne à garnissage arrosé à co-courant et à contre-courant de gaz-liquide. Représentation de sa texture par un modèle de films, filets, et gouttes," *Chim. Ind.—Genie Chim.* **99**(6):803–826 (1968).
7. F. DeMaria and R. R. White, "Transient Response Study of Gas Flowing through Irrigated Packing," *AIChE J.* **6:**473–481 (1960).
8. E. Dutkai and E. Ruckenstein, "Liquid Distribution in Packed Columns," *Chem. Eng. Sci.* **23:**1365–1373 (1968).
9. C. J. Hoohendoorn and J. Lips, "Axial Mixing of Liquids in Gas-Liquid Flow through Packed Beds," *Can. J. Chem. Eng.* 125–131 (June 1965).

10. G. J. Jameson, "A Model for Liquid Distribution in Packed Columns and Trickle-Bed Reactors," *Trans. Inst. Chem. Engr.* **44:**T198–T206 (1966).

11. L. Musil, C. Prost, and P. LeGoff, "Hydrodynamique des colonnes noyées à garnissage avec contre-courant de gaz-liquide. Comparaison avec les colonnes arosées," *Chim. Ind.—Genie Chim.* **100**(5):674–682 (1968).

12. K. E. Porter, "Liquid Flow in Packed Columns. Part I: The Rivulet Model," *Trans. Inst. Chem. Engrs.* **46:**T69–T73 (1968).

12*a*. K. E. Porter, V. D. Barnett, and J. J. Templeman, "Liquid Flow in Packed Columns. Part II: The Spread of Liquid over Random Packings," *Trans. Inst. Chem. Engr.* **46:**T74–T85 (1968).

13. K. E. Porter and J. J. Templeman, "Liquid Flow in Packed Columns. Part III: Wall Flow," *Trans. Inst. Chem. Engr.* **46:**T86–T94 (1968).

14. J. J. Templeman and K. E. Porter, "Experimental Determination of Wall Flow in Packed Columns," *Chem. Eng. Sci.* **20:**1139–1140 (1965).

15. W. P. M. van Swaaij, J. C. Charpentier, and J. Villermeaux, "Residence Time Distribution in The Liquid Phase of Trickle Flow in Packed Columns," *Chem. Eng. Sci.* **24:**1083–1095 (1969).

16. William E. Schiesser and Leon Lapidus, "Further Studies of Fluid Flow and Mass Transfer in Trickle Beds," *AIChE J.* **7:**163–171 (1961).

17. Vern W. Weekman, Jr. and John E. Myers, "Heat Transfer Characteristics of Concurrent Gas-Liquid Flow in Packed Beds," *AIChE J.* **11:**13–17 (1965). (Special copyright permission from the American Institute of Chemical Engineers.)

18. S. F. Chung and C. Y. Wen, "Longitudinal Dispersion of Liquid Flowing through Fixed and Fluidized Beds," *AIChE J.* **14:**857–866 (1968).

19. J. M. Hochman and E. Effron, "Two-Phase Cocurrent Downflow in Packed Beds," *Ind. Eng. Chem. Fundamentals* **8:**64–71 (1969).

20. M. B. Glaser and I. Lichtenstein, "Interrelation of Packing and Mixed Phase Flow Parameters with Liquid Residence Time Distribution," *AIChE J.* **9:**30–34 (1963).

21. Leon Lapidus, "Flow Distribution and Diffusion in Fixed-Bed Two-Phase Reactors," *Ind. Eng. Chem.* **49:**1000–1006 (1957).

22. Jim L. Turpin and R. L. Huntington, "Prediction of Pressure Drop for Two-Phase, Two-Component Concurrent Flow in Packed Beds," *AIChE J.* **13:**1196–1202 (1967).

23. Vern W. Weekman, Jr. and John E. Myers, "Fluid Flow Characteristics of Concurrent Gas-Liquid Flow in Packed Beds," *AIChE J.* **10:**951–958 (1964).

24. Sayeed Akhtar, Sam Friedman, and Paul M. Yavorsky, "Low Sulfur Fuel Oil from Coal," U.S. Bureau of Mines Coal Desulfurization Program, Tech. Progr. Rep. 35 (July 1971).

25. Sayeed Akhtar, Sam Friedman, and Paul M. Yavorsky, "Process for Hydrodesulfurization of Coal in a Turbulent Flow Fixed-Bed Reactor," paper

presented at the 71st Am. Inst. Chem. Engrs. National Meeting, Dallas, Feb. 20–23, 1972.

26. Sayeed Akhtar, Sam Friedman, and Paul M. Yavorsky, "Low-Sulfur Liquid Fuels From Coal," paper presented at the Am. Chem. Soc. Symposium on Quality of Synthetic Fuels, Boston, Mass., April 9–14, 1972.
27. Sayeed Akhtar, James J. Lacey, M. Weintraub, Alan A. Reznik, and Paul M. Yavorsky, "The Synthoil Process—Material Balance and Thermal Efficiency," paper presented at the 67th Am. Inst. Chem. Engrs. Natl. Meeting, Washington, Dec. 1–5, 1974.
28. Paul M. Yavorsky, Sayeed Akhtar, and Sam Friedman, "Converting Coal into Non-Polluting Fuel Oil," *Chem. Eng. Progr.* **69**(3):51–52 (1973).
29. Charles N. Satterfield, *Mass Transfer in Heterogenous Catalysis,* MIT Press, Cambridge, 1970, pp. 86–88.
30. D. E. Sweeney, "A Correlation for Pressure Drop in Two-Phase Co-Current Flow in Packed Beds," *AIChE J.* **13:**663–669 (1967).
31. Sabri Ergun and A. A. Orning, "Fluid Flow through Randomly Packed Columns and Fluidized Beds, *Ind. Eng. Chem.* **41:**1179–1184 (1949).
32. Thomas K. Sherwood, G. H. Shipley, and F. A. L. Holloway, "Flooding Velocities in Packed Columns," *Ind. Eng. Chem.* **30:**765–769 (1938).
33. Ralph Strigle, Jr., Frank Rukovena, and Leonard Rollison, "Generalized Pressure Drop Correlation," Sheet Gr-109 R6 Norton Chemical Process Products Division, Akron, Ohio.
34. V. E. Sater and Octave Levenspiel, "Two-Phase Flow in Packed Beds," *Ind. Eng. Chem. Fundamentals* **5:**86–92 (1966).
35. David E. Mears, "The Role of Axial Dispersion in Trickle-Flow Laboratory Reactors," *Chem. Eng. Sci.* **26:**1361–1366 (1971).
36. H. L. Shulman, C. F. Ullrich and N. Wells, "Performance of Packed Columns: Total, Static, and Operating Holdups," *AIChE J.* **1:**247–253 (1955).
37. Leon D. Ross, "Performance of Trickle-Bed Reactors," *Chem. Eng. Progr.* **61**(10):77–82 (1965).
38. Charles N. Satterfield, A. A. Pelosof, and Thomas K. Sherwood, "Mass Transfer Limitations in a Trickle-Bed Reactor," *AIChE J.* **15:**226–234 (1969).
39. H. Clarke Henry and John B. Gilbert, "Scale-up of Pilot Plant Data for Catalytic Hydroprocessing," *Ind. Eng. Chem. Process Design Develop.* **12:**328–334 (1973).
40. J. F. Davidson, "The Hold-Up and Liquid Film Coefficient of Packed Towers. Part II: Statistical Models of the Random Packing," *Trans. Inst. Chem. Engr.* **37:**131 (1959).
41. T. Otake and K. Okada, "Liquid Holdup in Packed Towers: Operating Holdup without Gasflow," *Chem. Eng.* (*Japan*) **17:**176–184 (1953).

42. D. M. Mohunta and G. S. Laddha, "Prediction of Liquid-Phase Holdup in Random Packed Beds," *Chem. Eng. Sci.* **20:**1069–1072 (1965).

43. Charles N. Satterfield, "Contacting Effectiveness in Trickle-Bed Reactors," Chem. Reaction Eng. Reviews, Intern. Symp., 1974, *Advan. Chem. Ser.* **148:**50–74 (1975).

44. Arnold A. Bondi, "Handling Kinetics in Trickle-Phase Reactors," *Chem-Tech.* **1:**185–188 (1971).

45. Vern W. Weekman, Jr., "Heat Transfer and Fluid Flow for Concurrent Gas-Liquid Flow in Packed Beds," Ph.D. thesis, Purdue University, 1963.

46. Sakae Yagi and Daizo Kunii, "Studies on Effective Thermal Conductivities in Packed Beds," *AIChE J.* **3:**373–381 (1957).

47. Charles N. Satterfield and Peter F. Way, "The Role of the Liquid Phase in the Performance of a Trickle-Bed Reactor," *AIChE J.* **18:**305–311 (1972). (Special copyright permission from the American Institute of Chemical Engineers.)

48. James J. Carberry, "Heat and Mass Diffusional Intrusions in Catalytic Reactor Behavior," *Catalysis Rev.* **3**(1):61–91 (1969).

49. J. Hanika, K. Sporka, and V. Ruzicka, "Investigation of Hydrogenation in Liquid Phase. XVI. Theoretical Models of Hydrogenation in Liquid Film. Flat Plate," *Collection Czech. Chem. Commun.* **35:**2111–2123 (1970).

50. J. Hanika, K. Sporka, and V. Ruzicka, "Investigation of Hydrogenation in Liquid Phase. XVII. Theoretical Model of Hydrogenation in Liquid Film on a Vertical Column of Spheres," *Collection Czech. Chem. Commun.* **36:**1358–1369 (1971).

51. J. Hanika, K. Sporka, and V. Ruzicka, "Investigation of Hydrogenation in Liquid Phase. XVIII. Experimental Verification of a Theoretical Model of a Trickle-Bed Reactor," *Collection Czech. Chem. Commun.* **36:**2903–2913 (1971).

52. Charles N. Satterfield, Yi Hua Ma, and Thomas K. Sherwood, "The Effectiveness Factor in Liquid-Filled Porous Catalyst," in *Inst. Chem. Engs. Symposium Ser.* No. 28, Institution of Chemical Engineers, London, 1968, pp. 22–29.

53. R. R. Cecil, F. X. Mayer, and E. N. Cart, Jr., "Fuel Oil Hydrodesulfurization Studies in Pilot Plant Reactors," paper presented at AIChE Meeting, Los Angeles, December 1968.

54. Peter F. Way, "The Performance of Trickle-Bed Reactors," Ph.D. thesis, MIT, Cambridge, 1971.

Chapter 7 PROCESS DESIGN OF TRICKLE-BED REACTORS

The design of trickle-bed reactors is considerably more complicated than that of fixed-bed gas reactors. There are no standard published methods. Many oil companies have developed and are using their own proprietary design procedures. In the following we will attempt to develop a procedure based on the present-day best published knowledge of trickle-bed reactor design.

7.1 GENERAL PROCEDURE

The first thing the designer should do is study the reacting system with all its kinetic and mass-transfer peculiarities, because this information will determine the kind of design model selected. There is a choice between a plug-flow and a partially backmixed reactor. In either case the reactor will be concurrent downflow and adiabatic. The use of criteria discussed in Sec. 6.2 will determine whether the reactor is plug-flow or not. We will select a process and design one reactor of each type in this book.

A *hydrocarbon oil desulfurization* reactor is selected as the example. The following assumptions can be made:

- The reaction occurs between the liquid phase and the catalyst surface.
- The reaction is adiabatic.
- The key reactants are sulfur compounds dissolved in the oil feed and a hydrogen-containing gas.
- The liquid volume in the reactor remains constant.

Although our main purpose is to design a reactor for the conversion of sulfur compounds, we must take account of all the side reactions occurring in the reactor because they all contribute to heat evolution and make up the composition of the reacting mass. Because the number of individual reactions is too large, it is customary to lump them into groups of reactions. We may write one equation for each of the following lumped reaction groups:

- Hydrodesulfurization
- Hydrodeoxygenation
- Hydrodenitrogenation
- Hydrocracking
- Saturative hydrogenation

Because economics dictates the recycling of the unused hydrogen, the recycled gases normally contain certain impurities. Hydrogen sulfide, the product of hydrodesulfurization, can be easily removed from the recycle gas.[1] Thus the major impurity will be methane, a product of the hydrocracking side reaction. It is customary to remove at least part of this methane from the effluent gas and to produce hydrogen from it.[2] Other impurities are water and ammonia. Ammonia is normally removed together with the hydrogen sulfide in a monoethanolamine absorber, and water vapor is removed from the desulfurized gas in a molecular sieve or equivalent dryer.

In order to develop the design equation, reference is made to Fig. 7-1, which represents a cylindrical packed bed of catalyst. In this bed a

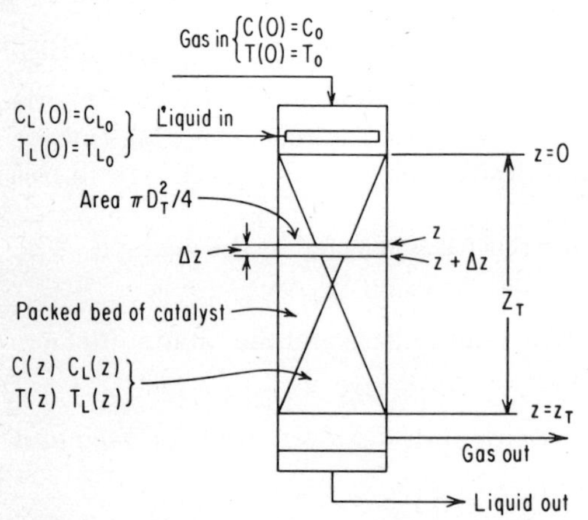

FIG. 7-1 Schematic representation of a typical downflow gas-liquid fixed-bed reactor.

differential height Δz is considered for which a materials balance and a heat balance will be obtained. The design will be determined for the liquid-phase reaction, and gas concentrations will be calculated from the liquid-phase reaction at all points.

Let us designate:

C_H = molar hydrogen concentration in bulk phase, kmol/m^3

C_L = molar concentration of key reactant in liquid phase or molar concentration of hydrocarbons containing an atom of sulfur, kmol/m^3

A_c = cross-sectional area of the catalyst bed = $\pi D_T^2/4$, m^2

z = axial coordinate in the reactor

Z_T = total reactor length, m

Let us introduce the concept of *phase fraction,* which is the fraction of the reactor bed volume occupied by any one phase. The total volume V of the packed catalyst beds consists of the volume taken by the catalyst particles V_p (which includes both the volume of the solids and that of the pores), the gas volume V_G, and the liquid volume V_L. The following equations can be written:

$$V = V_p + V_L + V_G \qquad \text{and} \qquad 1 = \frac{V_p}{V} + \frac{V_L}{V} + \frac{V_G}{V}$$

If we set

$$\frac{V_p}{V} = \varepsilon_p \qquad \frac{V_L}{V} = \varepsilon_L \qquad \text{and} \qquad \frac{V_G}{V} = \varepsilon_G$$

it follows that

$$\varepsilon_p + \varepsilon_L + \varepsilon_G = 1 \tag{7-1}$$

where ε_G = gas-phase fraction

ε_L = liquid-phase fraction or liquid holdup

ε_p = catalyst particle phase fraction

also ε = void fraction = $\varepsilon_G + \varepsilon_L$ (7-2)

While ε_p and hence ε are constant along the bed length, ε_G and ε_L may vary somewhat in some cases and appreciably in others. We will compute ε_L according to Satterfield's Eq. (6-19):

$$\varepsilon_L = 9.9(Gd/\mu)^{1/3}\,(d^3 g\,\rho^2/\mu^2)^{-1/3} \tag{6-19}$$

Plug-Flow Trickle-Bed Reactor

The case of the plug-flow industrial size reactor will be considered first. Let us make a materials balance for the liquid phase of the differential reactor volume increment:

(Molar inflow axially) − (molar outflow axially)
− (molar disappearance by reaction) = 0

Let us calculate the value of each set of parentheses in general terms:

$$\text{Molar inflow axially} = \frac{\pi}{4} D_T^2\, u_L\, \varepsilon_L\, C_L\big|_z$$

$$\text{Molar outflow axially} = \frac{\pi}{4} D_T^2\, u_L\, \varepsilon_L\, C_L\big|_{z+\Delta z}$$

$$\text{Molar disappearance by reaction} = -\varepsilon_L \frac{\pi}{4} D_T^2\, \Delta z\, \mathcal{R}$$

where D_T is the reactor diameter in meters and u_L is the superficial velocity of the liquid phase in meters per second. Using these expressions in the materials balance equation and dividing both sides of the resulting equation by $(\pi/4)D_T^2\, u_L\, \Delta z\, \varepsilon_L$ gives:

$$\frac{C_L\big|_z - C_L\big|_{z+\Delta z}}{\Delta z} - \frac{\mathcal{R}_1}{u_L} = 0$$

where $\mathcal{R}_1$ is the rate of the hydrodesulfurization reaction in kilomoles per cubic meter per second. This equation can be rearranged to

$$\frac{C_L\big|_{z+\Delta z} - C_L\big|_z}{\Delta z} = -\frac{\mathcal{R}_1}{u_L}$$

When $\Delta z \rightarrow 0$, the left-hand side of this equation tends toward dC_L/dz and

$$\frac{dC_L}{dz} = -\frac{\mathcal{R}_1}{u_L} \tag{7-3}$$

Equation (7-3) can be converted to a dimensionless form by substitution:

$$C_r = \frac{C_L}{C_{L0}} \quad \text{and} \quad Z = \frac{z}{d_p}$$

Thus we obtain:

$$\frac{dC_r}{dZ} = -\frac{d_p\, \mathcal{R}_1}{C_{L0}\, u_L} \tag{7-4}$$

where C_{L0} is the initial value of C_L.

An analogous set of equations can be developed for the heat balance. Referring to Fig. 7-1, we can write for the differential volume:

(Heat inflow axially) − (heat outflow axially)
+ (heat generated by reaction) = 0

The various heat flows to substitute in the equation are:

$$\text{Heat inflow axially in liquid phase} = T|_z \frac{\pi}{4} D_T^2 u_L \rho_L c_{pL} \varepsilon_L$$

$$\text{Heat outflow axially in liquid phase} = T|_{z+\Delta z} \frac{\pi}{4} D_T^2 u_L \rho_L c_{pL} \varepsilon_L$$

$$\text{Heat generated by reactions} = \sum [(-\Delta H)\Re](\pi/4) D_T^2 \Delta z \varepsilon_L$$

$$\text{Heat inflow axially in gas phase} = T|_z \frac{\pi}{4} D_T^2 u\rho c_p \varepsilon_G$$

$$\text{Heat outflow axially on gas phase} = T|_{z+\Delta z} \frac{\pi}{4} D_T^2 u\rho c_p \varepsilon_G$$

$$(T|_z - T|_{z+z}) \frac{\pi}{4} D_T^2 (u\rho c_p \varepsilon_G + u_L \rho_L c_{pL} \varepsilon_L) + \sum [\Re(-\Delta H)] \frac{\pi}{4} D_T^2 \Delta z \varepsilon_L = 0 \quad (7\text{-}5)$$

Equation (7-5) can be divided by $(\pi/4)D_T^2(u\rho c_p \varepsilon_G + u_L \rho_L c_{pL} \varepsilon_L)\Delta z$ and rearranged:

$$\frac{T|_{z+\Delta z} - T|_z}{\Delta z} = \sum [(-\Delta H)\Re] \cdot \frac{\varepsilon_L}{\varepsilon_G \rho c_p u + \varepsilon_L \rho_L c_{pL} u_L}$$

When $\Delta z \rightarrow 0$,

$$\frac{T|_{z+\Delta z} - T|_z}{\Delta z} \rightarrow \frac{dT}{dz} \quad \text{and}$$

$$\frac{dT}{dz} = \sum [(-\Delta H)\Re] \varepsilon_L/(\varepsilon_G \rho c_p u + \varepsilon_L \rho_L c_{pL} u_L) \quad (7\text{-}6)$$

Again, dimensionless variables can be substituted into Eq. (7-6):

$$Z = z/d_p \qquad T_r = T/T_0$$

and after simplification we will have:

$$\frac{dT}{dZ} = \sum [(-\Delta H)\Re] d_p\varepsilon_L/T_0(\varepsilon_G \rho c_p u + \varepsilon_L \rho_L c_{pL} u_L) \quad (7\text{-}7)$$

Because the reaction occurs in the catalyst particle, the exothermic heat is released right inside the particle and is propagated across the exterior surface of the particle to the bulk liquid and from there to the gas flow. Consequently, there should be a temperature gradient between the inside of the particle and its outside surface. However, because of the high thermal conductivity of solid catalysts, it is reasonable to assume that, for moderately exothermic reactions, the temperature inside the particle is constant. (A similar assumption was made in the case of NINAF reactors.) Then the continuously liquid-washed catalyst particles would be substantially at the temperature of the bulk fluid streams.

Let us now define the lumped chemical reactions we will consider:

Sulfur-containing hydrocarbons:

$$\text{Hydrocarbon}{=}\text{S} + 2\ \text{H}_2 \rightarrow \text{hydrocarbon}{=}\text{H}_2 + \text{H}_2\text{S} \tag{7-8}$$

Oxygenated hydrocarbons, e.g., phenols:

$$\text{Hydrocarbon—OH} + \text{H}_2 \rightarrow \text{hydrocarbon—H} + \text{H}_2\text{O} \tag{7-9}$$

Hydrogenated hydrocrackable hydrocarbons:

$$\text{Hydrocarbon—CH}_3 + \text{H}_2 \rightarrow \text{hydrocarbon—H} + \text{CH}_4 \tag{7-10}$$

Nitrogenated hydrocarbons, e.g., pyridines, quinolines:

$$\text{Hydrocarbon}{\equiv}\text{N} + 3\ \text{H}_2 \rightarrow \text{hydrocarbon}{\equiv}\text{H}_3 + \text{NH}_3 \tag{7-11}$$

Unsaturated hydrocarbons with double bonds:

$$\text{Hydrocarbon} + \text{H}_2 \rightarrow \text{hydrocarbon}{=}\text{H}_2 \tag{7-12}$$

Literature values for the kinetic constants of the above reactions fall in a very wide range. It is obviously possible to develop a cobalt molybdate-on-alumina catalyst that would work according to any of the kinetic data published. Consequently, while some of the kinetic data in this book are taken from the literature, others were simply assumed from the general range of the published data. The reactor designer should of course obtain new data that must correspond to the particular catalyst to be used.

The following kinetic expressions will be used in this book:

$$\mathcal{R}_1 = \eta_1(-dC_L/dt) = \eta_1\ 1.008 \times 10^8 \exp(-82{,}060/RT)\ C_L \tag{7-13}$$

$$\mathcal{R}_2 = \eta_2(-dC_{\text{ox}}/dt) = \eta_2\ 3.6 \times 10^8 \exp(-50{,}208/RT)\ C_{\text{ox}} \tag{7-14}$$

$$\mathcal{R}_3 = \eta_3(-dC_{\text{N}}/dt) = \eta_3\ 6.48 \times 10^6 \exp(-72{,}060/RT)\ C_{\text{N}} \tag{7-15}$$

$$\mathcal{R}_4 = \eta_4(-dC_{\text{hy}}/dt) = \eta_4\ 9.0 \times 10^{18} \exp(-243{,}500/RT)\ C_{\text{hy}} \tag{7-16}$$

$$\mathcal{R}_5 = \eta_5(-dC_{\text{hc}}/dt) = \eta_5\ 3.6 \times 10^6 \exp(-46{,}860/RT)\ C_{\text{hc}} \tag{7-17}$$

where C_{ox} = molar concentration of compounds each containing one atom of oxygen

C_N = molar concentration of compounds each containing one atom of nitrogen
C_{hy} = molar concentration of hydrocrackable hydrocarbons, i.e., the entire unreacted feedstock
C_{hc} = molar concentration of unreacted unsaturated or saturable aromatic hydrocarbons
η = effectiveness factors of various reactions

The reaction rate constants of Eqs. (7-13) to (7-17) are all expressed in hr^{-1}.

Sulfur compounds can be lumped into *aliphatic sulfur* and *thiophenic sulfur.* The latter react more slowly and require more severe conditions for hydrodesulfurization. R. A. Flinn et al.[3] and R. R. Cecil et al.[4] use the following expression for the two kinds of sulfur:

$$S = S_1^0 e^{-k_1\theta} + S_2^0 e^{-k_2\theta} \tag{7-18}$$

where S = sulfur content of the product
S_1^0 = initial content of type 1 (aliphatic) sulfur
S_2^0 = initial content of type 2 (thiophenic) sulfur
k_1 = reaction rate constant for type 1 sulfur
k_2 = reaction rate constant for type 2 sulfur
θ = 1/LHSV, where LHSV is the liquid hourly space velocity.

Flinn et al.[3] showed that this relationship does not quite represent the experimental data. Rather, the reaction appears to follow the rate constant k_1 up to a certain temperature, above which there is a bend in the corresponding curve and the reaction then proceeds according to k_2. Although k_1 and k_2 values were given, no E_1, E_2, A_1, and A_2 values were published. Consequently, in the absence of data for sulfur types, this book uses total sulfur data. Thus, C_L represents the molar concentration of both type 1 and type 2 sulfur or total sulfur, i.e., the molar concentration of compounds each containing one atom of sulfur, and C_r is the reduced molar total sulfur concentration.

Similarly, the other molar concentrations, C_{ox}, C_N, C_{hy}, and C_{hc} can also be expressed in reduced forms:

$$C_{rox} = C_{ox}/C_{ox0};\ C_{rN} = C_N/C_{N0};\ C_{rhy} = C_{hy}/C_{hy0};\ C_{rhc} = C_{hc}/C_{hc0}$$

where C_{ox0}, C_{N0}, C_{hy0}, and C_{HC0} are initial values for C_{ox}, C_N, C_{hy}, and C_{hc}, respectively.

Design equations similar to Eq. (7-4) can be developed for C_{rox}, C_{rN}, C_{rhy}, and C_{rhc}:

$$\frac{dC_{rox}}{dZ} = \frac{d_p\,\mathfrak{R}_2}{C_{ox0}\,u_L} \tag{7-19}$$

$$\frac{dC_{rN}}{dZ} = \frac{d_p \, \Re_3}{C_{N0} \, u_L} \tag{7-20}$$

$$\frac{dC_{rhy}}{dZ} = \frac{d_p \, \Re_4}{C_{hy0} \, u_L} \tag{7-21}$$

$$\frac{dC_{rhc}}{dZ} = \frac{d_p \, \Re_5}{C_{hc0} \, u_L} \tag{7-22}$$

Because the major reactant feed components are rather high-boiling liquids, there is no reason to be concerned with the mass transfer of these components from one phase to the other. However, if it is necessary to calculate the mass transfer of H_2 from the gas phase to the liquid phase and the mass transfer of reaction products such as H_2S, CH_4, H_2O, and NH_3 from the liquid phase to the gas phase, the following equations can be written:

$$k_{gH}a\,(C_{LeH} - C_{LH}) = \sum (\text{H}_2\text{-consuming reactions}) \tag{7-23}$$

$$k_{gH_2S}\, a(C_{LH_2S} - C_{LeH_2S}) = \Re_1 \tag{7-24}$$

$$k_{gCH_4}\, a(C_{LCH_4} - C_{LeCH_4}) = \Re_4 \tag{7-25}$$

$$k_{gH_20}\, a(C_{LH_2O} - C_{LeH_2O}) = \Re_2 \tag{7-26}$$

$$k_{gNH_3}\, a(C_{LNH_3} - C_{LeNH_3}) = \Re_3 \tag{7-27}$$

where subscript H denotes hydrogen, L denotes liquid phase, and Le denotes liquid phase in equilibrium with gas phase. The heat transfer from the catalyst to the liquid and to the gas is assumed to have very little resistance since catalysts, liquids, and the bulk gas are all the same temperature.

To summarize, the relationships that can be used to describe the plug-flow trickle-bed reactor system are Eqs. (7-4), (7-19) to (7-22), (7-13) to (7-17), and (7-7). After substituting the values of $\Re_i$ in the six first-order ODEs, Eqs. (7-4), (7-7), and (7-19) to (7-22), these equations can be solved numerically and simultaneously as initial-value ODEs. The initial values can be written as follows:

Inlet $Z = 0$ $\quad C_r = 1.0 \quad C_{rox} = 1.0 \quad C_{rN} = 1.0$

$C_{rhy} = 1.0 \quad C_{rhc} = 1.0 \quad T_r = 1.0$

The numerical values of the various heats of reaction are:

$-\Delta H_1 = 251{,}000$ kJ/kmol for hydrodesulfurization

$-\Delta H_2 = 68{,}200$ kJ/kmol for hydrodeoxygenation

$-\Delta H_3 = 64{,}850$ kJ/kmol for hydrodenitrogenation

$-\Delta H_4 = 41{,}000$ kJ/kmol for hydrocracking

$-\Delta H_5 = 125{,}520$ kJ/kmol for hydrosaturation

Equations (7-13) to (7-17) can also be expressed in kilomoles per square meter per second and the concentration terms can be replaced by products of reduced concentrations by initial concentrations:

$$\mathcal{R}_1 = \eta_1\, 2.8 \times 10^4 \exp(-82{,}060/RT) C_r\, C_{L0} \tag{7-28}$$

$$\mathcal{R}_2 = \eta_2\, 1.0 \times 10^5 \exp(-50{,}200/RT) C_{rox}\, C_{ox0} \tag{7-29}$$

$$\mathcal{R}_3 = \eta_3\, 1.8 \times 10^3 \exp(-72{,}060/RT) C_{rN}\, C_{N0} \tag{7-30}$$

$$\mathcal{R}_4 = \eta_4\, 2.5 \times 10^{15} \exp(-243{,}500/RT) C_{rhy}\, C_{hy0} \tag{7-31}$$

$$\mathcal{R}_5 = \eta_5\, 1.0 \times 10^3 \exp(-46{,}860/RT) C_{rhc}\, C_{hc0} \tag{7-32}$$

Trickle-Bed Reactor with Axial Dispersion

Small trickle-bed reactors such as those used in laboratories and pilot plants have some axial dispersion. Let us write the material balance for the liquid phase of the differential reactor volume increment in Fig. 7-1.

(Molar inflow axially) − (molar outflow axially)
+ (molar inflow by axial dispersion)
− (molar outflow by axial dispersion)
− (molar disappearance by reaction) = 0 (7-33)

$$\text{Molar inflow by axial dispersion} = \frac{\pi}{4} D_T^2\, \varepsilon_L \left(-D \left. \frac{dC_L}{dz} \right|_z \right)$$

$$\text{Molar outflow by axial dispersion} = \frac{\pi}{4} D_T^2\, \varepsilon_L \left(-D \left. \frac{dC_L}{dz} \right|_{z+\Delta z} \right)$$

where $-D(dC_L/dz)$ is the flux in axial direction according to Fick's law and D is the diffusivity of the reacting molecules in the liquid phase. Using these expressions in the balance equation, Eq. (7-33), dividing by $(\pi/4)D_T^2\, u_L\, \Delta z\, \varepsilon_L$, and rearranging gives:

$$\frac{C_L|_{z+\Delta z} - C_L|_z}{\Delta z} = \frac{D\, dC_L/dz|_{z+\Delta z} - D\, dC_L/dz|_z}{\Delta z u_L} = \frac{\mathcal{R}_1}{u_L}$$

When $\Delta z \rightarrow 0$, the difference expressions in the foregoing equation tend to become differentials and we obtain

$$\frac{dC_L}{dz} = \frac{D}{u_L} \cdot \frac{d^2 C_L}{dz^2} - \frac{\mathcal{R}_1}{u_L} \tag{7-34}$$

Equation (7-34) can be converted to a dimensionless form by substituting

$$C_r = C_L/C_{L0} \quad \text{and} \quad Z = z/d_p$$

$$\frac{dC_r}{dZ} = \frac{D}{u_L\, d_p} \cdot \frac{d^2C_r}{dZ^2} - \frac{\mathcal{R}_1\, d_p}{u_L\, C_{L0}} \tag{7-35}$$

Here, the term $u_L d_p/D$ is the Péclet number Pe_{mal} for mass and axial dispersion in liquid phase.

Similar equations can be written for all the other lumped reactions occurring in the process. Also, an analogous heat balance equation can be developed:

(Heat inflow axially − heat outflow axially)
+ (heat inflow by axial dispersion − heat outflow by axial dispersion)
+ (heat generated by reactions) = 0 (7-36)

The axial heat flows are:

	Liquid phase	Gas phase
Inflow	$T\|_z \frac{\pi}{4}D_T^2\, u_L\, \rho_L\, c_{pL}\, \varepsilon_L$	$T\|_z \frac{\pi}{4}D_T^2\, u\rho c_p \varepsilon_G$
Outflow	$T\|_{z+\Delta z} \frac{\pi}{4}D_T^2\, u_L\, \rho_L\, c_{pL}\, \varepsilon_L$	$T\|_{z+\Delta z} \frac{\pi}{4}D_T^2 u\rho c_p \varepsilon_G$

The heat flux by axial dispersion across a cross-sectional area A_c is given by Fourier's law[5]:

$$-K_a\, A_c\, \frac{dT}{dz} \tag{7-37}$$

where K_a is the axial thermal diffusivity in packed beds in square meters per second. Thus the heat flows by axial dispersion are:

	Liquid phase	Gas phase
Influx	$-\frac{\pi}{4}D_T^2\, \varepsilon_L\, \rho_L\, c_{pL}\, K_{aL} \left.\frac{dT}{dz}\right\|_z$	$-\frac{\pi}{4}D_T^2\, \varepsilon_G\, \rho\, c_p\, K_a \left.\frac{dT}{dz}\right\|_z$
Outflux	$-\frac{\pi}{4}D_T^2\, \varepsilon_L\, \rho_L\, c_{pL}\, K_{aL} \left.\frac{dT}{dz}\right\|_{z+\Delta z}$	$-\frac{\pi}{4}D_T^2\, \varepsilon_G\, \rho\, c_p\, K_a \left.\frac{dT}{dz}\right\|_{z+\Delta z}$

The heat balance equation must include both the gas phase and the liquid phase, as well as all the reactions. This gives a very long expression, which after simplification, rearrangement, and conversion of differences to differentials gives:

$$\frac{dT}{dz} = \frac{d^2T}{dz^2}\left[\frac{\varepsilon_G\rho\, c_p\, K_a + \varepsilon_L\, \rho_L\, c_{pL}\, k_{aL}}{\varepsilon_G\rho\, c_p\, u + \varepsilon_L\, \rho_L\, c_{pL}\, u_L}\right] + \sum [\mathcal{R}_i(-\Delta H)_i]\left[\frac{\varepsilon_L}{\varepsilon_G\rho\, c_p\, u + \varepsilon_L\, \rho_L\, c_{pL}\, u_L}\right]$$

which can also be written in dimensionless form:

$$\frac{dT_r}{dZ} = \frac{d^2T_r}{dZ^2}\cdot\frac{1}{d_p}\cdot\left[\frac{\varepsilon_G\rho\, c_p\, K_a + \varepsilon_L\, \rho_L\, c_{pL}\, K_{aL}}{\varepsilon_G\rho\, c_p\, u + \varepsilon_L\, \rho_L\, c_{pL}\, u_L}\right] + \sum (\mathcal{R}_i(-\Delta H)_i]\,\frac{d_p}{T_0}\left[\frac{\varepsilon_L}{\varepsilon_G\rho\, c_p\, u + \varepsilon_L\, \rho_L\, c_{pL}\, u_L}\right]$$

We may define a *Péclet number for heat for two-phase axial dispersion*:

$$\mathrm{Pe}_{ha2} = \frac{d_p(\varepsilon_G\, \rho\, c_p\, u + \varepsilon_L\, \rho_L\, c_{pL}\, u_L)}{\varepsilon_G\, \rho\, c_p\, K_a + \varepsilon_L\, \rho_L\, c_{pL}\, K_{aL}} \tag{7-38}$$

with which the heat balance equation becomes:

$$\frac{dT_r}{dZ} = \frac{1}{\mathrm{Pe}_{ha2}}\cdot\frac{d^2T_r}{dZ^2} + \sum [\mathcal{R}_i(-\Delta H)_i]\,\frac{d_p\, \varepsilon_L}{T_0\,(\varepsilon_G\, \rho\, c_p\, u + \varepsilon_L\, \rho_L\, c_{pL}\, u_L)} \tag{7-39}$$

In Eq. (7-39) everything except the Péclet number is relatively easily obtainable. The Péclet number Pe_{ha2} is a function of gas-phase and liquid-phase axial dispersion coefficients, which have to be determined.

The reactions, which take place in the catalyst particle, release the exothermic heat right inside the particle. This heat is propagated across the exterior surface of the particle to the bulk liquid and from there to the gas stream. As in the case of the NINAF reactors, the temperature inside the particle is assumed to be constant.

Now let us summarize the relationships that can be used to describe the trickle-bed reactor system with axial dispersion:

The five reaction rates given by Eqs. (7-28) to (7-32) are of course the same as in the plug-flow case. The design equations are Eq. (7-39) as the heat balance equation and

$$\frac{dC_r}{dZ} = \frac{1}{\mathrm{Pe}_{mal}}\cdot\frac{d^2C_r}{dZ^2} - \frac{d_p\, \mathcal{R}_1}{u_L\, C_{L0}} \tag{7-40}$$

$$\frac{dC_{rox}}{dZ} = \frac{1}{\text{Pe}_{mal}} \cdot \frac{d^2C_{rox}}{dZ^2} - \frac{d_p\,\mathfrak{R}_2}{u_L\,C_{ox0}} \tag{7-41}$$

$$\frac{dC_{rN}}{dZ} = \frac{1}{\text{Pe}_{mal}} \cdot \frac{d^2C_{rN}}{dZ^2} - \frac{d_p\,\mathfrak{R}_3}{u_L\,C_{N0}} \tag{7-42}$$

$$\frac{dC_{rhy}}{dZ} = \frac{1}{\text{Pe}_{mal}} \cdot \frac{d^2C_{rhy}}{dZ^2} - \frac{d_p\,\mathfrak{R}_4}{u_L\,C_{hy0}} \tag{7-43}$$

$$\frac{dC_{rhc}}{dZ} = \frac{1}{\text{Pe}_{mal}} \cdot \frac{d^2C_{rhc}}{dZ^2} - \frac{d_p\,\mathfrak{R}_5}{u_L\,C_{hc0}} \tag{7-44}$$

The following boundary conditions must be written:

Inlet $\quad Z = 0 \quad C_r = 1.0 \quad C_{rox} = 1.0 \quad C_{rN} = 1.0$

$C_{rhy} = 1.0 \quad C_{rhc} = 1.0 \quad T_r = 1.0$

Outlet $\quad Z = Z_T \quad \dfrac{dC_r}{dZ} = 0.0 \quad \dfrac{dT_r}{dZ} = 0.0$

It is not possible to write boundary conditions for each ODE. One can design a reactor for the conversion of a specific fraction of the sulfur, the oxygen, or the nitrogen or for a certain amount of hydrocracking or saturation, but not for all these specific conversions at the same time. If it is decided to design for sulfur conversion, one has to accept whatever one obtains from the other reactions.

7.2 DESIGN EXAMPLES FOR PETROLEUM HYDRODESULFURIZATION

Let us now calculate two specific examples for the petroleum oil hydrodesulfurization reactor that was discussed generally in the previous section. Selected design parameters related to both examples are listed below:

- Desired final fractional sulfur conversion $x_D = 0.65$
- Feedstock boiling in the 260 to 365°C range and containing 4% sulfur, no oxygen, 0.35% nitrogen, and olefins corresponding to a bromine number of 5.0
- Temperature 375°C = 648.2 K
- Pressure = 55.0 bars
- H_2/oil ratio = 0.5 m^3 H_2(NTP)/kg oil
- Catalyst: cobalt molybdate on alumina, 5-mm square cylinder pellets of $\rho_B = 950$ kg/m^3

- Kinetics: key reaction is first-order, kinetic data are given in Eqs. (7-28) to (7-32); $\eta_1 = 0.4$; weight hourly space velocity (WHSV) = 2000 kg/(m^3·h)
- Void space in catalyst bed $\varepsilon = 0.36$
- Oil density at ambient temperature, ρ_{L0}, is given as 35.3° API or 141/(35.5 + 131.5) = 843.3 kg/m^3
- Thermal expansion of the oil, 1.49 at 375°C, gives density at reaction temperature $\rho_L = (843.3/1.49) = 569.3$ kg/m^3
- $c_{pL} = 3.3095$ kJ/(kg·K)

Plug-Flow Industrial Reactor

Most industrial-size reactors are of the plug-flow type. The general design configuration of such a trickle-bed reactor is shown in Fig. 7-2. The reacting gas *G* enters the reactor vessel from the top. The reacting liquid *L* also enters from the top but is distributed by means of a liquid distributor over the catalyst bed. As will be seen further below, the reactor will need two catalyst beds with a gas quench in between as a means of interbed cooling. The effluent gas leaves the vessel at the bottom. The reacted liquid accumulates at the bottom and is released from the reactor by means of a level controller.

Design parameters specific to the plug-flow reactor are given below:

The plant capacity is 250,000 t/yr.

The approximate reactor volume can be calculated from the weight

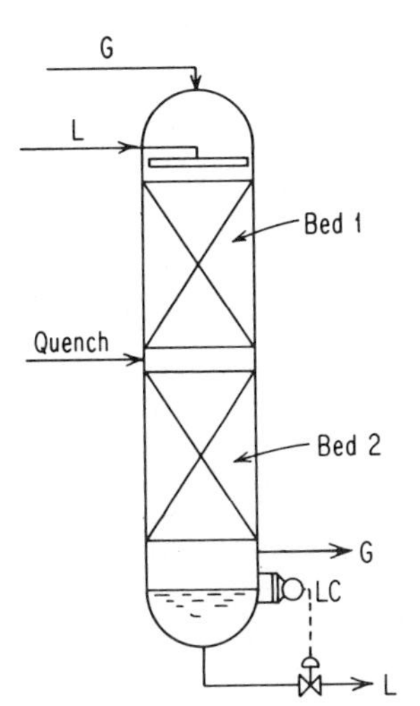

FIG. 7-2 Trickle-bed reactor with interbed quenching.

hourly space velocity. Assuming an on-stream time of 310 days/yr, the hourly capacity is

$$\frac{250{,}000 \text{ kg/yr}}{(310 \text{ days/yr})(24 \text{ h/day})} = 33{,}602 \text{ kg/h} = 9.33393 \text{ kg/s}$$

Then the approximate reactor volume is

$$\frac{33{,}602 \text{ kg/h}}{2000 \text{ kg/(h}\cdot\text{m}^3)} = 16.801 \text{ m}^3$$

In order to determine the reactor's *height/diameter ratio,* we must assure that the reactor will indeed operate as a trickle-bed reactor. For this, we may refer to Fig. 6-4 and calculate the gas/liquid ratio as follows. We note that 0.5 Nm^3 H_2/kg oil is equivalent to (0.5)(2.016)/(22.4 m^3/kmol) which equals 0.045 kg H_2/kg oil. Then, since 5000 lb oil/(h·ft^2) appears to be safely in the gas-continuous region up to 250 lb gas/(h·ft^2), the hydrogen rate, assuming pure hydrogen is used, is [5000 lb/(h·ft^2)] · (0.045 lb/lb) = 225 lb H_2/(h·ft^2). Indeed, 225 lb/(h·ft^2) is in a safe region in Fig. 6-4 and the process is certain to be trickle-bed. The minimum reactor cross-sectional area is:

$$\frac{(33{,}602 \text{ kg/h}) \cdot (0.0929 \text{ m}^2/\text{ft}^2)}{[5000 \text{ lb/(h}\cdot\text{ft}^2)] \cdot (0.453 \text{ kg/lb})} = 1.3782 \text{ m}^2$$

Since we already know the volume, the reactor height will be 16.801 m^3/1.3782 m^2 = 12.19 m and the reactor diameter 1.324 m, which are quite reasonable values. A lower height/diameter ratio would also be permissible since the process would then be slower.

An economic study should be made of the cost of the reactor at different height/diameter ratios. At large diameters and high pressures, the reactor wall must be thicker and hence more expensive. On the other hand, the cost of the reactor is also a function of its external surface area, which for perfect cylinders is given by the relationship:

$$\frac{\text{Surface area}}{\text{Volume}} = \frac{4}{H}\left(\frac{H}{D} + 0.5\right)$$

where H is height and D is diameter. This relationship gives a minimum surface/volume ratio for $H = D$. Because in this example we do not want to go into cost problems, we will simply select a somewhat larger diameter, namely $D_T = 1.5$ m. The corresponding cross-sectional area A_c is 1.7671 m^2 and the approximate reactor height is 9.5 m.

The *sulfur content of the feedstock* is given as 4.0 wt% of sulfur. This corresponds to 4.0/(32.064)(100 kg) = 0.12475 kg-atoms S°/100 kg of S°-containing material.

When designing a reactor that is actually going to be built, the designer should use actual molecular weight data obtained in a reliable laboratory on properly sampled representative feedstocks. However, for the purpose of this book we can look up the molecular weight of oil from page 21 of Maxwell's book[6] from which we obtain a value of 670 for an oil with a mean boiling point of 594°F (322.2°C) and API gravity of 35.3°. Then 100 kg of oil contains 100/670 = 0.14925 kmol. Thus the mole fraction of S-containing oil is:

$$\frac{0.12475 \text{ mol S/100 kg}}{0.14925 \text{ mol/100 kg}} = 0.8358 = y_0$$

This means that 83.58% of all molecules contain one atom of sulfur.

Let us calculate C_{L0}:

$$C_{L0} = \frac{(4.0)\ (569.3 \text{ kg/m}^3)}{(32.064)(100 \text{ kg})} = 0.7102 \text{ kmol S/m}^3$$

Also, O_x wt % oxygen = $O_x/16$ kmol/100 kg of oxygen-containing material. The gas oil selected contains no oxygen. However, for reasons of completeness, equations for oxygenated compounds will still be developed:

$$C_{ox0} = \frac{O_x\ \rho_L}{(16)\ (100)} \text{ kmol/m}^3$$

The *content of unsaturates* is best expressed as a *bromine number.* A *bromine number* of 1.0 means that 1.0 g of bromine is added to the double bonds contained in 100 g of feedstock. The molar concentration of double bonds in the feed can be expressed as follows:

$$C_{hc0} = \frac{\text{Br.} - \text{no. } \rho_L\ (0.001)}{(159.832)(0.1 \text{ kg})} = 0.1781 \text{ kmol unsaturates/m}^3$$

The *content of hydrocrackable compounds* is difficult to define. Only the reaction results show the extent of hydrocracking. The basis of feed concentration is the entire feed:

$$C_{hy0} = \frac{\rho_L}{(\text{mol wt of oil})} = \frac{569.3 \text{ kg/m}^3}{670} = 0.8497 \text{ kmol/m}^3$$

The *nitrogen concentration* is 0.35 wt % N in feed. The molar concentration of nitrogen-containing compounds is:

$$C_{N0} = \frac{(0.35)\ \rho_L}{(100)(14.008 \text{ kg/kg-atom})} = 0.14224 \text{ kmol N compounds/m}^3$$

The *molar concentration of sulfur* in liquid phase will then be

C_{L0} = (4.0)(569.3)/(100)(32.064) = 0.7102 kmol/m^3 initially and C_L = 0.7102(1 − x) at any point in the reactor after that. Since the liquid volume is assumed to remain constant throughout the reactor, conversion x may be defined in terms of concentrations:

$$x_1 = \frac{C_{L0} - C_L}{C_{L0}} = 1 - C_r$$

Similarly

$$x_2 = 1 - C_{rox}$$

$$x_3 = 1 - C_{rN}$$

$$x_4 = 1 - C_{rhy}$$

$$x_5 = 1 - C_{rhc}$$

One kilomole of gaseous process mixture at 375°C and 55 bar occupies the volume of

$$\frac{(22.414 \text{ m}^3\text{NTP})(648.2 \text{ K})(1.01325 \text{ bar})}{(55 \text{ bar})(273.2 \text{ K})} = 0.97972 \text{ m}^3$$

Furthermore, 1 m^3 of reactor void space will contain at reaction conditions 1/0.97972 = 1.0207 kmol/m^3, which is also the initial hydrogen concentration C_{H0}.

The *H/oil mole ratio* can be calculated from the H/oil ratio:

$$\frac{(0.5 \text{ m}^3 \text{ H}_2)(670 \text{ kg/kmol})}{(22.414 \text{ m}^3\text{NTP/kmol})\ (1 \text{ kg oil})} = 14.946 \text{ kmol H}_2\text{/kmol oil}$$

For simplicity's sake in calculations, the reactor is assumed to use pure hydrogen, although this is not common. Thus C_{H0} = 1.0342 kmol/m^3.

The *density of oil* is given as 35.3° API. This corresponds to 141.5/(35.3 + 131.5) = 0.8483 g/cm^3 or 848.3 kg/m^3. The thermal expansion of this oil is 1.49 at 375°C according to page 143 of Maxwell's data book.[6] Thus the density at reaction temperature is 848.3/1.49 = 569.3 kg/m^3 = ρ_L. This figure may be used as a constant because it does not vary significantly in the temperature range of the reactor. However the *gas density* does vary with conversion and should be expressed by the function:

$$\rho = (273.2\ P/22.711\ T)[2.016(1. - Q_1x_1 - Q_2x_2 - Q_3x_3 - Q_4x_4 - Q_5x_5) + 34.032\ Q_1x_1 + 18.016\ Q_2x_2 + 16.043\ Q_3x_3 + 5.6773\ Q_4x_4]$$

where

$$Q_1 = (4.0\%\ \text{S}/100)(670 \text{ kg oil/kmol})/(32.066 \text{ kg S/kmol}).\ (14.946 \text{ kmol H}_2 \text{ available/kmol oil})$$

If all the sulfur would react, it would involve Q_1 fraction of the initial

H_2. Similarly, if all oxygen in the oil would react with H_2, it would involve Q_2 fraction of the initial H_2, etc.

Q_2 = (% O_2/100)(670 kg oil/kmol)(1.0 kmol H_2/katom O)/(16.0 kg O/katom)(14.946 kmol H_2 available/kmol oil)

Q_3 = (0.35 % N/100)(670 kg oil/kmol)(1.5 kmol H_2/katom N)/(14.011 kg N/katom)(14.946 kmol H_2 available/kmol oil)

We will assume that every hydrocarbon mole is hydrocrackable.

Q_4 = (kmol H_2/kmol oil)(22.414 m^3/kmol)/(0.5 m^3 H_2/kg oil)(670 kg/kmol)
= 0.0669

Q_5 = Br no./159.832)(0.01)(670 kg/mol)(22.414 m^3/kmol)/(14.946 kmol H_2 available/kmol oil)

Reynolds numbers are calculated as follows:

$$\mathrm{Re}_G = d_p G/\mu \qquad \text{and} \qquad \mathrm{Re}_L = d_p G_L/\mu_L$$

Here d_p is the diameter of a sphere that has the same outside surface as the catalyst pellet we use. The surface of the square cylinder pellet is $2\pi r^2 + (2r)(2\pi r) = 6\pi r^2$. When r = 0.0025 m, the surface area is 0.00011781 m^2 which equals the surface of the sphere, $4\pi r_s^2$. Then $r_s = (0.00011781/4\pi)^{0.5}$ = 0.0030618, and thus d_p = 0.00612 m.

Viscosity of hydrogen at 375°C = 0.015 cp = 0.00015 g/(cm·s) = 0.000015 kg/(m·s). (See *Chemical Engineers' Handbook,*[7] pp. 3–21.)

Viscosity of oil = 0.0021 g/(cm·s) = 0.00021 g/(m·s). (See page 163 of Maxwell's book.[6])

$$G_L = (9.3339 \text{ kg oil/s})/(1.767 \text{ m}^2) = 5.2819 \text{ kg/(m}^2\text{·s)}$$

$$G = (5.2819 \text{ kg/m}^2\text{·s})(0.045 \text{ kg H}_2\text{/kg oil}) = 0.2377 \text{ kg/(m}^2\text{·s)}$$

$$\mathrm{Re}_G = (0.00612 \text{ m})(0.2377 \text{ kg/m}^2\text{·s})/[0.000015 \text{ kg/(m·s)}] = 96.98$$

$$\mathrm{Re}_L = (0.00612 \text{ m})(5.2819 \text{ kg/m}^2\text{·s})/[0.00021 \text{ kg/(m·s)}] = 153.93$$

In order to calculate the *linear velocities* u_G and u_L in the reactor, we must first calculate the phase fractions ε_G and ε_L.

Liquid flow = (9.3339 kg/s)/(569.3 kg/m^3) = 0.016395 m^3/s

Gas flow = (9.3339 kg/s)(0.5 m^3/kg)(648.2 K)(1.01325 bars)/ 273.2 K · 55.0 bars = 0.20399 m^3/s

The void fraction is assumed to be ε = 0.36. Thus $\varepsilon_L + \varepsilon_G$ = 0.36. Equation (6-16) is used to estimate ε_L.

$$\varepsilon_L = 9.9\ \mathrm{Re}^{1/3}\left(\frac{d^3 g\rho^2}{\mu^2}\right)^{-1/3}$$

where Re = 153.93

$$d = d_p = 0.00612 \text{ m}$$
$$\mu_L = 0.00021 \text{ kg/(m·s)}$$
$$\rho_L = 569.3 \text{ kg/m}^3$$
$$g = 9.807 \text{ m/s}^2$$
$$\varepsilon_L = 0.20833 \approx 0.208$$

Thus $\varepsilon_G = 0.36 - 0.208 = 0.152$

Now we can calculate u_G and u_L at the inlet:

$$u_G = \frac{0.20399 \text{ m}^3\text{/s}}{(1.767 \text{ m}^2)(0.152)} = 0.7595 \text{ m/s}$$
$$u_L = \frac{0.016395 \text{ m}^3\text{/s}}{(1.767 \text{ m}^2)(0.208)} = 0.0446 \text{ m/s}$$

We can also calculate the *residence times of the gas and the liquid* in the bed:

$$\theta_G = \frac{(16.801 \text{ m}^3)(0.152)}{0.20399 \text{ m}^3\text{/s}} = 12.519 \text{ s}$$
$$\theta_L = \frac{(16.801 \text{ m}^3)(0.208)}{0.016395 \text{ m}^3\text{/s}} = 213.15 \text{ s} = 3.5525 \text{ min}$$

The *specific heat of the oil* is assumed to be constant and equal to 3.3095 kJ/(kg·K). However, the *specific heat of the gas* is a function of gas composition and will change with conversion. We need numerical values of the specific heats of water, H_2, H_2S, NH_3, and CH_4:

$$c_p\,(H_2O) = 34.401 + 0.000628\,T + 1.34 \times 10^{-6}\,T^2$$
$$c_p(H_2) = 27.698 + 0.003389\,T$$
$$c_p(H_2S) = 30.1248 + 0.01506\,T$$
$$c_p(NH_3) = 28.0328 + 0.02636\,T$$
$$c_p(CH_4) = 22.343 + 0.04812\,T$$

where T is absolute temperature in kelvins and other dimensions are given in kilojoules per kilomole per Kelvin.

$$c_p = c_p(H_2)\,(1. - Q_1x_1 - Q_2x_2 - Q_3x_3 - Q_4x_4 - Q_5x_5) + c_p(H_2S)Q_1x_1/2 + c_p(H_2O)\,Q_2x_2 + c_p(NH_3)(1/3)Q_3x_3 + c_p(CH_4)Q_4x_4$$

There are several ways of computing the *effectiveness factor* of the trickle-bed reactor, none of which appears to be rigorous and fully convincing. In view of this uncertainty, several methods will be used to compute η and results will be compared.

The value $\eta = 0.4$ was assumed for Cecil et al.'s[4] catalyst with $E =$ 41,000 kcal/kmol, or 171,544 kJ/kmol.

One method of calculating η can be derived from the method of Henry and Gilbert.[8] For a first-order reaction, one can write the following expression for the apparent rate constant:

$$k_{app} = \frac{\text{LHSV}}{\varepsilon_L} \ln\left(\frac{1 - x_{L0}}{1 - x_{LF}}\right)$$

where the subscript LF means the final value of the liquid-phase reaction and the subscript *app* means apparent.

From the definition

$$\eta = \frac{k_{app}}{k} \tag{7-45}$$

one can calculate

$$\eta = \frac{\text{LHSV}}{\varepsilon_L\, k} \ln\left(\frac{1 - x_{L0}}{1 - x_{LF}}\right) \tag{7-46}$$

where $x_{LF} = 0.65$ and $x_{L0} = 0$

The liquid hourly space velocity (LHSV) can be calculated from the WHSV, 2000 kg/(m$^3 \cdot$ h), and the oil density at ambient temperature, $\rho_{L0} = 843.3$ kg/m^3:

$$\text{LHSV} = (2000 \text{ kg/m}^3 \cdot \text{h})/(848.3 \text{ kg/m}^3) = 2.3577 \text{ h}^{-1}$$

$$\eta = \frac{2.358 \text{ h}^{-1}}{0.208\, k} \ln \frac{1}{1 - 0.65} = \frac{11.901}{k}$$

Here we must use the hourly k value

$$k = 1.99 \times 10^{15} \exp[-171{,}500/(8.314 \times 648.2)] = 29.7841$$

Thus

$$\eta = (11.901/29.7841) = 0.3996$$

Another method of calculating the effectiveness factor in trickle-bed reactors, which uses the Thiele modulus φ_H, has been proposed by Satterfield, Ma, and Sherwood[9] as follows:

$$\eta = \frac{\tanh \varphi_H}{\varphi_H} \qquad \varphi_H = \frac{1}{a}\sqrt{\frac{k\,\rho_p\,C_L}{D_{Heff}\,3600}} \tag{7-47}$$

where D_{Heff} = effective diffusion coefficient = $D_H\,\theta'/\tau$, cm^2/s

k = intrinsic reaction rate constant = 29.7841 h^{-1}

ρ_p = particle density, g/cm^3

θ' = porosity of catalyst = 0.60, dimensionless

τ = tortuosity factor = 3.9, dimensionless

C_L = molar concentration of reactant in liquid phase = $C_r \cdot C_{L0}$ = 0.7102 C_r

a = ratio of external surface area of catalyst particle to volume = 12.0

D_H = molecular diffusion coefficient for hydrogen, cm^2/s

The calculation of η must be made in the cgs system in order to avoid excessively large numbers in computing tanh φ_H.

The particle density can be calculated from the relation:

$$\rho_p = \rho_B/(1-\varepsilon) = 0.95\ \text{g/cm}^3/(1-0.36) = 1.484\ \text{g/cm}^3$$

For estimating D_H Wilke and Chang[10] have proposed:

$$D_H = 7.4 \times 10^{-10}\,\frac{T(XM_L)^{1/2}}{\mu V_b^{0.6}} \quad \text{cm}^2/\text{s} \tag{7-48}$$

where T = absolute reaction temperature = 648.2 K

X = an empirical "association parameter" of the liquid, taken as 1.0 for petroleum oils

M_L = molecular weight of the oil = 670

μ = viscosity of the liquid at reaction temperature = 0.0021 poise

V_b = molar volume of diffusing solute, 3.7 cm^3/(g-mol) [obtained from Kopp's law (p. 16, Satterfield's book[11])]

$$D_H = 7.4 \times 10^{-10}\,(648.2)(670)^{1/2}/(0.0021)(3.7^{0.6}) = 0.002697\ \text{cm}^2/\text{s}$$

$$D_{Heff} = (0.002697\ \text{cm}^2/\text{s})(0.6)/3.9 = 0.0004149\ \text{cm}^2/\text{s}$$

$$\varphi_{\mathrm{H}} = \frac{1}{3}\left(\frac{(29.7841)(1.484)(0.7102\ C_r)}{(0.0004149)(3600)}\right)^{1/2} = 1.5281\sqrt{C_r}$$

The value $C_r = 1.0$ can be assumed at the start of the reaction, i.e., at the inlet.

$$\tanh \varphi_{\mathrm{H}} = \frac{\exp(\varphi_{\mathrm{H}}) - \exp(\varphi_{\mathrm{H}})}{\exp(\varphi_{\mathrm{H}}) + \exp(\varphi_{\mathrm{H}})} = 0.91$$

$$\eta = \frac{\tanh \varphi_{\mathrm{H}}}{\varphi_{\mathrm{H}}} = \frac{0.91}{1.5281} = 0.595$$

Now we can compare the three numbers we have:
According to Cecil et al.

$$\eta = 0.4$$

According to Henry and Gilbert

$$\eta = 0.3996$$

According to Satterfield et al.

$$\eta = 0.595$$

We will use $\eta = 0.4$.

The Computer Program RDMOT4

The computer program RDMOT4, which was developed to solve the plug-flow trickle-bed problem will now be explained. Figure 7-3 shows a block diagram of the RDMOT4 program and Fig. 7-4 lists the definitions of symbols used in programs RDMOT4 and RDMOT3.

Figure 7-5 is a listing of the RDMOT4 Fortran program. Like RDMOT1, RDMOT4 is designed for a multibed reactor with intermediate gas quench. The integration of the ODEs is stopped when the temperature exceeds a preset value TRMAX; the amount of hydrogen gas needed to quench the reaction fluids from TRMAX to the inlet temperature is calculated; this amount of hydrogen is added to the reaction mix; and the integration of ODEs is continued for a second bed. Variables such as Z, Y1, Y2, are saved at the end of each bed in form of dummy variables called SAVEZ, SAVEY1, SAVEY2, and reconverted to the actual variables at the start of the new bed. A DO loop (labeled 5) repeats bed calculations up to a bed number of IBED. It turned out that only two beds were needed.

An *equivalence* statement establishes convertibility between variables of the main program and those of the FUNCTION RUNGE. Input data

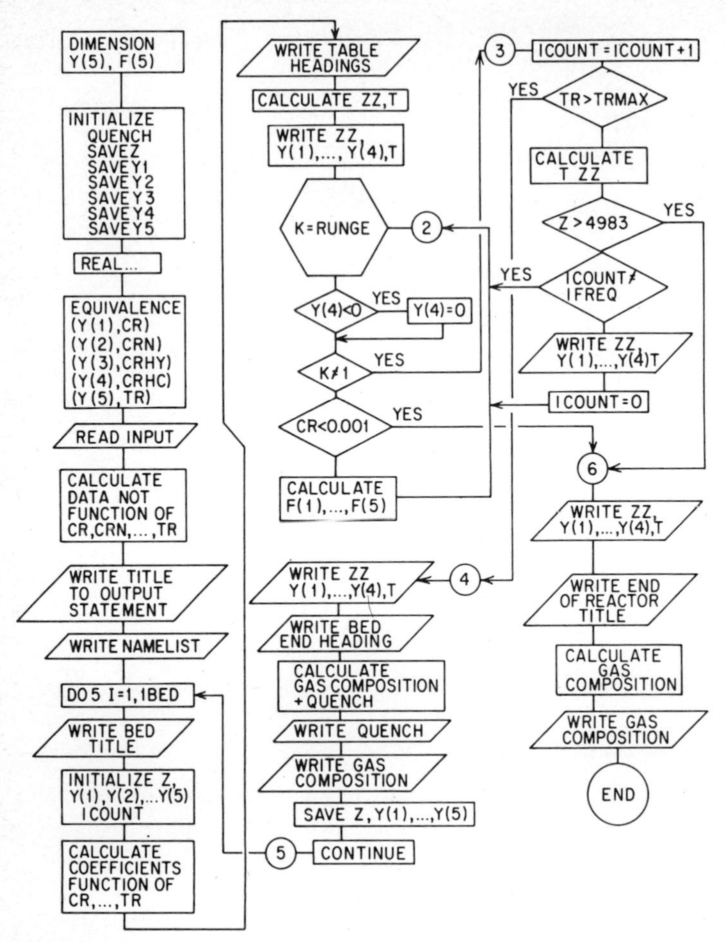

FIG. 7-3 Block diagram of the RDMOT4 computer program for designing commercial trickle-bed reactors.

are read in and a number of quantities are computed that are independent of concentrations and temperature.

The titles of the output are printed, and the input data are printed as a name list.

Concentration and temperature variables are then initialized and quantities that are functions of these variables are computed. Values at the inlet of the bed are printed, and FUNCTION RUNGE is then called to simultaneously integrate the ODEs for mass and heat. A number of safety statements are used for each variable. For example, no concentration is permitted to exceed unity, and the concentration is set to zero

DEFINITION OF SYMBOLS FOR PROGRAMS RDMOT3 AND RDMOT4

```
A        CATALYST MASS-TRANSFER SURFACE AREA/UNIT VOLUME, 1/M
AA       SUBDIAGONAL ARRAY IN SUBROUTINE TRIDAG
AC       CROSS-SECTIONAL AREA OF REACTOR, M**2
AM       AMMONIA MOL FRACTION IN GAS PHASE, DIMENSIONLESS
AMMF     MOLAR FLOW OF AMMONIA, KMOL/S
A1       FREQUENCY FACTOR OF REACTION 1
A3       FREQUENCY FACTOR OF REACTION 3
A4       FREQUENCY FACTOR OF REACTION 4
A5       FREQUENCY FACTOR OF REACTION 5
B        DIAGONAL ARRAY IN SUBROUTINE TRIDAG
B1, B3, B4, B5 DUMMY VARIABLES IN  RDMOT3
BETA     VARIABLE IN SUBROUTINE TRIDAG
BRNO     BROMINE NUMBER OF FEED
C        SUPERDIAGONAL ARRAY IN SUBROUTINE TRIDAG
C11, C121, C122, C123, C124, C125, C13, C21, C22, C23, C24
         COEFFICIENTS IN TRIDIAGONAL SYSTEM, IN RDMOT3
CC1, CC3, CC4, CC5 DUMMY VARIABLES IN RDMOT3
CHC      MOLAR CONCENTRATION OF UNSATURATED HYDROCARBONS,KMOL/M**3
CHCS     CHC ON CATALYST SURFACE, KMOL/M**3
CHCO     INLET VALUE OF CHC, KMOL/M**3
CHYS     MOLAR CONCENTRATION OF HYDROCRACKABLE HYDROCARBONS
         ON CATALYST SURFACE, KMOL/M**3
CHYO     INLET VALUE OF CHY, KMOL/M**3
CH4      METHANE MOL FRACTION IN GAS PHASE, DIMENSIONLESS
CH4MF    MOLAR FLOW OF METHANE, KMOL/S
CLO      INLET CONCENTRATION OF SULFUR IN LIQUID PHASE, KMOL/M**3
CNS      CN ON CATALYST SURFACE, KMOL/M**3
CNO      INLET VALUE OF CN , KMOL/M**3
CP       SPECIFIC HEAT OF GAS , KJ/KG.K
CPCH4    SPECIFIC HEAT OF METHANE, KJ/KG.K
CPH2     SPECIFIC HEAT OF H2 , KJ/KG.K
CPH2S    SPECIFIC HEAT OF H2S, KJ/KG.K
CPL      SPECIFIC HEAT OF LIQUID, KJ/KG.K
CPNH3    SPECIFIC HEAT OF NH3, KJ/KG.K
CR       REDUCED MOL CONCENTRATION OF SULFUR IN LIQUID PHASE
CRHC     REDUCED MOL.CONCN.OF UNSATURATED HYDROCARNONS
CRHY     REDUCED MOL.CONCN.OF HYDROCRACKABLE HYDROCARBONS
CRN      REDUCED MOL.CONCN.OF COMPDS. CONTG. EACH ONE ATOM OF N
CS       CONCENTRATION OF SULFUR ON CATALYST SURFACE, KMOL/M**3
D        RIGHT-HAND SIDE ARRAY IN SUBROUTINE TRIDAG
DAH      DAMKOEHLER NUMBER FOR HEAT, DIMENSIONLESS
DAM1,DAM3,DAM4,DAM5  DAMKOEHLER NUMBER FOR MASS  FOR REACTIONS
         1, 3, 4, AND 5,  RESPECTIVELY, DIMENSIONLESS
DELTAZ   LONGITUDINAL INCREMENT OR STEPSIZE = ZT/(DP*M)  (RDMOT3)
DFTS     DERIVATIVE OF FTS IN NEWTON-RAPHSON ITERATION
DH       TOTAL REACTION HEAT, KJ/KMOL
DH1      HEAT OF REACTION 1, KJ/KMOL
DH3      HEAT OF REACTION 3, KJ/KMOL
DH4      HEAT OF REACTION 4, KJ/KMOL
DH5      HEAT OF REACTION 5, KJ/KMOL
DP       CATALYST PARTICLE DIAMETER, M
DT       INTERNAL DIAMETER OF REACTOR, M
EFF1     EFFECTIVENESS FACTOR OF REACTION 1
EPS      VOID FRACTION , DIMENSIONLESS
EPSG     GAS PHASE FRACTION, DIMENSIONLESS
EPSL     LIQUID PHASE FRACTION , DIMENSIONLESS
E1       ACTIVATION ENERGY FOR REACTION 1, KJ/KMOL
E3       ACTIVATION ENERGY FOR REACTION 3, KJ/KMOL
E4       ACTIVATION ENERGY FOR REACTION 4, KJ/KMOL
E5       ACTIVATION ENERGY FOR REACTION 5, KJ/KMOL
F        DERIVATIVE IN RDMOT4
FEED     OIL FEED, KG/S
FTS      FUNCTION OF TSI IN NEWTON-RAPHSON ITERATION
GAMMA    VARIABLE IN SUBROUTINE TRIDAG
GL       MASS FLOW RATE, KG OIL/S.M**2
H        STEPSIZE IN PLUG-FLOW REACTOR (RDMOT4)
HMF      MOLAR FLOW OF HYDROGEN, KMOL/S
```

FIG. 7-4 Definition of symbols for the programs RDMOT3 and RDMOT4.

```
HOIL     HYDROGEN-TO-OIL RATIO, M**3(NTP)/KG
HTC      HEAT TRANSFER COEFFICIENT, KJ/M**2.S.K
HYD      HYDROGEN MOL FRACTION IN GAS PHASE, DIMENSIONLESS
H2S      MOL FRACTION OF HYDROGEN SULFIDE IN GAS PHASE
H2SMF    MOLAR FLOW OF HYDROGEN SULFIDE, KMOL/S
I        SUBSCRIPT = LONGITUDINAL NUMBER OF INCREMENT DELTAZ
ICOUNT   COUNTER FOR FUNCTION RUNGE (RDMOT4)
IF       NUMBER OF EQUATIONS IN SUBROUTINE TRIDAG
IBED     NUMBER OF BEDS IN RDMOT4
IFREQ    FREQUENCY OF PRINTING IN RDMOT4
IFP1     DUMMY VARIABLE IN SUBROUTINE TRIDAG
ITER     TEST FOR TRIDAG ITERATION = TRUE OR FALSE
KC       MASS TRANSFER COEFFICIENT FROM LIQ. TO CAT. SURFACE,M/S
K1, K3, K4, K5  RATE CONSTANTS OF REACTIONS 1, 3, 4, AND 5, RESP.
L        LAST EQUATION IN SUBROUTINE TRIDAG
LAST     VARIABLE IN SUBROUTINE TRIDAG
M        NUMBER OF STEPS IN RDMOT3
MWL      MOLECULAR WEIGHT OF OIL FEED
NITRO    % OF NITROGEN BY WEIGHT IN FEED
NOITER   NUMBER OF TRIDAG ITERATIONS, COUNTER, DIMENSIONLESS
P        PRESSURE, BAR
PEHA2    PECLET NUMBER FOR 2-PHASE HEAT TRANSFER,AXIAL DISPERSION
PEMAL    PECLET NUMBER FOR MASS , AXIAL DISPERSION, LIQ.PHASE
PHI      DUMMY VARIABLE IN FUNCTION RUNGE IN RDMOT4
Q1       FRACTION OF H2 CONSUMED AT COMPLETE REACTION OF SULFUR
Q3       FRACTION OF H2 CONSUMED AT COMPLETE REACTION OF NITROGEN
Q4       FRACTION OF H2 CONSUMED AT COMPLETE HYDROCRACKING REACTION
Q5       FRACTION OF H2 CONSUMED AT COMPLETE SATURATION REACTION
RG       GAS CONSTANT = 8.314 KJ/KMOL.K
RHO      DENSITY OF GAS PHASE, KG/M**3
RHOL     DENSITY OF LIQUID PHASE, KG/M**3
RMU      VISCOSITY OF LIQUID, PAS
R1       RATE OF REACTION 1, KMOL/S.M**3
R3       RATE OF REACTION 3, KMOL/S.M**3
R4       RATE OF REACTION 4, KMOL/S.M**3
R5       RATE OF REACTION 5, KMOL/S.M**3
S        WEIGHT % OF SULFUR IN FEED
SAVEY1,SAVEY3,SAVEY4,SAVEY5,SAVEZ  DUMMY VARIABLES IN RDMOT4
SIGMA    DUMMY VARIABLE IN PLUG-FLOW REACTOR IN CALCULATIONG
         HEAT BALANCE ODE
SIGMA1   DUMMY VARIABLE IN NEWTON-RAPHSON ITERATION IN LAB REACTOR
SIGMA2   DUMMY VARIABLE IN NEWTON-RAPHSON ITERATION IN LAB REACTOR
SIGMA3   DUMMY VARIABLE IN CALCULATING DAH(I) IN LAB REACTOR
SIGMAD   DUMMY VARIABLE IN CALCULATING F(5) IN LAB REACTOR
SUM      SUM OF GAS MOLAR FLOWS, KMOL/S
T        ABSOLUTE TEMPERATURE, K
TR       REDUCED ABSOLUTE BULK TEMPERATURE =T/TO ,DIMENSIONLESS
TRX      UNKNOWN REDUCED ABSOLUTE BULK TEMPERATURE,DIMENSIONLESS
TS       ABSOLUTE CATALYST SURFACE TEMPERATURE, K
TSI      DUMMY VARIABLE FOR TS(I)
TO       ABSOLUTE TEMPERATURE AT INLET, K
U        SUPERFICIAL GAS VELOCITY, M/S
UL       SUPERFICIAL LIQUID VELOCITY, M/S
V        SOLUTION VECTOR IN SUBROUTINE TRIDAG,
Y1,Y3,Y4,Y5  INPUT VARIABLES IN FUNCTION RUNGE
Z        REDUCED LONGITUDINAL COORDINATE = ZZ/DP ,DIMENSIONLESS
ZZ       LONGITUDINAL COOIRDINATE, M
```

FIG. 7-4 Definition of symbols for the programs RDMOT3 and RDMOT4 (*continued*).

when it becomes less than 0.00001 in order to prevent so-called underflows, which would terminate computer executions. Similar safety statements are used for derivatives. Integration calculations are ended when the reduced sulfur concentration is decreased below 0.001. For each reduced concentration the derivative function F(N) is computed; safety statements are used to prevent these derivatives from becoming positive.

```
C
C         PROCESS DESIGN OF TRICKLE-BED REACTOR
C                        FOR
C          PETROLEUM OIL HYDRODESULFURIZATION
C
C      .... PLUG-FLOW INDUSTRIAL REACTOR ....
C      .... CS = C  ;   TS = T   ....
C
      DIMENSION Y(5),F(5)
      DATA QUENCH,SAVEZ,SAVEY1,SAVEY2,SAVEY3,SAVEY4,SAVEY5/0.,0.,1.,1.,
     1     1.,1.,1./
      INTEGER RUNGE
      REAL K1,K3,K4,K5,MWL,NITRO,Q1,Q3,Q4,Q5
      EQUIVALENCE (Y(1),CR),(Y(2),CRN),(Y(3),CRHY),
     1            (Y(4),CRHC), (Y(5),TR)
C
C     ....DEFINE COEFFICIENTS WHICH ARE NOT FUNCTIONS OF CR OR TR....
      READ(5,100)A,A1,A3,A4,A5,BRNO,CPL,DH1,DH3,DH4,DH5,DP,DT,E1,E3,E4,
     1 E5,EFF1,EPS,FEED,H,HOIL,HTC,MWL,NITRO,P,RG,RHOL,RMU,S,TO,
     2 TRMAX,IBED,IFREQ
  100 FORMAT (7E10.3 / 7E10.3 / 7E10.3/7E10.3/4E10.3/I2,I6)
      CLO  = S * RHOL/3206.4
      AC   = 3.1416 *(DT/2.)**2
      GL   = FEED/AC
      EPSL = 9.9 * (GL*DP/RMU)**0.333/
     1    (DP**3 * 9.8066 *RHOL**2/(RMU**2))**0.333
      EPSG = EPS - EPSL
      UL   = GL/(RHOL * EPSL)
      CNO  = NITRO*RHOL/1400.8
      CHCO = BRNO*RHOL/15983.2
      CHYO = RHOL/MWL
      NAMELIST/DATA/A,A1,A3,A4,A5,AC,BRNO,CLO,CNO,CHYO,CHCO,CPL,DH1,DH3,
     1 DH4,DH5,DP,DT,E1,E3,E4,E5,EFF1,EPS,EPSG,EPSL,FEED,H,HOIL,HTC,
     2 IBED,IFREQ,MWL,NITRO,P,RG,RHOL,RMU,S,SAVEZ,SAVEY1,SAVEY2,SAVEY3,
     3 SAVEY4,SAVEY5,TO,TRMAX,UL
      WRITE(6,150)
  150 FORMAT(1H1,46X,29HDESIGN OF TRICKLE-BED REACTOR)
      WRITE (6, 151)
  151 FORMAT(1H0,55X,11HINPUT  DATA)
      WRITE (6, DATA)
C
      DO 5 I=1, IBED
      WRITE(6, 99) I
   99 FORMAT(1H1, 20X, 10HFIXED BED , I2)
C
C     .... INITIALIZE Z, Y(1), Y(2), Y(3), Y(4), Y(5), AND ICOUNT ....
      Z   =  SAVEZ
      Y(1) =  SAVEY1
      Y(2) =  SAVEY2
      Y(3) =  SAVEY3
      Y(4) =  SAVEY4
      Y(5) =  SAVEY5
      ICOUNT = 0
C     .... CALCULATE COEFFICIENTS THAT ARE FUNCTICNS OF CRN AND CRHC....
      U = (GL*TO*1.01325/(273.2*EPSG*P))*(HOIL-((CNO*(1.-CRN/3.)) +
     1      (CHCO*(1.-CRHC)))/RHOL)
      WRITE(6,152)
  152 FORMAT(1H0,4X,3HZZ=,6X,3HCR=,7X,4HCRN=,6X,5HCRHY=,5X,5HCRHC=,6X,
     1    2HT=/1H ,3X,5HMETER,44X,8HDEGREE K)
C     ....CALL ON THE FOUTRTH-ORDER RUNGE-KUTTA FUNCTION....
      ZZ = Z * DP
      T  = TO * TR
      WRITE (6,200) ZZ,Y(1),Y(2),Y(3),Y(4),T
    2 K=RUNGE(5,Y,F,Z,H)
      IF(Y(4).LT.0.0) Y(4)=0.0
C     ....IF K=1 COMPUTE DERIVATIVE VALUES....
      IF (K.NE.1.0) GO TO 3
C     ....MATERIAL BALANCE ODE FOR SULFUR....
      IF(CR.GT.1.0) CR=1.0
      IF(CR.LT.0.001) GO TO 6
      K1=A1*EXP(-E1/(RG*TO*TR))
```

FIG. 7-5 Fortran program RDMOT4 for designing a plug-flow industrial-size trickle-bed reactor for petroleum oil hydrodesulfurization.

```
      F(1)= -EFF1*K1*DP*CR/UL
      IF(F(1).GT.0.) F(1)=0.0
C     ....MATERIAL BALANCE ODE FOR NITROGEN....
      IF(CRN.GT. 1.0) CRN=1.0
      IF(CRN.LT.0.00001) CRN=0.0
      K3=A3*EXP(-E3/(RG*T0*TR))
      F(2) = -EFF1*K3*DP*CRN/UL
      IF (F(2).GT.0.0) F(2)=0.0
C     ....MATERIAL BALANCE ODE FOR HYDROCRACKABLES....
      IF(CRHY.GT. 1.0) CRHY=1.0
      IF(CRHY.LT.0.00001) CRHY=0.0
      K4=A4*EXP(-E4/(RG*T0*TR))
      F(3) = -EFF1*K4*DP*CRHY/UL
      IF (F(3).GT.0.0) F(3)=0.0
C     .... MATERIAL BALANCE ODE FOR UNSATURATES....
      IF(CRHC.GT.1.0) CRHC=1.0
      IF(CRHC.LT.0.00001) CRHC=0.0
      K5=A5*EXP(-E5/(RG*T0*TR))
      F(4) = -EFF1*K5*DP*CRHC/UL
      IF (F(4).GT.0.0) F(4)=0.0
C     ....HEAT BALANCE ODE....
      R1= EFF1*K1*CL0*CR
      R3= EFF1*K3*CN0*CRN
      R4= EFF1*K4*CHY0*CRHY
      R5= EFF1*K5*CHC0*CRHC
      SIGMA = (DH1*R1) + (DH3*R3) + (DH4*R4) + (DH5*R5)
C     .... CALCULATION OF GAS DENSITY RHO ....
      Q1 = 2.08656E-05*S*MWL
      Q3 = 7.16304E-05*NITRO*MWL
      Q4 = 22.414/(HOIL*MWL)
      Q5 = 9.38276E-05*BRNO*MWL
      RHO= 12.028*P/(TR*T0)*(2.016*(1.-(Q1*(1.-CR)) -
     1     (Q3*(1.-CRN)) - (Q4*(1.-CRHY)) - (Q5*(1.-CRHC)))) +
     2     (34.032*Q1*(1.-CR)) + (16.043*Q3*(1.-CRN)) +
     3     (5.6773*Q4*(1.-CRHY))
C     .... CALCULATION OF THE SPECIFIC HEAT CP OF REACTING GAS MIX ....
      CPH2 = 27.698 + (0.003389* T0 * TR)
      CPH2S= 30.1248 + (0.01506 * T0 * TR)
      CPCH4= 22.343 +(0.04812 * T0 * TR)
      CPNH3= 28.0328 + (0.02636 * T0 * TR)
      CP= CPH2*(1.-Q1*(1.-CR)-Q3*(1.-CRN)-Q4*(1.-CRHY)-Q5*(1.-CRHC)) +
     1     (CPH2S*Q1*(1.-CR)/2.0) + (CPNH3*Q3*(1.-CRN)/3.0) +
     2     (CPCH4*Q4*(1.-CRHY))
      F(5)= SIGMA*DP*EPSL/(T0*((EPSG*RHO*CP*U) + (EPSL*RHOL*CPL*UL)))
      IF(F(5).LT.0.0) F(5)=0.0
      GO TO 2
    3 ICOUNT = ICOUNT + 1
C     .... IT TR GREATER THAN TRMAX, END THE BED ....
      IF(TR.GT.TRMAX) GO TO 4
C     .... IF REACTOR LENGTH EXCEEDS 30 METERS, END CALCULATIONS ....
      T = T0 * TR
      ZZ = Z * DP
      IF(Z.GT.4983.0) GO TO 6
      IF (ICOUNT.NE.IFREQ) GO TO 2
      WRITE(6,200) ZZ,Y(1),Y(2),Y(3),Y(4),T
  200 FORMAT(1H ,1P6E10.3)
      ICOUNT = 0
      GO TO 2
C     .... END OF BED ....
    4 WRITE (6,200) ZZ,Y(1),Y(2),Y(3),Y(4),T
      WRITE (6,201) I
  201 FORMAT(1H ,5X,11HEND OF BED ,I2)
C     .... COMPUTE GAS COMPOSITION AND QUENCH AT BED OUTLET ....
      HMF  =(FEED*0.5/22.414)*(1.-Q1*(1.-CR) - Q3*(1.-CRN) -
     1      Q4*(1.-CRHY) - Q5*(1.-CRHC))
      H2SMF = FEED*S*(1.-CR)/3206.6
      AMMF  = FEED*NITRO*(1.-CRN)/1400.8
      CH4MF = FEED*(1.-CRHY)/MWL
      SUM   = HMF + H2SMF + AMMF + CH4MF
      QUENCH= ((FEED*CPL/MWL) + (SUM*CP))*(TR*T0 - T0)/(29.895 *
     1        (T0 - 298.2))
      WRITE(6, 202) QUENCH
  202 FORMAT(1H0, 5X,9HQUENCH = ,F10.5,7H KMOL/S)
      WRITE(6,230)
```

FIG. 7-5 Fortran program RDMOT4 for designing a plug-flow industrial-size trickle-bed reactor for petroleum oil hydrodesulfurization (*continued*).

```
  230 FORMAT(1H0,15X,29HGAS CCMPCSITION, MOL FRACTION/1H0,9X,
     1 8HHYDROGEN,5X,3HH2S,7X,3HNH3,7X,3HCH4)
      HYD = HMF/SUM
      H2S = H2SMF/SUM
      AM  = AMMF/SUM
      CH4 = CH4MF/SUM
      WRITE(6,231)  HYD,H2S, AM, CH4
  231 FORMAT(1H0, 8X,F8.5,2X,F8.5,2X,F8.5,2X,F8.5)
      SAVEZ = Z
      SAVEY1= Y(1)
      SAVEY2= Y(2)
      SAVEY3= Y(3)
      SAVEY4= Y(4)
    5 SAVEY5= 1.0
C   5 CONTINUE
C     USE THE TOP "5" IF THE NEW BED SHOULD START AT TR=1.
C     USE THE BOTTOM "5" IF THE NEW BED SHOULD START AT TR=INPUT VALUE.
C     .... END OF REACTOR ....
    6 WRITE(6, 200) ZZ, Y(1), Y(2), Y(3), Y(4), T
      WRITE(6, 203)
  203 FORMAT(1H ,5X,14HEND OF REACTOR)
C     .... COMPUTE GAS COMPOSITION AT REACTOR END ....
      HMF =  (FEED*0.5/22.414)*(1.-Q1*(1.-CR) - Q3*(1.-CRN) -
     1        Q4*(1.-CRHY) - Q5*(1.-CRHC))
      H2SMF  = FEED*S*(1.-CR)/3206.6
      AMMF   = FEED*NITRO*(1.-CRN)/1400.8
      CH4MF  = FEED*(1.-CRHY)/MWL
      SUM    = HMF + H2SMF + AMMF + CH4MF
      HYD    = HMF/SUM
      H2S    = H2SMF/SUM
      AM     = AMMF/SUM
      CH4    = CH4MF/SUM
      WRITE(6, 230)
      WRITE(6, 231) HYD, H2S, AM, CH4
      STOP
      END
C
      FUNCTION RUNGE (N, Y, F, Z, H)
      INTEGER RUNGE
      DIMENSION PHI(50), SAVEY(50), Y(N), F(N)
      DATA M/0/
      M = M + 1
      GO TO (1,2,3,4,5), M
C     ....PASS 1 ....
    1 RUNGE = 1
      RETURN
C     ....PASS 2 ....
    2 DO 22 J = 1, N
      SAVEY(J) = Y(J)
      PHI(J) = F(J)
   22 Y(J) = SAVEY(J) + 0.5 * H * F(J)
      Z = Z + 0.5 * H
      RUNGE = 1
      RETURN
C     .... PASS 3 ....
    3 DO 33 J = 1, N
      PHI(J) = PHI(J) + 2.0 * F(J)
   33 Y(J) = SAVEY(J) + 0.5 * H * F(J)
      RUNGE = 1
      RETURN
C     .... PASS 4 ....
    4 DO 44 J = 1, N
      PHI(J) = PHI(J) + 2.0 * F(J)
   44 Y(J) = SAVEY(J) + H * F(J)
      Z = Z + 0.5 * H
      RUNGE = 1
      RETURN
C     .... PASS 5 ....
    5 DO 55 J = 1, N
   55 Y(J) = SAVEY(J) + (PHI(J) + F(J)) * H/6.0
      M = 0
      RUNGE = 0
      RETURN
      END
```

FIG. 7-5 Fortran program RDMOT4 for designing a plug-flow industrial-size trickle-bed reactor for petroleum oil hydrodesulfurization (*continued*).

```
1.200E+03 2.800E+04 1.800E+03 2.500E+15 1.000E+03 5.000E+00 3.310E+00
2.512E+05 6.485E+04 4.100E+04 1.255E+05 0.602E-02 1.5  E+00 8.206E+04
7.206E+04 2.435E+05 4.686E+04 0.4  E+00 0.36 E+00 9.334E+00 0.2  E+00
0.5  E+00 1.298E+00 6.7  E+02 0.35 E+00 5.5  E+01 8.314E+00 5.693E+02
0.21 E-03 4.0  E+00 6.482E+02 1.C7 E+00
5   500
```

```
A=1200.0          CHCO=0.1780       E4=243500.0       IBED=5              SAVEY1=1.0
A1=28000.0        CPL=3.3100        E5=46860.0        IFREQ=500           SAVEY2=1.0
A3=1800.0         DH1=251200.0      EFF1=0.4          MWL=670.0           SAVEY3=1.0
A4=0.25E+16       DH3=64850.0       EPS=0.360         NITRO=0.350         SAVEY4=1.0
A5=1000.0         DH4=41000.0       EPSG=0.14856      P=55.0              SAVEY5=1.0
AC=1.7671         DH5=125500.0      EPSL=0.2114       RG=8.3140           TO=648.2
BRNO=5.0          DP=0.602E-02      FEED=9.3340       RHOL=569.30         TRMAX=1.07
CLO=0.7102        DT=1.50           H=0.2             RMU=0.210E-03       UL=0.439E-01
CNO=0.1422        E1=82060.0        HOIL=0.50         S=4.0
CHYO=0.8497       E3=72060.0        HTC=1.2980        SAVEZ=0.0
```

FIG. 7-6 Input data for computer program RDMOT4.

In order to integrate the heat ODE, the rates of all reactions and the density and specific heat of the gas mix are calculated. A safety statement is used to prevent the heat derivative from becoming negative.

This first part of the DO loop is repeated until the FUNCTION RUNGE completes its five passes and all the ODEs are integrated. Because we do not want the results of every integration step to be printed, a counter named ICOUNT is used. This counter counts the completed integration steps. When ICOUNT becomes equal to IFREQ, it prints the results of the last integration step.

The values of T and ZZ are calculated (see Fig. 7-4 for meaning of symbols). If the total bed length exceeds a predetermined number such as 30 m, the reactor calculations are ended (if they have not been ended before for some other reason). At each bed end the last results are printed and then bed end titles are printed. Now the QUENCH is computed and printed and the gas composition at bed end is calculated and printed. At the end of the reactor the results are printed and gas composition is calculated and printed.

The input data used in the above program are listed in Fig. 7-6 and the output data are listed in Fig. 7-7. We see that the first bed reaches TRMAX in 5.799 m of reactor length. At that point CR=0.5161, CRN=0.7774, CRHY=0.9776, CRHC=0, and T=693.6 (which equals 420.4°C). The gas phase contains only 95.463% H_2.

The second bed is calculated to a total reactor length of 30 m. However, the designer should stop the integration calculations for the second bed at a desirable CR of 0.35 at ZZ=11.2 m. It can be seen that the two beds are about equal in length. The interbed cooling can be implemented according to Fig. 7-2. These results are the solution of the plug-flow trickle-bed reactor problem.

Laboratory Reactor with Backmixing

An experimental trickle-bed reactor that meets Mears' condition of a back-mixed reactor[12] will be considered here. The condition is

$$Z_T > \frac{20\ \alpha\ d_s}{\text{Bo}} \ln \frac{C_0}{C_f} \tag{6-18}$$

where α = 1 = reaction order

C = concentration of key reactant, kmol/m^3

Z_T = total length of reactor bed, m

d_s = equivalent spherical diameter of catalyst particle, m

$= [0.005^2 + (0.005/2)^2]^{0.5} = 0.00612$ m

Subscripts f and 0 denote final and initial, respectively.

$$C_f = C_0(1 - x_f)$$

where x_f is also the desired conversion $C_0/C_f = C_0/C_0(1 - x_f) = 1/(1 - x_f) = 1/(1 - 0.65) = 2.857$ and Bo = Bodenstein number.
The *Bodenstein number,* Bo, is a Péclet number based on particle diameter d_s instead of d_p (see Sec. 6.2). Actually, Eq. (6-18) is a condition for plug-flow regime. Consequently, the condition for a backmixed reactor would be an inequality with the opposite sign of that of Eq. (6-18). Let us calculate the Z_T value that separates the plug flow and the backmixed regimes. Then we have to take Eq. (6-18) as an equality, rather than an inequality. In Eq. (6-18), Bo is an indirect function of reactor length Z_T, consequently Z_T can be calculated by trial and error by starting with an assumed Z_T. Let us assume that $Z_T = 1.25$ m. Assuming the same length/diameter ratio used in the plug-flow example, the reactor diameter would be $D_T = (1.25/6.3333) = 0.19737$, and the bed cross section and total volume are $A_c = 0.030594$ m^2 and $V = 0.03824$ m^3, respectively.

The oil throughput is (2000 kg/m^3 · hr)(0.03824 m^3) = 76.486 kg/h

$$G_L = (76.486 \text{ kg/h})/(3600 \times 0.030594) = 0.6944 \text{ kg/(s} \cdot \text{m}^2)$$
$$G_G = (0.6944)(0.045 \text{ kg } H_2\text{/kg oil}) = 0.03125 \text{ kg/(s} \cdot \text{m}^2)$$
$$\text{Re}_G = (0.00612)(0.03125)/(0.000015) = 12.75$$
$$\text{Re}_L = (0.00612)(0.69445)/(0.00021) = 20.24$$

The Bodenstein number is really a Péclet number based on a particle diameter, so we can use Eq. (6-17) to calculate it:

$$\text{Bo} = 0.034\ \text{Re}_L^{0.5}\ 10^{0.003(\text{Re})_G} = 0.167$$
$$Z_T \text{ (calculated)} = (20)(1)(0.00612)(2.857)/(0.167) = 2.09 \text{ m}$$

```
                       FIXED BED  1

   ZZ=         CR=         CRN=        CRHY=       CRHC=        T=
  METER                                                      DEGREE K
0.0         1.000E+00 1.000E+00 1.000E+00 1.000E+00 6.482E+02
6.020E-01 9.592E-01 9.832E-01 9.995E-01 3.771E-01 6.566E+02
1.204E+00 9.135E-01 9.643E-01 9.988E-01 1.297E-01 6.623E+02
1.805E+00 8.650E-01 9.438E-01 9.978E-01 4.151E-02 6.668E+02
2.407E+00 8.146E-01 9.221E-01 9.965E-01 1.247E-02 6.709E+02
3.008E+00 7.628E-01 8.991E-01 9.947E-01 3.521E-03 6.749E+02
3.609E+00 7.102E-01 8.750E-01 9.925E-01 9.321E-04 6.790E+02
4.210E+00 6.569E-01 8.497E-01 9.896E-01 2.308E-04 6.830E+02
4.811E+00 6.034E-01 8.233E-01 9.859E-01 5.330E-05 6.870E+02
5.412E+00 5.502E-01 7.957E-01 9.812E-01 1.146E-05 6.910E+02
5.799E+00 5.161E-01 7.774E-01 9.776E-01 0.0          6.936E+02
  END OF BED  1

  QUENCH  =      0.01276 KMOL/S

                 GAS COMPOSITION, MOL FRACTION

       HYDROGEN       H2S          NH3          CH4

       0.95463     0.03953     0.00364     0.00219
```

FIG. 7-7 Computer output of program RDMOT4 for designing industrial-size trickle-bed reactors.

We can repeat this calculation by assuming $Z_T = 1.5$ m and find a calculated value of 1.88 m. The limiting value for Eq. (6-18) must be between 1.50 and 1.88 m. Any number smaller than this limiting number would correspond to a backmixed reactor. Hence 1.5 m is a good number for Z_T.

The diameter of the bed will be 1.5/6.3333 = 0.197 m; or around 0.2 m; also, $A_C = 0.0311416\ \text{m}^2$; $V = (0.0311416)(1.5) = 0.047123\ \text{m}^3$. The throughput of oil is $(0.047123\ \text{m}^3)(2000\ \text{kg/m}^3 \cdot \text{h}) = 94.248$ kg/h, or 0.02618 kg/s.

The reaction conditions are the same as those given for the plug-flow reactor.

$$\text{Throughput of gas} = (0.02618\ \text{kg/s})(0.045\ \text{kg H}_2/\text{kg oil}) = 0.0011781\ \text{kg/s}$$

$$\text{Volume flow of oil} = (0.02618\ \text{kg/s})/569.3\ \text{kg/m}^3 = 0.000045986\ \text{m}^3/\text{s}$$

$$\text{Volume flow of H}_2 = \frac{(0.0011781\ \text{kg/s})(22.414\ \text{m}^3/\text{kg-mol})(648.2\ \text{K})(1.01325\ \text{bars})}{(2.016\ \text{kg/kmol})(55\ \text{bars})(273.2\ \text{K})} = 0.00057252\ \text{m}^3/\text{s}$$

$$G_G = (0.0011781\ \text{kg/s})/(0.0311416\ \text{m}^2) = 0.03783\ \text{kg/(s} \cdot \text{m}^2)$$

$$G_L = (0.02618\ \text{kg/s})/(0.03114\ \text{m}^2) = 0.8407\ \text{kg/(s} \cdot \text{m}^2)$$

$$\text{Re}_G = (0.00612)(0.03783)/(0.000015) = 15.43$$

$$\text{Re}_L = (0.00612)(0.8407)/(0.00021) = 24.50$$

FIXED BED 2

ZZ= METER	CR=	CRN=	CRHY=	CRHC=	T= DEGREE K
5.801E+00	5.161E-01	7.774E-01	9.776E-01	0.0	6.482E+02
6.402E+00	4.969E-01	7.653E-01	9.772E-01	0.0	6.494E+02
7.003E+00	4.778E-01	7.532E-01	9.768E-01	0.0	6.507E+02
7.604E+00	4.589E-01	7.409E-01	9.764E-01	0.0	6.519E+02
8.205E+00	4.403E-01	7.285E-01	9.760E-01	0.0	6.531E+02
8.806E+00	4.219E-01	7.161E-01	9.755E-01	0.0	6.544E+02
9.407E+00	4.037E-01	7.035E-01	9.750E-01	0.0	6.556E+02
1.001E+01	3.859E-01	6.908E-01	9.744E-01	0.0	6.569E+02
1.061E+01	3.684E-01	6.781E-01	9.738E-01	0.0	6.581E+02
1.121E+01	3.512E-01	6.653E-01	9.731E-01	0.0	6.593E+02
1.181E+01	3.344E-01	6.524E-01	9.724E-01	0.0	6.604E+02
1.241E+01	3.180E-01	6.395E-01	9.716E-01	0.0	6.613E+02
1.301E+01	3.021E-01	6.267E-01	9.708E-01	0.0	6.623E+02
1.362E+01	2.867E-01	6.139E-01	9.699E-01	0.0	6.632E+02
1.422E+01	2.718E-01	6.011E-01	9.690E-01	0.0	6.641E+02
1.482E+01	2.574E-01	5.883E-01	9.681E-01	0.0	6.650E+02
1.542E+01	2.434E-01	5.756E-01	9.670E-01	0.0	6.660E+02
1.602E+01	2.300E-01	5.630E-01	9.659E-01	0.0	6.669E+02
1.662E+01	2.170E-01	5.504E-01	9.647E-01	0.0	6.678E+02
1.722E+01	2.045E-01	5.379E-01	9.635E-01	0.0	6.685E+02
1.782E+01	1.926E-01	5.255E-01	9.622E-01	0.0	6.691E+02
1.842E+01	1.813E-01	5.133E-01	9.609E-01	0.0	6.697E+02
1.903E+01	1.705E-01	5.012E-01	9.595E-01	0.0	6.703E+02
1.963E+01	1.601E-01	4.892E-01	9.581E-01	0.0	6.709E+02
2.023E+01	1.503E-01	4.775E-01	9.566E-01	0.0	6.716E+02
2.083E+01	1.410E-01	4.658E-01	9.551E-01	0.0	6.722E+02
2.143E+01	1.321E-01	4.543E-01	9.535E-01	0.0	6.728E+02
2.203E+01	1.237E-01	4.430E-01	9.518E-01	0.0	6.734E+02
2.263E+01	1.157E-01	4.318E-01	9.501E-01	0.0	6.737E+02
2.323E+01	1.082E-01	4.209E-01	9.483E-01	0.0	6.740E+02
2.383E+01	1.012E-01	4.102E-01	9.466E-01	0.0	6.743E+02
2.444E+01	9.453E-02	3.997E-01	9.447E-01	0.0	6.746E+02
2.503E+01	8.828E-02	3.894E-01	9.429E-01	0.0	6.749E+02
2.562E+01	8.241E-02	3.793E-01	9.410E-01	0.0	6.752E+02
2.620E+01	7.690E-02	3.694E-01	9.391E-01	0.0	6.755E+02
2.679E+01	7.171E-02	3.597E-01	9.372E-01	0.0	6.758E+02
2.738E+01	6.685E-02	3.502E-01	9.352E-01	0.0	6.761E+02
2.797E+01	6.228E-02	3.409E-01	9.332E-01	0.0	6.765E+02
2.856E+01	5.801E-02	3.318E-01	9.312E-01	0.0	6.768E+02
2.914E+01	5.401E-02	3.229E-01	9.291E-01	0.0	6.771E+02
2.973E+01	5.027E-02	3.142E-01	9.270E-01	0.0	6.772E+02
3.000E+01	4.865E-02	3.103E-01	9.260E-01	0.0	6.772E+02

END OF REACTOR

GAS COMPOSITION, MOL FRACTION

HYDROGEN	H2S	NH3	CH4
0.90338	0.07803	0.01133	0.00726

FIG. 7-7 Computer output of program RDMOT4 for designing industrial-size trickle-bed reactors (*continued*).

Let us calculate the Péclet number Pe_{mal} according to the following two correlations:

Sater and Levenspiel[13] $Pe_{mal} = 7.58 \times 10^{-3} \, Re_L^{0.703} = 0.0718$

Hochman and Effron[14] $Pe_{mal} = 0.034 \, Re_L^{0.5} \, 10^{0.003 \, Re_G}$

$= 0.1993$

As a conservative measure, we will select the correlation that gives the smallest Péclet number, namely that of Sater and Levenspiel, $Pe_{mal} = 0.0718$.

No correlations are available for the mixed Péclet number Pe_{ha2} for heat and two-phase flow. Heat Péclet numbers may be estimated by analogy from mass Péclet numbers. We can assume (for the lack of a better method) that the two-phase Péclet number is made up of the Péclet numbers of each phase in the same proportion as the phase fractions. We have no proof of this fact, but it seems like a reasonable assumption that might not be too far from reality. We can use it in this book until actual experimental data are available.

Thus
$$Pe_{ha2} = Pe_{mal}\frac{\varepsilon_L}{\varepsilon_G + \varepsilon_L} + Pe_{mag}\frac{\varepsilon_G}{\varepsilon_G + \varepsilon_L} \tag{7-49}$$

There are three correlations for Pe_{mag}:

Sater and Levenspiel[13] $Pe_{mag} = 3.4\ Re_G^{-0.67}\ 10^{-0.0026\ Re_L} = 0.4694$

DeMaria and White[15] $Pe_{mag} = 2.4\ Re_G^{-0.2}\ 10^{-0.002\ Re_L} = 1.24$

Hochman and Effron[14] $Pe_{mag} = 1.8\ Re_G^{-0.7}\ 10^{-0.005\ Re_L} = 0.20$

Again the smallest number is selected, 0.20, and that gives $Pe_{ha2} = 0.4993$.

The Computer Program RDMOT3

The backmixed trickle-bed reactor problem can be solved by using the Fortran program RDMOT3, developed in Chap. 2, Sec. 2.6, as Case 2 with $C_s \neq C$ and $T_s \neq T$ for first-order reactions. The version of this program for several reactions in parallel is discussed in Sec. 2.8. The application of this program to the backmixed trickle-bed reactor problem is explained below. Figure 7-8 shows a block diagram of the RDMOT3 program, and Fig. 7-9 is a listing of the program.

First, the concentration and temperature variables, both in the bulk phase and on the catalyst surface, are dimensioned, as are the reaction rate constants, reaction rates, Damköhler numbers, reactor lengths, and the variables of the subroutine TRIDAG. The number of integration steps M is then read in: M = 400.

Bulk-phase concentrations and temperature are initialized by means of a DO loop (labeled 7) from step 1 to M1. Input data are read in and quantities independent of concentrations and temperature are calculated. The titles of the output are printed and the input data are printed in the form of a name list. A DO loop (labeled 8) prints reactor lengths ZZ(I) and TRIDAG coefficients independent of reactor length are calculated. A DO loop (labeled 9) initializes catalyst surface concentrations by equating them to their respective initial bulk-phase concentrations. Also, surface temperature is equated to bulk temperature.

A counter called NOITER is used to count the number of TRIDAG iterations. A test called ITER is used to terminate TRIDAG iterations. A DO loop (labeled 10) is used to calculate the TRIDAG coefficients for the sulfur concentration ODE. Here TS(I) is calculated for each reactor length increment by a Newton-Raphson iteration, and from that result other quantities are calculated for the same reactor length increment. Finally, the coefficients of the Subroutine TRIDAG are computed. All the calculated values are stored in "dimension" storages.

The boundary values are set and subroutine TRIDAG is called. The reduced sulfur concentrations calculated by TRIDAG are printed. We select for printing 10 values starting with I = 41 and ending with I = 401, thus printing every fortieth increment. Again safety statements are used to make certain that CR is positive and smaller than 1.0. This type of computation is repeated for the mass ODEs for nitrogen, hydrocrackables, and unsaturates.

The integration of the heat ODE is basically similar, except that it includes the calculation of the density, specific heat, and superficial velocity of the gas mixture.

Thus the RDMOT3 program successively integrates all the ODEs for the entire reactor length, starting from initial conditions, and then repeats this procedure in a series of iterations, each time improving on the previous calculations, until the results change less than a given test value. Our test is applied to TR and the test value is 0.001. Once this test is met, the reactor design results are printed. Finally, the composition of the gas phase is calculated and printed for the 10 points along the reactor length for which concentrations and temperatures are printed.

Figure 7-10 is a listing of the input data for RDMOT3. Figure 7-11 is the output of RDMOT3: first it lists the input data as a name list; then it lists the reactor lengths, the concentrations and the temperatures for the 10 selected points along the reactor length for each successive iteration. To meet the test 11 iterations are needed. Then the definitive reactor design data are printed and the gas compositions for the 10 points are given.

We can see from the output data that 1.20 m is an excessive length for the laboratory reactor, since CR is decreased to 0.000787 at the end of this reactor. However, it is all right to build an experimental reactor somewhat oversized. The desired conversion of 65% or CR = 0.35 is reached at about 0.28 m. The reduced temperature TR shoots quickly above 1.07, which was used as TRMAX in RDMOT4 and levels off at 1.378. In practice, we would not bother designing this experimental reactor as a multibed reactor with interbed quench but would rather want to see what happens to temperature. If we want an experimental reactor with 65% conversion, we would simply build a reactor that is only 0.28 m long.

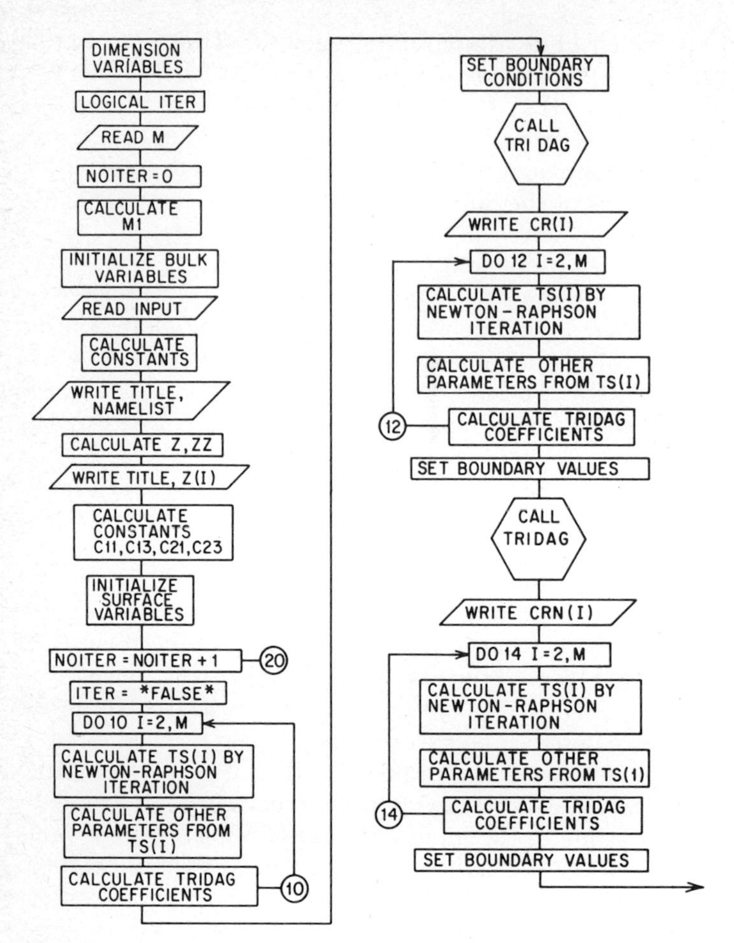

FIG. 7-8 Block diagram of the RDMOT3 program.

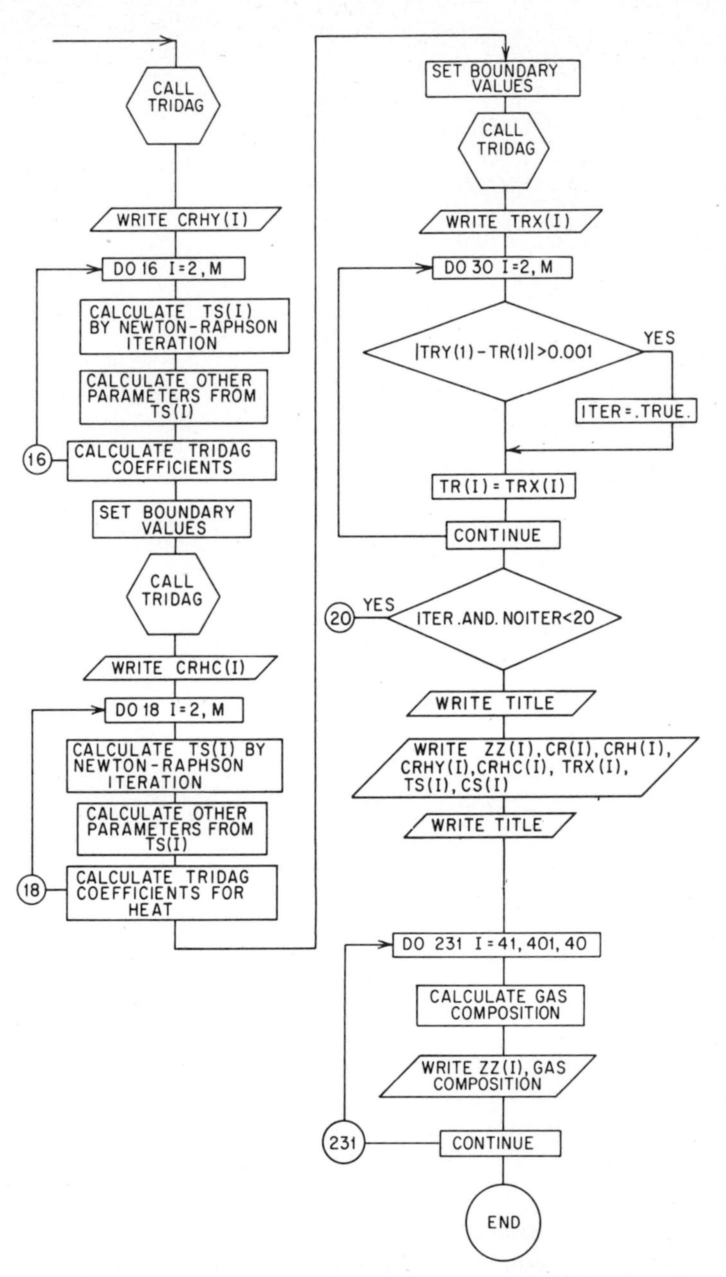

FIG. 7-8 **Block diagram of the RDMOT3 program (*continued*).**

```
C
C          PROCESS DESIGN OF TRICKLE-BED REACTOR
C                         FOR
C           PETROLEUM OIL HYDRODESULFURIZATION
C
C     ....CS AND TS SUBSTITUTION SCHEME 2 ....
C     ....CS NOT = C  ;  TS NOT = T  ....
C
      DIMENSION CR(401),CRN(401),CRHY(401),CRHC(401),TR(401),
     1 CS(401),CNS(401),CHYS(401),CHCS(401),TS(401),K1(401),
     2 K3(401),K4(401),K5(401),R1(401),R3(401),R4(401),R5(401),
     3 DAM1(401),DAM3(401),DAM4(401),DAM5(401),DAH(401),Z(401),
     4 ZZ(401)
      DIMENSION AA(401),B(401),C(401),D(401),TRX(401)
      REAL K1,K3,K4,K5,KC,MWL,NITRO,Q1,Q3,Q4,Q5
      LOGICAL ITER
      READ(5,99) M
   99 FORMAT (I10)
      NOITER = 0
C
C     ....INITIALIZE   CR, CRN, CRHY, CRHC, AND TR ....
      M1 = M + 1
      DO 7 I=1, M1
      CR(I)  = 1.
      CRN(I)  = 1.
      CRHY(I)  = 1.
      CRHC(I)  = 1.
    7 TR(I)  = 1.
C
C     ....DEFINE COEFFICIENTS WHICH ARE NOT FUNCTIONS OF CR OR TR....
      READ(5,100) A,CPL,DH1,DP,DT,E1,EPS,FEED,HTC,HOIL,KC,P,PEMAL,PEHA2,
     1 RG,RMU,S,TO,DELTAZ,RHOL,A1,EFF1,E3,E4,E5,A3,A4,A5,DH3,DH4,DH5,
     2 NITRO,BRNO,MWL
  100 FORMAT (7E10.3 / 7E10.3 / 7E10.3/7E10.3/6E10.3)
      CLO   = S * RHOL/3206.4
      AC    = 3.1416 *(DT/2.)**2
      GL    = FEED/AC
      EPSL = 9.9 *  (GL*DP/RMU)**0.333/
     1    (DP**3 * 9.8066 *RHOL**2/(RMU**2))**0.333
      EPSG = EPS - EPSL
      UL    = GL/(RHOL * EPSL)
      CNO   = NITRO*RHOL/1400.8
      CHCO  = BRNO*RHOL/15983.2
      CHYO  = RHOL/MWL
      NAMELIST/DATA/M,DELTAZ,A,A1,A3,A4,A5,AC,CLO,CPL,DH1,DH3,DH4,DH5,
     1 DP,DT,E1,E3,E4,E5,EPS,EPSG,EPSL,FEED,HOIL,KC,P,PEMAL,PEHA2,RG,
     2 RHOL,RMU,S,TO,UL,HTC,
     3 CNO,CHYO,CHCO
      WRITE(6,150)
  150 FORMAT(1H1,46X,29HDESIGN OF TRICKLE-BED REACTOR)
      WRITE(6,151)
  151 FORMAT(1H0,55X,11HINPUT  DATA)
      WRITE(6,DATA)
      DO 8 I=1, M1
      DEL   = FLOAT(I)
      Z(I) = DELTAZ * DEL
    8 ZZ(I)= Z(I) * DP
C
      WRITE(6,210)
  210 FORMAT(1H0,20X,31HI T E R A T I O N   C Y C L E S)
C
      WRITE (6, 197)  (Z(I), I=41, 401, 40)
  197 FORMAT  (10H0 Z(I)    =, 1P10E12.3)
      C11 = 1./(PEMAL*DELTAZ**2)
      C13 = C11 - (1./DELTAZ)
```

FIG. 7-9 Fortran program RDMOT3 for designing a backmixed laboratory-size trickle-bed reactor for petroleum oil hydrodesulfurization.

```
      C21 = 1./(PEHA2*DELTAZ**2)
      C23 = C21 - (1./DELTAZ)
C
C     ....INITIALIZE CS ,CNS, CHYS, CHCS, AND TS ....
      DO 9 I=1, M1
      CS(I) = CL0
      CNS(I)  = CN0
      CHYS(I) = CHY0
      CHCS(I) = CHC0
    9 TS(I) = T0
C
C     ....COMPUTE VALUES FOR EACH I-VALUE OF ALL COEFFICIENTS AND FEED
C     THEM INTO THE ODE'S AND ALSO STORE  THEM IN DIMENSION STATEMENTS.
C     THE SUBROUTINE TRIDAG UPGRADES THESE COEFFICIENT VALUES  AND THE
C     ODE'S BY ITERATION UNTIL A TEST IS MET....
C
   20 NOITER = NOITER + 1
      ITER= .FALSE.
C     .... INTEGRATE MASS ODE FOR SULFUR ....
      DO 10 I=2, M
C     ....CALCULATION OF TS(I) BY NEWTON-RAPHSON ITERATION....
   21 TSI  = TS(I)
      K1(I)= A1*EXP(-E1/(RG*TS(I)))
      K3(I)= A3*EXP(-E3/(RG*TS(I)))
      K4(I)= A4*EXP(-E4/(RG*TS(I)))
      K5(I)= A5*EXP(-E5/(RG*TS(I)))
      R1(I)= EFF1*K1(I)*CS(I)
      R3(I)= EFF1*K3(I)*CNS(I)
      R4(I)= EFF1*K4(I)*CHYS(I)
      R5(I)= EFF1*K5(I)*CHCS(I)
      SIGMA1= (EFF1*DH1*K1(I)*CR(I)   *CL0 /(1.+(EFF1*K1(I)/(KC*A)))) +
     1        (EFF1*DH3*K3(I)*CRN(I)  *CN0 /(1.+(EFF1*K3(I)/(KC*A)))) +
     2        (EFF1*DH4*K4(I)*CRHY(I)*CHY0/(1.+(EFF1*K4(I)/(KC*A)))) +
     3        (EFF1*DH5*K5(I)*CRHC(I)*CHC0/(1.+(EFF1*K5(I)/(KC*A))))
      FTS  = (TR(I)*T0) + (SIGMA1/(HTC*A))
      SIGMA2= (EFF1*DH1*K1(I)*CR(I)*CL0*E1/(1.+
     1                                       (EFF1*K1(I)/(KC*A)))**2) +
     2        (EFF1*DH3*K3(I)*CRN(I)*CN0*E3/(1.+
     3                                       (EFF1*K3(I)/(KC*A)))**2) +
     4        (EFF1*DH4*K4(I)*CRHY(I)*CHY0*E4/(1.+
     5                                       (EFF1*K4(I)/(KC*A)))**2) +
     6        (EFF1*DH5*K5(I)*CRHC(I)*CHC0*E5/(1.+
     7                                       (EFF1*K5(I)/(KC*A)))**2)
      DFTS =SIGMA2/(HTC*A*RG*TS(I)**2)
      TS(I)= (FTS - TS(I)*DFTS)/(1.- DFTS)
      IF(ABS(TSI-TS(I)).GE..05) GO TO 21
C     ....CALCULATION OF OTHER PARAMETERS....
C     ....PARAMETERS ARE  K1(I), R1(I), DAM1(I), AND DAH(I) ....
      K1(I)= A1*EXP(-E1/(RG*TS(I)))
      DAM1(I)  = EFF1*K1(I)/(A*KC)
      CS(I)= CR(I)*CL0/(1.+DAM1(I))
      R1(I)= EFF1*K1(I)*CS(I)
      SIGMA3= (DH1*R1(I)) + (DH3*R3(I)) + (DH4*R4(I)) + (DH5*R5(I))
      DAH(I)  = SIGMA3 /(A*HTC*T0)
C     ....DEFINE COEFFICIENTS WHICH ARE FUNCTIONS OF CR AND TR....
      CC1  = (CL0/(1.+DAM1(I)))*EXP(-E1/(RG*TS(I)))
      B1   = DP*EFF1*A1/(UL*CL0)
      C121 = -(2.*C11) - (B1*CC1)+(1./DELTAZ)
C     ....DEFINE AA, B, C, AND D FOR MASS EQUATIONS FOR SULFUR....
      AA(I) = C11
      B(I)  = C121
      C(I)  = C13
   10 D(I)  = 0.
C     ...SET BOUNDARY VALUES....
      D(2)  = -C11
```

FIG. 7-9 Fortran program RDMOT3 for designing a backmixed laboratory-size trickle-bed reactor for petroleum oil hydrodesulfurization (*continued*).

```
      B(M) = C13 + C121
C
      CALL TRIDAG (2,M,AA,B,C,D,CR)
      CR(M1) = CR(M)
      WRITE (6, 198) (CR(I), I=41, 401, 40)
  198 FORMAT (10H0 CR(I)  =, 1P10E12.3)
      DO 11  I= 2, M1
      IF(CR(I).LT.0.)CR(I)=0.
   11 IF(CR(I).GT.1.)CR(I)=1.
C
C     ....INTEGRATE MASS ODE FOR NITROGEN....
      DO 12  I=2, M
C     ....CALCULATION OF TS(I) BY NEWTCN-RAPHSON ITERATION....
   22 TSI = TS(I)
      K1(I)=A1*EXP(-E1/(RG*TS(I)))
      K3(I)=A3*EXP(-E3/(RG*TS(I)))
      K4(I)=A4*EXP(-E4/(RG*TS(I)))
      K5(I)=A5*EXP(-E5/(RG*TS(I)))
      R1(I)=EFF1*K1(I)*CS(I)
      R3(I)=EFF1*K3(I)*CNS(I)
      R4(I)=EFF1*K4(I)*CHYS(I)
      R5(I)=EFF1*K5(I)*CHCS(I)
      SIGMA1=(EFF1*DH1*K1(I)*CR(I)   *CLO  /(1.+(EFF1*K1(I)/(KC*A)))) +
     1        (EFF1*DH3*K3(I)*CRN(I)  *CNO  /(1.+(EFF1*K3(I)/(KC*A)))) +
     2        (EFF1*DH4*K4(I)*CRHY(I)*CHYO/(1.+(EFF1*K4(I)/(KC*A)))) +
     3        (EFF1*DH5*K5(I)*CRHC(I)*CHCO/(1.+(EFF1*K5(I)/(KC*A))))
      FTS = (TR(I)*TO) + (SIGMA1/(HTC*A))
      SIGMA2= (EFF1*DH1*K1(I)*CR(I)   *CLO  *E1/(1.+
     1                                  (EFF1*K1(I)/(KC*A)))**2) +
     2         (EFF1*DH3*K3(I)*CRN(I)  *CNO  *E3/(1.+
     3                                  (EFF1*K3(I)/(KC*A)))**2) +
     4         (EFF1*DH4*K4(I)*CRHY(I)*CHYO*E4/(1.+
     5                                  (EFF1*K4(I)/(KC*A)))**2) +
     6         (EFF1*DH5*K5(I)*CRHC(I)*CHCO*E5/(1.+
     7                                  (EFF1*K5(I)/(KC*A)))**2)
      DFTS= SIGMA2/(HTC*A*RG*TS(I)**2)
      TS(I) = (FTS - TS(I)*DFTS)/(1.- DFTS)
      IF(ABS(TSI-TS(I)).GE.0.05) GO TO 22
C     ....CALCULATION OF OTHER PARAMETERS ....
C     ....PARAMETERS ARE: K3(I), R3(I), DAM3(I), DAH(I), AND CNS(I)....
      K3(I)    = A3*EXP(-E3/(RG*TS(I)))
      DAM3(I)  = EFF1*K3(I)/(A*KC)
      CNS(I)   = CRN(I)*CNO/(1. + DAM3(I))
      R3(I)    = EFF1*K3(I)*CNS(I)
      SIGMA3= (DH1*R1(I)) + (DH3*R3(I)) + (DH4*R4(I)) + (DH5*R5(I))
      DAH(I)   = SIGMA3 / (A*HTC*TO)
C     ....DEFINE COEFFICIENTS WHICH ARE FUNCTIONS OF CRN AND TR ....
      CC3  = (CNO/(1.+DAM3(I)))*EXP(-E3/(RG*TS(I)))
      B3   = DP*EFF1*A3/(UL*CNO)
      C123 = -(2.*C11) - (B3*CC3) + (1./DELTAZ)
C     .... DEFINE AA, B, C, AND D FOR MASS ODE FOR NITROGEN ....
      AA(I)  = C11
      B(I)   = C123
      C(I)   = C13
   12 D(I)  = 0.
C     .... SET BOUNDARY VALUES ....
      D(2)  = -C11
      B(M)  = C13 + C123
C
      CALL TRIDAG (2,M,AA,B,C,D,CRN)
      CRN(M1) = CRN(M)
      WRITE (6, 199) (CRN(I), I=41, 401, 40)
  199 FORMAT (10H0 CRN(I) =,1P10E12.3)
      DO 13 I= 2, M1
      IF(CRN(I).LT.0.0) CRN(I)=0.
```

FIG. 7-9 Fortran program RDMOT3 for designing a backmixed laboratory-size trickle-bed reactor for petroleum oil hydrodesulfurization (*continued*).

```
   13 IF(CRN(I).GT.1.0)CRN(I)=1.
C
C     .... INTEGRATE MASS ODE FOR HYDROCRACKABLE COMPOUNDS ....
      DO 14 I=2, M
C     .... CALCULATION OF TS(I) BY NEWTON-RAPHSON ITERATION ....
   23 TSI   = TS(I)
      K1(I)= A1*EXP(-E1/(RG*TS(I)))
      K3(I)= A3*EXP(-E3/(RG*TS(I)))
      K4(I)= A4*EXP(-E4/(RG*TS(I)))
      K5(I)= A5*EXP(-E5/(RG*TS(I)))
      R1(I)= EFF1*K1(I)*CS(I)
      R3(I)= EFF1*K3(I)*CNS(I)
      R4(I)= EFF1*K4(I)*CHYS(I)
      R5(I)= EFF1*K5(I)*CHCS(I)
      SIGMA1=(EFF1*DH1*K1(I)*CR(I)   *CL0 /(1.+(EFF1*K1(I)/(KC*A)))) +
     1       (EFF1*DH3*K3(I)*CRN(I)  *CN0 /(1.+(EFF1*K3(I)/(KC*A)))) +
     2       (EFF1*DH4*K4(I)*CRHY(I)*CHY0/(1.+(EFF1*K4(I)/(KC*A)))) +
     3       (EFF1*DH5*K5(I)*CRHC(I)*CHC0/(1.+(EFF1*K5(I)/(KC*A))))
      FTS   = (TR(I)*T0) + (SIGMA1/(HTC*A))
      SIGMA2= (EFF1*DH1*K1(I)*CR(I)   *CL0 *E1/(1.+(EFF1*K1(I)/
     1                                         (KC*A)))**2)  +
     2         (EFF1*DH3*K3(I)*CRN(I)  *CN0 *E3/(1.+(EFF1*K3(I)/
     3                                         (KC*A)))**2)  +
     4         (EFF1*DH4*K4(I)*CRHY(I)*CHY0*E4/(1.+(EFF1*K4(I)/
     5                                         (KC*A)))**2)  +
     6         (EFF1*DH5*K5(I)*CRHC(I)*CHC0*E5/(1.+(EFF1*K5(I)/
     7                                         (KC*A)))**2)
      DFTS = SIGMA2 /(HTC*A*RG*(TS(I)**2))
      TS(I) = (FTS - TS(I)*DFTS)/(1.- DFTS)
      IF(ABS(TSI-TS(I)).GE.0.05) GO TO 23
C     .... CALCULATION OF OTHER PARAMETERS ....
C     .... PARAMETERS ARE K4(I), R4(I), DAM4(I), AND DAH(I) ....
      K4(I)   = A4*EXP(-E4/(RG*TS(I)))
      DAM4(I)= EFF1*K4(I)/(A*KC)
      CHYS(I)= CRHY(I)*CHY0/(1.+DAM4(I))
      R4(I)   = EFF1*K4(I)*CHYS(I)
      SIGMA3 = (DH1*R1(I)) + (DH3*R3(I)) + (DH4*R4(I)) + (DH5*R5(I))
      DAH(I) = SIGMA3 / (A*HTC*T0)
C     .... DEFINE COEFFICIENTS WHICH ARE FUNCTIONS OF CRHY AND TR ....
      CC4    = CHY0*EXP(-E4/(RG*TS(I)))/(1.+DAM4(I))
      B4     = DP*EFF1*A4/(UL*CHY0)
      C124   = -(2.*C11) - (B4*CC4) +(1./DELTAZ)
C     .... DEFINE AA, B, C, AND D FOR MASS ODE FOR HYDROCRACKABLES ....
      AA(I)    = C11
      B(I)     = C124
      C(I)     = C13
   14 D(I)     = 0.
C     .... SET BOUNDARY VALUES ....
      D(2)     = -C11
      B(M)     = C13 + C124
C
      CALL TRIDAG (2,M,AA,B,C,D,CRHY)
      CRHY(M1)= CRHY(M)
      WRITE (6, 200) (CRHY(I), I=41, 401, 40)
  200 FORMAT (10H0 CRHY(I)=, 1P10E12.3)
      DO 15 I= 2, M1
      IF(CRHY(I).LT.0.)CRHY(I) = 0.
   15 IF(CRHY(I).GT. 1.)CRHY(I) = 1.
C
C     .... INTEGRATE MASS ODE FOR UNSATURATES ....
C
      DO 16 I=2, M
C     .... CALCULATION OF TS(I) BY NEWTON-RAPHSON ITERATION ....
   24 TSI = TS(I)
      K1(I)=A1*EXP(-E1/(RG*TS(I)))
```

FIG. 7-9 Fortran program RDMOT3 for designing a backmixed laboratory-size trickle-bed reactor for petroleum oil hydrodesulfurization (*continued*).

```
      K3(I)=A3*EXP(-E3/(RG*TS(I)))
      K4(I)=A4*EXP(-E4/(RG*TS(I)))
      K5(I)=A5*EXP(-E5/(RG*TS(I)))
      R1(I)=EFF1*K1(I)*CS(I)
      R3(I)=EFF1*K3(I)*CNS(I)
      R4(I)=EFF1*K4(I)*CHYS(I)
      R5(I)=EFF1*K5(I)*CHCS(I)
      SIGMA1= (EFF1*DH1*K1(I)*CR(I)   *CLO /(1.+(EFF1*K1(I)/(KC*A)))) +
     1        (EFF1*DH3*K3(I)*CRN(I)  *CNO /(1.+(EFF1*K3(I)/(KC*A)))) +
     2        (EFF1*DH4*K4(I)*CRHY(I)*CHYO/(1.+(EFF1*K4(I)/(KC*A)))) +
     3        (EFF1*DH5*K5(I)*CRHC(I)*CHCO/(1.+(EFF1*K5(I)/(KC*A))))
      FTS  = (TR(I)*TO) + (SIGMA1/(HTC*A))
      SIGMA2= (EFF1*DH1*K1(I)*CR(I)   *CLO *E1/(1.+(EFF1*K1(I)/
     1                                         (KC*A)))**2) +
     2        (EFF1*DH3*K3(I)*CRN(I)  *CNO *E3/(1.+(EFF1*K3(I)/
     3                                         (KC*A)))**2) +
     4        (EFF1*DH4*K4(I)*CRHY(I)*CHYO*E4/(1.+(EFF1*K4(I)/
     5                                         (KC*A)))**2) +
     6        (EFF1*DH5*K5(I)*CRHC(I)*CHCO*E5/(1.+(EFF1*K5(I)/
     7                                         (KC*A)))**2)
      DFTS = SIGMA2 / (HTC*A*RG*(TS(I)**2))
      TS(I)= (FTS - TS(I)*DFTS)/(1.-DFTS)
      IF(ABS(TSI-TS(I)).GE.0.05) GO TO 24
C     .... CALCULATION OF OTHER PARAMETERS ....
C     .... PARAMETERS ARE K5(I), R5(I), DAM5(I), AND DAH(I) ....
      K5(I)   = A5*EXP(-E5/(RG*TS(I)))
      DAM5(I) = EFF1*K5(I)/(A*KC)
      CHCS(I) = CRHC(I)*CHCO/(1.+DAM5(I))
      R5(I)   = EFF1*K5(I)*CHCS(I)
      SIGMA3 = (DH1*R1(I)) + (DH3*R3(I)) + (DH4*R4(I)) + (DH5*R5(I))
      DAH(I)  = SIGMA3 / (A*HTC*TO)
C     .... DEFINE COEFFICIENTS WHICH ARE FUNCTIONS OF CRHC AND TR ....
      CC5  = (CHCO/(1.+ DAM5(I)))*EXP(-E5/(RG*TS(I)))
      B5   = DP*EFF1*A5/(UL*CHCO)
      C125 = -(2.*C11) - (B5*CC5) + (1./DELTAZ)
C     ....DEFINE AA, B, C, AND D FOR MASS ODE FOR UNSATURATES ....
      AA(I)   = C11
      B(I)    = C125
      C(I)    = C13
   16 D(I)  = 0.
C     .... SET BOUNDARY VALUES ....
      D(2)  = -C11
      B(M)  = C13 + C125
C
      CALL TRIDAG (2,M,AA,B,C,D,CRHC)
      CRHC(M1)  = CRHC(M)
      WRITE(6, 201) (CRHC(I), I=41, 401, 40)
  201 FORMAT (10H0 CRHC(I)=, 1P10E12.3)
      DO 17 I= 2, M1
      IF(CRHC(I).LT.0.)CRHC(I)=0.
   17 IF(CRHC(I).GT.1.)CRHC(I)=1.
C
C     .... INTEGRATE HEAT ODE FOR ALL REACTIONS ...
C
C     ....DEFINE AA,B,C, AND D FOR HEAT EQUATION ....
      DO 18 I=2, M
C     ....CALCULATION OF TS(I) BY NEWTON-RAPHSON ITERATION....
   25 TSI = TS(I)
      K1(I)=A1*EXP(-E1/(RG*TS(I)))
      K3(I)=A3*EXP(-E3/(RG*TS(I)))
      K4(I)=A4*EXP(-E4/(RG*TS(I)))
      K5(I)=A5*EXP(-E5/(RG*TS(I)))
      R1(I)=EFF1*K1(I)*CS(I)
      R3(I)=EFF1*K3(I)*CNS(I)
      R4(I)=EFF1*K4(I)*CHYS(I)
```

FIG. 7-9 Fortran program RDMOT3 for designing a backmixed laboratory-size trickle-bed reactor for petroleum oil hydrodesulfurization (*continued*).

```
      R5(I)=EFF1*K5(I)*CHCS(I)
      SIGMA1= (EFF1*DH1*K1(I)*CR(I)   *CLO  /(1.+(EFF1*K1(I)/(KC*A)))) +
     1        (EFF1*DH3*K3(I)*CRN(I)  *CNO  /(1.+(EFF1*K3(I)/(KC*A)))) +
     2        (EFF1*DH4*K4(I)*CRHY(I) *CHYO/(1.+(EFF1*K4(I)/(KC*A)))) +
     3        (EFF1*DH5*K5(I)*CRHC(I)*CHCO/(1.+(EFF1*K5(I)/(KC*A))))
      FTS = (TR(I)*TO) + (SIGMA1/(HTC*A))
      SIGMA2= (EFF1*DH1*K1(I)*CR(I)   *CLO *E1/(1.+(EFF1*K1(I)/
     1                                          (KC*A)))**2) +
     2        (EFF1*DH3*K3(I)*CRN(I)  *CNO *E3/(1.+(EFF1*K3(I)/
     3                                          (KC*A)))**2) +
     4        (EFF1*DH4*K4(I)*CRHY(I) *CHYO*E4/(1.+(EFF1*K4(I)/
     5                                          (KC*A)))**2) +
     6        (EFF1*DH5*K5(I)*CRHC(I)*CHCO*E5/(1.+(EFF1*K5(I)/
     7                                          (KC*A)))**2)
      DFTS = SIGMA2 / (HTC*A*RG*(TS(I)**2))
      TS(I)= (FTS - TS(I)*DFTS)/(1.-DFTS)
      IF(ABS(TSI-TS(I)).GE.0.05) GO TO 25
C     ....CALCULATION OF OTHER PARAMETERS....
C     ....PARAMETERS ARE DAH(I), RHO, CP, U, AND SIGMAD ....
      SIGMA3 = (DH1*R1(I)) + (DH3*R3(I)) + (DH4*R4(I)) + (DH5*R5(I))
      DAH(I) = SIGMA3 / (A*HTC*TO)
C     .... CALCULATION OF GAS DENSITY RHO ....
      Q1 = 2.08656E-C5*S*MWL
      Q3 = 7.16304E-05*MWL*NITRO
      Q4 = 22.414/(HOIL*MWL)
      Q5 = 9.38276E-05*BRNO*MWL
      RHO= 12.028*P/(TR(I)*TO)*(2.016*(1.-(Q1*(1.-CR(I))) -
     1     (Q3*(1.-CRN(I))) - (Q4*(1.-CRHY(I))) - (Q5*(1.-CRHC(I))))) +
     2     (34.032*Q1*(1.-CR(I))) + (16.043*Q3*(1.-CRN(I))) +
     3     (5.6773*Q4*(1.-CRHY(I)))
C     .... CALCULATION OF THE SPECIFIC HEAT CP OF REACTING GAS MIX ....
      CPH2  = 27.698 + (0.003389 * TO * TR(I))
      CPH2S = 30.1248 + (0.01506 * TO * TR(I))
      CPCH4 = 22.343 + (0.04812 * TO * TR(I))
      CPNH3 = 28.0328 + (0.02636 * TO *TR(I))
      CP   = CPH2 *(1.-(Q1*(1.-CR(I))) - (Q3*(1.-CRN(I))) -
     1 (Q4*(1.-CRHY(I))) - (Q5*(1.-CRHC(I)))) + (CPH2S*Q1*(1.-CR(I))/2.)
     2 + (CPNH3*Q3*(1.-CRN(I))/3.) + (CPCH4*Q4*(1.-CRHY(I)))
C     .... CALCULATION OF SUPERFICIAL GAS VELOCITY U ....
      U = (GL*TO*1.01325/(273.2*EPSG*P))*(HOIL-((CNO*(1.-CRN(I)/3)) +
     1 (CHCO*(1.-CRHC(I))))/RHCL)
C
      BB =DP*EPSL/(TO*((EPSG*RHO*CP*U) + (EPSL*RHOL*CPL*UL)))
      SIGMAD = (DH1*R1(I)/DAM1(I)) + (DH3*R3(I)/DAM3(I)) +
     1         (DH4*R4(I)/DAM4(I)) + (DH5*R5(I)/DAM5(I))
      C22  = -(2.*C21)+(1./DELTAZ)
      C24=-BB* SIGMAD
      AA(I) = C21
      B(I) = C22
      C(I) = C23
   18 D(I) = C24
C     ....SET BOUNDARY VALUES....
      D(2) = D(2) - C21
      B(M) = C23 + C22
      CALL TRIDAG (2,M,AA,B,C,D,TRX)
      TRX(M1) = TRX(M)
      WRITE (6,202) (TRX(I), I=41, 401, 40)
  202 FORMAT (10H0 TRX(I) =,1P10E12.3)
      DO 19  I = 2, M1
   19 IF(TRX(I).LT.1.)TRX(I)=1.
C
C     ....TEST....
      DO 30 I=2, M
      IF(ABS(TRX(I)-TR(I)).GT. 0.001) ITER=.TRUE.
      TR(I)=TRX(I)
```

FIG. 7-9 Fortran program RDMOT3 for designing a backmixed laboratory-size trickle-bed reactor for petroleum oil hydrodesulfurization (*continued*).

```
   30 CONTINUE
      IF (ITER.AND.NOITER.LT.20) GO TO 20
      WRITE(6, 220)
  220 FORMAT(1H0,13X,43HR E A C T O R   D E S I G N   R E S U L T S)
C
      WRITE (6, 203) (ZZ(I),   I=41, 401, 40)
  203 FORMAT(10H0 ZZ(I)  =,1P10E12.3)
      WRITE (6, 198) (CR(I),   I=41, 401, 40)
      WRITE (6, 199) (CRN(I),  I=41, 401, 40)
      WRITE (6, 200) (CRHY(I), I=41, 401, 40)
      WRITE (6, 201) (CRHC(I), I=41, 401, 40)
      WRITE (6, 202) (TRX(I),  I=41, 401, 40)
      TS(M1) = TS(M)
      WRITE (6, 204) (TS(I),   I=41, 401, 40)
  204 FORMAT(10H0 TS(I)  =, 1P10E12.3)
      CS(M1) = CS(M)
      WRITE (6, 205) (CS(I),   I=41, 401, 40)
  205 FORMAT(10H0 CS(I)  =, 1P10E12.3)
      WRITE(6, 230)
  230 FORMAT(1H0,15X,29HGAS COMPOSITION  MOL-FRACTION/1H0,10X,
     1  5HZZ(I),4X,8HHYDROGEN,5X,3HH2S,7X,3HNH3,7X,3HCH4)
      DO 231 I=41, 401, 40
      HMF = (FEED*0.5/22.414)*(1.-Q1*(1.-CR(I)) - Q3*(1.-CRN(I)) -
     1      Q4*(1.-CRHY(I)) - Q5*(1.-CRHC(I)))
      H2SMF= FEED*S*(1.-CR(I))/3206.6
      AMMF = FEED*NITRO*(1.-CRN(I))/1400.8
      CH4MF= FEED*(1.-CRHY(I))/MWL
      SUM  = HMF + H2SMF + AMMF + CH4MF
      HYD  = HMF/SUM
      H2S  = H2SMF/SUM
      AM   = AMMF/SUM
      CH4  = CH4MF/SUM
      WRITE (6, 232) ZZ(I), HYD, H2S, AM, CH4
  231 CONTINUE
  232 FORMAT (1H0, 10X, F6.4, 4X, F6.5, 4X, F6.5, 4X, F6.5, 4X, F6.5)
      STOP
      END
C     SUBROUTINE TRIDAG
C     SUBROUTINE FOR SOLVING A SYSTEM OF LINEAR SIMULTANEOUS EQUATIONS
C     HAVING A TRIDIAGONAL COEFFICIENT MATRIX.  THE EQUATIONS ARE
C     NUMBERED FROM IF THROUGH L, AND THEIR SUBDIAGONAL, DIAGONAL,AND
C     SUPERDIAGONAL COEFFICIENTS ARE STORED IN THE ARRAYS A, B, AND C.
C     THE COMPUTED SOLUTION VECTOR V(IF)....V(L) IS STORED IN THE ARRAY
C     V.
      SUBROUTINE TRIDAG (IF,L,A,B,C,D,V)
      DIMENSION A(400),B(400),C(400),D(400),V(400),BETA(400),GAMMA(400)
C
C     ....COMPUTE INTERMEDIATE ARRAYS BETA AND GAMMA
      BETA(IF)=B(IF)
      GAMMA(IF)=D(IF)/BETA(IF)
      IFP1=IF+1
      DO 1 I=IFP1, L
      BETA(I)=B(I)-A(I)*C(I-1)/BETA(I-1)
    1 GAMMA(I)=(D(I)-A(I)*GAMMA (I-1))/BETA(I)
C
C     ....COMPUTE FINAL SOLUTION VECTOR V ....
      V(L)=GAMMA(L)
      LAST =  L-IF
      DO 2 K = 1, LAST
      I = L - K
    2 V(I) = GAMMA(I) - C(I)*V(I+1)/BETA(I)
      RETURN
      END
```

FIG. 7-9 **Fortran program RDMOT3 for designing a backmixed laboratory-size trickle-bed reactor for petroleum oil hydrodesulfurization (*continued*).**

```
      400
1.2  E+03 3.31 E+00 2.512E+05 6.020E-03 0.2  E+00 8.206E+04 0.360E+00
2.12 E-02 1.298E+00 0.5  E+00 1.5  E-04 5.5  E+01 0.26 E+00 0.2  E+00
8.314E+00 0.21 E-03 4.0  E+00 6.482E+02 0.5  E+00 5.693E+02 2.800E+04
0.4  E+00 7.206E+04 2.435E+05 4.686E+04 1.800E+03 2.500E+15 1.000E+03
6.485E+04 4.1  E+04 1.255E+05 0.35 E+00 5.000E+00 6.7  E+02
```

FIG. 7-10 Input data for computer program RDMOT3.

7.3
VARIETIES OF TRICKLE-BED REACTORS

There are quite a variety of types of trickle-bed reactors, as shown in Fig. 6-1. We will not treat them all here.

We want to discuss the kinetics of a trickle-bed reactor in which the reaction occurs both in the gas and in the liquid phase, as developed by Frye and Mosby.[16] The process is the hydrodesulfurization of petroleum oils that are partially vaporized under the reaction conditions. However, the concept of reactions on catalytic surfaces used by these workers are those of Langmuir and Hinshelwood, as developed by Hougen and Watson,[17] and not the power law generally used in this book. The isothermal equation developed for the desulfurization of single compounds is:

$$\ln(X_0/X) = (kP_0P_H/SV)\left[1 - v' + \left(v' + \frac{H}{M}\right)\frac{P_0}{P}\right]$$

$$[1 + k_{H_2S}\,P_{H_2S} + k_AP_A]^2 \qquad (7\text{-}50)$$

where
X = mole fraction of compound S in liquid
X_0 = mole fraction of compound S in feed liquid
k = volumetric reaction rate constant for a single sulfur compound
P_0 = vapor pressure of sulfur compound
P_H = partial pressure of hydrogen
S = amount of a single sulfur compound
v' = mole fraction of liquid vaporized
H/M = the hydrogen/oil mole ratio
P_A = partial pressure of aromatic hydrocarbons
P = total pressure
k_{H_2S} = adsorption equilibrium constant for a single sulfur compound = 2.8 exp(2760/RT)
K_A = average adsorption equilibrium constant for aromatic hydrocarbons = 0.38 exp(11,700/RT)
$kP_0 \cong \exp(-129{,}000/RT)$

DESIGN OF TRICKLE-BED REACTOR

INPUT DATA

```
&DATA
M=          400,DELTAZ=   .500000000     ,A=  1200.00000      ,A1=  28000.0000      ,A3=  1800.00000      ,A4=  .250000007E+16,A5=
  1000.00000      ,AC=   .314159634E-01,CL0=   .710204661      ,CPL=  3.31000042      ,DH1=  251200.000      ,DH3=  64850.0000      ,DH4=
  41000.0000      ,DH5=  125500.000      ,DP=   .601999834E-02,DT=   .199999988      ,E1=  82060.0000      ,E3=  72060.0000      ,E4=
  243500.000      ,E5=  46860.0000      ,EPS=   .360000014      ,EPSG=  .253436148      ,EPSL=  .106563866      ,FEED=  .212000012E-01,HOIL=
  .500000000      ,KC=  .150000007E-03,P=  55.0000000      ,PEMAL=  .259999990      ,PEHA2=  .199999988      ,RG=  8.31400013      ,RHOL=
  569.300049      ,RMU=  .209999998E-03,S=  4.00000000      ,T0=  648.199951      ,UL=  .111233145E-01,HTC=  1.29800034      ,CN0=
  .142243683      ,CHY0=  .849701524      ,CHC0=  .178093255
&END
```

I T E R A T I O N   C Y C L E S

Z (I) =	2.050E+01	4.050E+01	6.050E+01	8.050E+01	1.005E+02	1.205E+02	1.405E+02	1.605E+02	1.805E+02	2.005E+02
CR (I) =	9.711E-01	9.429E-01	9.156E-01	8.891E-01	8.634E-01	8.384E-01	8.141E-01	7.905E-01	7.676E-01	7.496E-01
CRN (I) =	9.880E-01	9.761E-01	9.643E-01	9.527E-01	9.412E-01	9.299E-01	9.187E-01	9.076E-01	8.967E-01	8.879E-01
CRHY (I) =	1.000E+00	1.000E+00	1.000E+00	1.000E+00	1.000E+00	1.000E+00	1.000E+00	1.001E+00	1.001E+00	1.001E+00
CRHC (I) =	6.125E-01	3.752E-01	2.299E-01	1.409E-01	8.630E-02	5.287E-02	3.239E-02	1.985E-02	1.216E-02	8.105E-03
TRX (I) =	1.278E+00	1.567E+00	1.860E+00	2.155E+00	2.452E+00	2.748E+00	3.043E+00	3.338E+00	3.631E+00	3.851E+00
CR (I) =	**7.235E-01**	**2.451E-01**	**5.917E-02**	**1.326E-02**	**2.913E-03**	**6.361E-04**	**1.385E-04**	**3.012E-05**	**6.546E-06**	**1.762E-06**
CRN (I) =	8.829E-01	4.978E-01	1.699E-01	4.471E-02	1.062E-02	2.420E-03	5.410E-04	1.197E-04	2.634E-05	7.151E-06
CRHY (I) =	**6.065E-01**	**1.346E-01**	**2.922E-02**	**6.339E-03**	**1.375E-03**	**2.984E-04**	**6.476E-05**	**1.405E-05**	**3.049E-06**	**8.199E-07**
CRHC (I) =	3.884E-01	1.025E-01	2.409E-02	5.439E-03	1.208E-03	2.662E-04	5.839E-05	1.278E-05	2.791E-06	7.544E-07
TRX (I) =	1.203E+00	1.264E+00	1.278E+00	1.282E+00	1.284E+00	1.285E+00	1.285E+00	1.285E+00	1.285E+00	1.285E+00
CR (I) =	**8.134E-01**	**5.210E-01**	**3.112E-01**	**1.824E-01**	**1.062E-01**	**6.162E-02**	**3.573E-02**	**2.072E-02**	**1.202E-02**	**7.646E-03**
CRN (I) =	9.283E-01	7.880E-01	6.495E-01	5.315E-01	4.340E-01	3.543E-01	2.892E-01	2.361E-01	1.928E-01	1.634E-01
CRHY (I) =	8.148E-01	3.249E-01	1.033E-01	3.147E-02	9.490E-03	2.854E-03	8.584E-04	2.584E-04	7.792E-05	2.812E-05

CRHC(I) =	4.172E-01	1.374E-01	4.355E-02	1.370E-02	4.298E-03	1.348E-03	4.229E-04	1.327E-04	4.165E-05	1.556E-05
TRX(I) =	1.203E+00	1.277E+00	1.294E+00	1.298E+00	1.299E+00	1.298E+00	1.298E+00	1.298E+00	1.297E+00	1.297E+00
CR(I) =	3.144E-01	5.026E-01	2.821E-01	1.558E-01	8.597E-02	4.756E-02	2.637E-02	1.465E-02	8.150E-03	5.009E-03
CRN(I) =	9.287E-01	7.779E-01	6.262E-01	5.004E-01	3.998E-01	3.197E-01	2.559E-01	2.050E-01	1.644E-01	1.372E-01
CRHY(I) =	8.161E-01	2.980E-01	8.457E-02	2.328E-02	6.402E-03	1.766E-03	4.890E-04	1.358E-04	3.781E-05	1.272E-05
CRHC(I) =	4.189E-01	1.361E-01	4.213E-02	1.295E-02	3.979E-03	1.224E-03	3.767E-04	1.160E-04	3.577E-05	1.315E-05
TRX(I) =	1.217E+00	1.327E+00	1.384E+00	1.417E+00	1.437E+00	1.449E+00	1.456E+00	1.461E+00	1.464E+00	1.466E+00
CR(I) =	7.990E-01	4.375E-01	1.922E-01	7.563E-02	2.803E-02	1.004E-02	3.522E-03	1.220E-03	4.193E-04	1.689E-04
CRN(I) =	9.218E-01	7.305E-01	5.160E-01	3.388E-01	2.124E-01	1.293E-01	7.726E-02	4.561E-02	2.672E-02	1.707E-02
CRHY(I) =	7.717E-01	2.225E-01	5.073E-02	1.123E-02	2.465E-03	5.394E-04	1.179E-04	2.574E-05	5.617E-06	1.518E-06
CRHC(I) =	4.128E-01	1.273E-01	3.603E-02	9.837E-03	2.637E-03	6.992E-04	1.843E-04	4.837E-05	1.266E-05	4.023E-06
TRX(I) =	1.212E+00	1.305E+00	1.345E+00	1.365E+00	1.375E+00	1.381E+00	1.385E+00	1.387E+00	1.389E+00	1.389E+00
CR(I) =	8.044E-01	4.645E-01	2.275E-01	1.035E-01	4.540E-02	1.949E-02	8.263E-03	3.476E-03	1.455E-03	6.974E-04
CRN(I) =	9.243E-01	7.509E-01	5.637E-01	4.063E-01	2.864E-01	1.993E-01	1.376E-01	9.453E-02	6.474E-02	4.730E-02
CRHY(I) =	7.869E-01	2.464E-01	5.930E-02	1.363E-02	3.090E-03	6.957E-04	1.561E-04	3.496E-05	7.819E-06	2.160E-06
CRHC(I) =	4.147E-01	1.305E-01	3.826E-02	1.093E-02	3.081E-03	8.632E-04	2.409E-04	6.704E-05	1.863E-05	6.243E-06
TRX(I) =	1.211E+00	1.303E+00	1.339E+00	1.352E+00	1.358E+00	1.360E+00	1.361E+00	1.361E+00	1.361E+00	1.361E+00
CR(I) =	8.050E-01	4.663E-01	2.315E-01	1.036E-01	4.990E-02	2.275E-02	1.034E-02	4.696E-03	2.133E-03	1.101E-03
CRN(I) =	9.246E-01	7.525E-01	5.695E-01	4.182E-01	3.035E-01	2.192E-01	1.581E-01	1.140E-01	8.219E-02	6.282E-02
CRHY(I) =	7.888E-01	2.486E-01	6.046E-02	1.411E-02	3.259E-03	7.497E-04	1.723E-04	3.956E-05	9.088E-06	2.572E-06
CRHC(I) =	4.150E-01	1.308E-01	3.856E-02	1.113E-02	3.190E-03	9.116E-04	2.603E-04	7.429E-05	2.121E-05	7.284E-06

FIG. 7-11 Computer output of program RDMOT3 for designing a laboratory-size trickle-bed reactor.

TRX(I) =	1.212E+00	1.308E+00	1.348E+00	1.366E+00	1.374E+00	1.378E+00	1.380E+00	1.381E+00	1.382E+00	1.382E+00
CR(I) =	8.039E-01	4.609E-01	2.232E-01	1.008E-01	4.415E-02	1.906E-02	8.170E-03	3.491E-03	1.489E-03	7.273E-04
CRN(I) =	9.241E-01	7.485E-01	5.590E-01	4.016E-01	2.831E-01	1.978E-01	1.376E-01	9.552E-02	6.625E-02	4.899E-02
CRHY(I) =	7.855E-01	2.431E-01	5.808E-02	1.332E-02	3.019E-03	6.809E-04	1.533E-04	3.446E-05	7.746E-06	2.150E-06
CRHC(I) =	4.146E-01	1.301E-01	3.802E-02	1.084E-02	3.057E-03	8.580E-04	2.403E-04	6.722E-05	1.880E-05	6.337E-06
TRX(I) =	1.212E+00	1.307E+00	1.346E+00	1.364E+00	1.372E+00	1.377E+00	1.379E+00	1.380E+00	1.381E+00	1.381E+00
CR(I) =	8.042E-01	4.624E-01	2.253E-01	1.024E-01	4.515E-02	1.959E-02	8.438E-03	3.619E-03	1.549E-03	7.581E-04
CRN(I) =	9.242E-01	7.496E-01	5.615E-01	4.048E-01	2.865E-01	2.009E-01	1.401E-01	9.749E-02	6.775E-02	5.017E-02
CRHY(I) =	7.863E-01	2.446E-01	5.866E-02	1.349E-02	3.063E-03	6.920E-04	1.560E-04	3.511E-05	7.898E-06	2.193E-06
CRHC(I) =	4.147E-01	1.303E-01	3.815E-02	1.090E-02	3.079E-03	8.659E-04	2.428E-04	6.801E-05	1.904E-05	6.423E-06
TRX(I) =	1.212E+00	1.306E+00	1.345E+00	1.362E+00	1.370E+00	1.374E+00	1.375E+00	1.376E+00	1.377E+00	1.377E+00
CR(I) =	8.043E-01	4.628E-01	2.260E-01	1.033E-01	4.583E-02	2.007E-02	8.729E-03	3.785E-03	1.639E-03	8.108E-04
CRN(I) =	9.242E-01	7.499E-01	5.625E-01	4.068E-01	2.891E-01	2.038E-01	1.431E-01	1.003E-01	7.021E-02	5.234E-02
CRHY(I) =	7.867E-01	2.450E-01	5.887E-02	1.357E-02	3.088E-03	6.996E-04	1.582E-04	3.572E-05	8.063E-06	2.246E-06
CRHC(I) =	4.147E-01	1.304E-01	3.820E-02	1.093E-02	3.096E-03	8.729E-04	2.456E-04	6.904E-05	1.940E-05	6.568E-06
TRX(I) =	1.212E+00	1.306E+00	1.346E+00	1.363E+00	1.371E+00	1.375E+00	1.377E+00	1.378E+00	1.378E+00	1.378E+00
CR(I) =	8.042E-01	4.624E-01	2.254E-01	1.027E-01	4.542E-02	1.981E-02	8.583E-03	3.706E-03	1.598E-03	7.874E-04
CRN(I) =	9.242E-01	7.496E-01	5.617E-01	4.055E-01	2.876E-01	2.023E-01	1.417E-01	9.900E-02	6.913E-02	5.141E-02
CRHY(I) =	7.864E-01	2.446E-01	5.870E-02	1.351E-02	3.072E-03	6.950E-04	1.569E-04	3.539E-05	7.979E-06	2.220E-06
CRHC(I) =	4.147E-01	1.303E-01	3.816E-02	1.091E-02	3.086E-03	8.692E-04	2.443E-04	6.856E-05	1.924E-05	6.505E-06
TRX(I) =	1.212E+00	1.306E+00	1.346E+00	1.363E+00	1.371E+00	1.375E+00	1.377E+00	1.378E+00	1.378E+00	1.378E+00

R E A C T O R   D E S I G N   R E S U L T S

ZZ(I) =	1.234E-01	2.438E-01	3.642E-01	4.846E-01	6.050E-01	7.254E-01	8.458E-01	9.662E-01	1.087E+00	1.207E+00
CR(I) =	8.042E-01	4.624E-01	2.254E-01	1.027E-01	4.542E-02	1.981E-02	8.583E-03	3.706E-03	1.598E-03	7.874E-04
CBN(I) =	9.242E-01	7.496E-01	5.617E-01	4.055E-01	2.876E-01	2.023E-01	1.417E-01	9.900E-02	6.913E-02	5.141E-02
CRHY(I) =	7.864E-01	2.446E-01	5.870E-02	1.351E-02	3.072E-03	6.950E-04	1.569E-04	3.539E-05	7.979E-06	2.220E-06
CRHC(I) =	4.147E-01	1.303E-01	3.816E-02	1.091E-02	3.086E-03	8.692E-04	2.443E-04	6.856E-05	1.924E-05	6.505E-06
TBX(I) =	1.212E+00	1.306E+00	1.346E+00	1.363E+00	1.371E+00	1.375E+00	1.377E+00	1.378E+00	1.378E+00	1.378E+00
TS(I) =	7.906E+02	8.515E+02	8.746E+02	8.846E+02	8.893E+02	8.915E+02	8.926E+02	8.931E+02	8.933E+02	8.934E+02
CS(I) =	4.623E-01	2.086E-01	9.009E-02	3.885E-02	1.677E-02	7.244E-03	3.130E-03	1.353E-03	5.850E-04	2.893E-04

GAS COMPOSITION MOL-FRACTION

ZZ(I)	HYDROGEN	H2S	NH3	CH4
0.1234	.96801	.01343	.00104	.01752
0.2438	.88499	.04145	.00387	.06969
0.3642	.84005	.06230	.00706	.09059
0.4846	.82088	.07317	.00971	.09625
0.6050	.81241	.07819	.01169	.09771
0.7254	.80835	.08043	.01311	.09811
0.8458	.80623	.08142	.01412	.09824
0.9662	.80503	.08185	.01483	.09830
1.0866	.80431	.08205	.01532	.09832
1.2070	.80392	.08213	.01562	.09834

FIG. 7-11 Computer output of program RDMOT3 for designing a laboratory-size trickle-bed reactor (*continued*).

Frye and Mosby conclude that this equation is specific to hydrodesulfurization. However, their approach is also applicable to hydrodenitrogenation.

NOMENCLATURE

A	Frequency factor
A_c	Cross-sectional area of catalyst bed, m^2
Bo	Bodenstein number, dimensionless
c_p	Specific heat of gas, kJ/(kg · K)
c_{pL}	Specific heat of liquid phase, kJ/(kg · K)
C	Molar concentration of key reactant, kmol/kg
C_H	Molar concentration of hydrogen in bulk gas phase, kmol/m^3
C_{hy}	Molar concentration of hydrocrackable hydrocarbons, i.e., the entire unreacted feedstock, kmol/m^3
C_{hy0}	Inlet molar concentration of hydrocrackable compounds, kmol/m^3
C_L	Molar concentration of key reactant in liquid phase or molar concentration of hydrocarbons containing an atom of sulfur, kmol/m^3
C_{L0}	Inlet value of C_L
C_N	Molar concentration of compounds each containing one atom of nitrogen, kmol/m^3
C_{N0}	Inlet value of C_N
C_{ox}	Molar concentration of compounds each containing one atom of oxygen, kmol/m^3
C_{ox0}	Inlet value of C_{ox}
C_r	Reduced molar concentration of key reactant (sulfur), dimensionless
C_{rhc}	Reduced molar concentration of unsaturated double bonds, dimensionless
C_{HC0}	Inlet concentration of unsaturated compounds, kmol/m^3
C_{rhy}	Reduced molar concentration of hydrocrackable compounds, dimensionless
C_{rN}	Reduced molar concentration of nitrogen-containing compounds, dimensionless

C_{rox}	Reduced molar concentration of oxygen-containing compounds, dimensionless
d_p	Catalyst particle diameter, m
d_s	Equivalent spherical diameter of catalyst particle, m
D	Diffusivity of reacting molecules in liquid phase, m^2/s
D_H	Molecular diffusion coefficient for hydrogen, cm^2/s
D_{Heff}	Effective diffusion coefficient for hydrogen, cm^2/s
D_T	Inside diameter of reactor, m
E	Activation energy, kJ/kmol
H/M	Hydrogen/oil mole ratio
k_1	Reaction rate constant for type 1 sulfur
k_2	Reaction rate constant for type 2 sulfur
k_{H_2S}	Adsorption equilibrium constant for hydrogen sulfide
K_a	Axial thermal diffusivity in packed beds, m^2/s
K_A	Average adsorption equilibrium [in Eq. (7-50)] constant for aromatic hydrocarbons
LHSV	Liquid hourly space velocity
P	Total pressure, bars
P_A	Partial pressure of aromatic hydrocarbons, bars
Pe_{mal}	Péclet number for mass and axial dispersion in liquid phase, dimensionless
P_H	Partial pressure of hydrogen, bars
P_0	Vapor pressure of sulfur compound, bars
$\mathcal{R}$	Global reaction rate, $kmol/(s \cdot m^3)$
S	Sulfur concentration in the product, $kmol/m^3$ or [in Eq. (7-50)] amount of a single sulfur compound
S_1^0	Initial content of type 1 (aliphatic) sulfur, $kmol/m^3$
S_2^0	Initial content of type 2 (thiophenic) sulfur, $kmol/m^3$
T	Absolute temperature, K
T_0	Absolute inlet temperature of feed to reactor, K
T_r	Reduced temperature, dimensionless
u	Superficial velocity of the gas phase, m/s
u_L	Superficial velocity of the liquid phase, m/s

v'	Mole fraction of liquid vaporized, dimensionless
V	Total volume of catalyst beds of the reactor, m^3
V_G	Gas volume in catalyst beds of the reactor, m^3
V_L	Liquid volume in catalyst beds of the reactor, m^3
V_p	Volume of catalyst particles in packed beds of the reactor, m^3
WHSV	Weight hourly space velocity
X	Mole fraction of compound S in liquid, dimensionless
X_0	Mole fraction of compound S in feed liquid, dimensionless
z	Axial coordinate in the reactor, m
Z	Dimensionless axial coordinate in the reactor
Z_T	Total reactor length, m
α	Reaction order, dimensionless
$-\Delta H$	Heat of reaction, kJ/kmol
η	Effectiveness factors of various reactions
ε	Void fraction, dimensionless
ε_G	Gas-phase fraction, dimensionless
ε_L	Liquid-phase fraction or liquid holdup, dimensionless
ε_p	Catalyst-particle-phase fraction, dimensionless
θ	Time = 1/LHSV, h
μ_L	Viscosity of the liquid phase, Pa · s or kg/(m · s)
ρ	Density of gas, kg/m^3
ρ_L	Density of liquid phase, kg/m^3
ρ_p	Particle density, g/cm^3
φ_H	Thiele modulus for hydrogen
τ	Tortuosity factor, dimensionless

Subscripts

0	Initial
f	Final

REFERENCES

1. Arthur Kohl and Fred Riesenfeld, *Gas Purification,* 2d ed., Gulf Publishing Co., 1974.

2. M. Orhan Tarhan and Louis H. Windsor, "Coke-Oven Oils Yield High Quality Benzene," *Chem. Eng. Progr.* **62**(2):67–72 (1966).
3. Richard A. Flinn, Harold Beuther, and B. K. Schmid, "Now You Can Improve Residue Treating," *Petrol. Refiner* **40**(4):139–44 (1961).
4. R. R. Cecil, F. X. Mayer, and E. N. Cart, Jr., "Fuel Oil Hydrodesulfurization Studies in Pilot Plant Reactors," paper presented at the Am. Inst. Chem. Engrs. Meeting, Los Angeles, December 1968.
5. J. B. Fourier, *Théorie analytique de la chaleur,* Oeuvres de Fourier, Gauthier-Villars et Fils, Paris, 1822.
6. J. B. Maxwell, *Data Book on Hydrocarbons,* The Esso Series, D. van Nostrand, New York, 5th Printing, 1958.
7. Robert H. Perry and Cecil H. Chilton, *Chemical Engineers' Handbook,* 5th ed. McGraw-Hill, New York, 1973.
8. H. C. Henry and J. B. Gilbert, "Scale-up of Pilot Plant Data for Catalytic Hydroprocessing," *Ind. Eng. Chem. Process Design Develop.* **12,** 328–334 (1973).
9. Charles N. Satterfield, Yi Hua Ma, and Thomas K. Sherwood, "The Effectiveness Factor in Liquid-Filled Porous Catalyst," *Inst.* Chem. Engrs. Symposium Series no. 28, Inst. Chem. Engrs., London, 1968 pp. 22–29.
10. Charles R. Wilke and P. Chang, "Correlation of Diffusion Coefficients in Dilute Solutions," *AIChE J.* **1:**264–270 (1955).
11. Charles N. Satterfield, *Mass Transfer in Heterogeneous Catalysis,* MIT Press, Cambridge, Mass., 1970.
12. David E. Mears, "The Role of Axial Dispersion in Trickle-Flow Laboratory Reactors," *Chem. Eng. Sci.* **26:**1361–1366 (1971).
13. V. E. Sater and Octave Levenspiel, "Two-Phase Flow in Packed Beds," *Ind. Eng. Chem. Fundamentals* **5:**86–92 (1966).
14. J. M. Hochman and E. Effron, "Two-Phase Cocurrent Downflow in Packed Beds," *Ind. Eng. Chem. Fundamentals* **8:**64–71 (1969).
15. F. DeMaria and R. R. White, "Transient Response Study of Gas Flowing through Irrigated Packing," *AIChE J.* **6:**473–481 (1960).
16. C. G. Frye and J. E. Mosby, "Kinetics of Hydrodesulfurization," *Chem. Eng. Progr.* **63**(9):66–77 (1967).
17. Olaf A. Hougen and Kenneth M. Watson, *Chemical Process Principles,* vol. 3, John Wiley, New York, 1947; 9th printing 1962.

Chapter 8 FIXED-BED BUBBLE REACTORS (FBBR)

If trickle-bed reactors have not been sufficiently studied, *fixed-bed bubble reactors* (FBBRs) have been even less well studied. In 1952 Schönemann[1] wrote that FBBRs had not yet been introduced into practice because the upflow would entrain the catalyst and this would limit the upflow. Of course, today, this is no big problem, as will be discussed further below.

Fixed-bed bubble reactors are reactors in which the liquid phase is the continuous phase and the gas phase is the disperse phase. The typical FBBR is an upflow concurrent gas-liquid reactor (type II in Fig. 6-1) with relatively low gas and liquid flow. If the liquid flow is increased beyond the fluidization velocity, the fixed bed of catalyst expands into an *ebullated bed,* which will be discussed in Chap. 9. However, it is possible to operate an upflow fixed-bed reactor as an FBBR at or above the fluidization velocity if the upward expansion of the fixed bed is prevented by installing hold-down plates right above the fixed bed. These plates are made of screens open enough to permit the passage of liquid and gas but fine enough to prevent catalyst particles from going through. If the liquid and/or gas flows are increased even higher, then the system will enter the pulsating regime, which is discussed in Sec. 8.3.

Interest in FBBRs arose during development work at Oak Ridge National Laboratory on a reactor to reduce uranium (VI) to uranium (IV) nitrate in aqueous solution with hydrogen over a supported palladium catalyst. Flooded concurrent upflow operation gave higher conversions than downflow trickle-bed regime.[2] Subsequently, Mochizuki et al.[3] found the FBBR to be more selective than the trickle-bed reactor in the hydrogenation of phenyl acetylene (PA) to styrene over Pd/Al_2O_3 catalyst, the undesirable reaction being the consecutive hydrogenation of styrene to ethyl benzene.

We really know very little about FBBRs, so we will discuss both the transport phenomena and the process design of this class of reactors in a single chapter.

8.1
TRANSPORT PHENOMENA IN FBBRS

Transport phenomena in FBBRs have great resemblance to those in suspended-bed reactors, which will be discussed in Chap. 9.

Pressure Drop across FBBRs

The pressure drop across an FBBR consists of three basic terms:

1. The pressure drop across the sparger
2. The pressure drop to overcome the liquid column of height H_L and density ρ_L (Fig. 8-1)
3. The pressure drop due to gas flow through the submerged fixed catalyst bed

A *sparger* is simply a pipe with many holes on it to distribute a gas in a liquid. The pipe may be of various shapes and sizes. The gas pressure in the pipe, the pressure in the liquid, the densities of the gas and the liquid, and the temperature and the size of the sparger holes determine the size and frequency of the bubbles.

The pressure drop across a sparger can be calculated by following

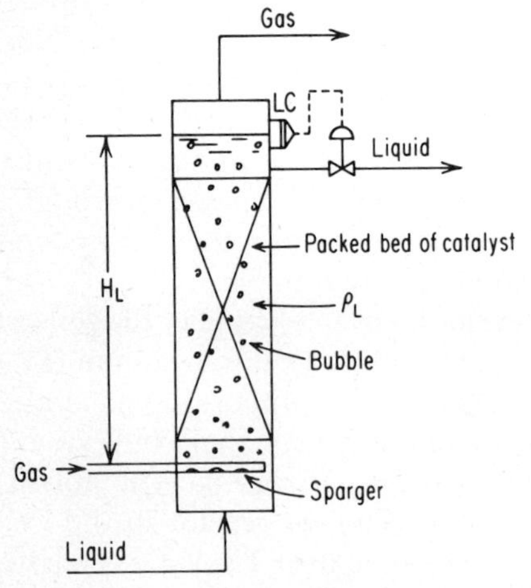

FIG. 8-1 Schematic representation of a fixed-bed bubble reactor (FBBR).

the procedure given in the *Chemical Engineers Handbook*[4] and also the procedure suggested by Litz.[5]

The pressure drop to overcome the liquid column in the fixed bed can be calculated jointly by using the method of Turpin and Huntington (see Sec. 6.2).

Gas Dispersion in FBBRs

While the liquid feed is pumped in bulk to the bottom of an FBBR, the gas must also be properly distributed in the form of bubbles at the bottom. Of course, the fixed bed itself is a good distributor. However, only in a small narrow reactor can one depend exclusively on the bed for gas distribution. In a large-diameter bed it becomes necessary to install a sufficient number of spargers all through the cross-sectional area under the bed. Again, the fine distribution is effected by the bed.

Unlike the suspended-bed reactors, in the case of the FBBRs the size of the bubbles is not critical because the dimensions of the rising bubbles are determined by factors independent of the sparger, e.g., the size and shape of the catalyst particles and the viscosities of the gas and the liquid.

Axial and Radial Dispersion in FBBRs

Hanns Hofmann[6] published correlations between the liquid-phase Péclet number for mass and the product of the Reynolds and Schmidt numbers (Re · Sc) for FBBRs. He found that bubble size had no effect on Pe. The correlation consists of families of curves depending on parameters such as u_G and u_L/u_G. Hofmann investigated the celebrated air-water system in an FBBR packed with 4-mm × 10-mm glass cylinders and 2-mm glass spheres. The shape of the curves were completely different. It is therefore fair to conclude that the Péclet number of any other gas-liquid system with any particular shape and size of catalyst would have to be experimentally determined.

Heat Transfer in FBBRs

For mildly endothermic or exothermic reactions FBBRs can be run as adiabatic reactors and the cooling and heating can be done by heat exchanging the liquid with a coolant or a heating medium between beds. For more strongly exothermic reactions it should be possible to install cooling coils right in the catalyst bed. The strong backmixing caused by the turbulence of the bubbles rising between catalyst particles should enhance the transfer of heat from the particles to the liquid and then from the liquid to the coil.

Mass Transfer in FBBRs

S. Goto et al.[7] studied the mass transfer in FBBRs and trickle-bed reactors and found that the catalyst-to-liquid mass transfer coefficient $k_s a$ and the liquid-to-gas mass transfer coefficient $k_L a$ do not differ greatly between concurrent upflow or downflow reactors. However, upflow gives somewhat higher $k_s a$ than downflow at high gas rates, low liquid rates, and smaller particle sizes. FBBRs give higher $k_L a$ than trickle beds at high gas and high liquid flow rates.

Snider and Perona[2] studied the mass transfer in an FBBR using the hydrogenation of α-methylstyrene in a differential reactor over two different palladium-on-alumina catalysts. They found that gas and liquid flow rates strongly influenced the reaction rate and that the gas flow increased the transfer rate. The effects of temperature and composition on reaction rates were much weaker. The rate of mass transfer of hydrogen in the liquid phase can be represented by the equation:

$$\mathcal{R}_c = \frac{k_L a}{\rho_c}(C^* - C_s) \tag{8-1}$$

where $\mathcal{R}_c$ = reaction rate, kmol/(s · kg of catalyst)

C^* = equilibrium hydrogen concentration in liquid phase, kmol/m^3

C_s = hydrogen concentration in liquid phase at catalyst surface, kmol/m^3

k_L = mass-transfer coefficient, m/s

a = external surface area of the catalyst pellets per unit bed volume, 1060 m^{-1}

ρ_c = bulk density of catalyst, kg/m^3 of bed volume

In order to calculate $k_L a$ from this equation, $\mathcal{R}_c$ and ρ_c are obtained from experiments, C^* is obtained from the reactor pressure and the Henry's law constant according to Johnson et al.,[8] and C_s is calculated from:

$$\mathcal{R}_c = \frac{A\, C_s\, C_B}{(1 + B(C_s^{1/2}))^2(1 + C_s C_B)} \tag{8-2}$$

where C_B is the concentration of α-methylstyrene in kilomoles per cubic meter and A, B, and C are empirical constants in Eq. (8-2) and are obtainable from Refs. 2 and 9 after proper adjustments for conversion from the cgs to the SI system.

Snider and Perona obtained low mass transfer coefficients for gas

Reynolds numbers above 50. They tentatively attributed this decline to the pulsing regime.

It appears that for any other reaction to be run in a FBBR, C_s has to be determined experimentally from the kinetic equation of that reaction.

8.2 PROCESS DESIGN OF FBBRs

The first step in designing an FBBR should be the determination of the rate-controlling step or steps. Once this is done, the reaction rate must be expressed in terms of this step.

The second step is to determine the rate of liquid upflow. This rate must be below the fluidization rate; otherwise the FBBR would become an ebullated-bed reactor. It is theoretically possible to use bed limiters or hold-down plates or the like to maintain the fixed bed beyond the fluidization rates. However, indications are that the mass transfer would suffer from pulsing under the higher rates. Thus the hourly capacity of the reactor would determine the cross-sectional area A_c.

The exothermicity or endothermicity of the reactions must be expressed by differential equations as a function of z and heat transfer means must be devised to remove or supply the heat.

The combined design equation for mass and heat must be integrated or resolved for the reactor height Z_T corresponding to the desired conversion x. If the desired x is higher than the practically possible x, the product may be distilled and unreacted feedstock recycled. Economics would dictate how high an x should be attained in the reactor and how much reactant should be recycled after the product distillation.

8.3 GAS-LIQUID-PHASE FIXED-BED REACTORS WHICH OPERATE IN THE PULSING OR SPRAY REGIMES

Reactor types that operate at higher flows than the trickle bed or the FBBR are receiving increasing attention. While, in the past, chemical engineers saw mostly their disadvantages, such as the unsteadiness and shaking of the pulsed reactor and the need for effective phase separation after processing in the spray-regime reactor, they are now beginning to see some of the advantages as well. We will attempt a brief review of these fast reactor types in the following.

Transport Phenomena

Most flow maps showing the transition from the gas-continuous trickle-bed regime to the pulsing regime are based on experimental data for the air-water system and cannot be used to predict the transition to the pulsing regime in other systems. T. S. Chou et al.[10] found that the transition from gas-continuous to pulse flow is very sharp in general and that no hysteresis occurs. It appears to the author of this book that, pending the availability of extensive data on various gas-liquid systems, the reactor designer will have to obtain detailed solid data on the particular gas-liquid system of interest.

One known property of pulsing and spray regimes is that the coefficient k_c for mass transfer between liquid and the catalyst particle increases as one progresses from the trickle-bed to the pulsing to the spray regime. A measure of this progress is the power dissipation by the liquid phase per unit packed volume and per unit mass of liquid holdup[11]:

$$E'_L = \frac{(-\Delta P/Z)_{LG}\, u_L}{\varepsilon_L\, \rho_L} \tag{8-3}$$

where

E'_L = power dissipation per unit packed volume and per unit mass of liquid holdup, W/kg

$(-\Delta P/Z)_{LG}$ = pressure drop for concurrent gas-liquid flow, Pa/m

ε_L = liquid holdup, dimensionless

ρ_L = liquid density, kg/m^3

u_L = superficial liquid velocity, m/s

A double logarithmic plot of k_c against E_L gives a straight line with a slope of $+0.22$.

Calderbank and Moo-Young[12] found that heat and mass transfer coefficients in a variety of systems and geometries depend on power dissipation to the one-fourth power. The relationship between k_c and E'_L can be expressed similarly:

$$k_c(\mathrm{Sc})^{2/3} = 0.20(E'_L\, \mu_L/\rho_L)^{1/4} \tag{8-4}$$

The root-means square error of this expression according to Lemay et al.[11] is 0.5×10^{-5} m/s, which corresponds to an average relative error for k_c of about 6%. This relationship is valid with certainty only for aqueous solutions of electrolytes contacting packed spheres.

The effect of radial position on k_c was studied by Lemay et al.,[11] who reviewed the models of Weekman and Meyers[13] and Beimesch and Kessler[14] and concluded that k_c is not especially sensitive to radial position.

Another known property of pulsing and spray regimes is the relationship between the liquid-phase mass-transfer coefficient k_La and the power dissipation E_L by the liquid phase per unit packed volume:

$$E_L = (-\Delta P/Z)_{LG} u_L \qquad \mathrm{W/m^3} \tag{8-5}$$

Lemay et al.[11] plotted $K_L a(\mathrm{Sc})^{1/2}$ against E_L in double logarithmic coordinates and correlated data by various workers. They found that $k_L a(\mathrm{Sc})^{1/2}$ increases with E_L but the line has a slight curvature. Thus, as the fluid velocity and the power dissipation increase in a gas-liquid packed bed, both k_c and $k_L a$ increase.

Choice of Fast Reactors and Process Design

Because gas-liquid-phase fixed-bed reactors operating in the pulsing and spray regimes have higher gas absorption capacities than similar reactors operating as trickle beds, these faster reactors should be used with reactions that have higher intrinsic reaction rates. Catalysts used in such reactors can be made more effective by depositing the active components in a thin layer near the geometric surface.

Designers should find reactors in pulsing and spray regimes quite attractive because such regimes will enable them to design faster and more economical reactors. However, this sort of design is pure pioneering in a yet unknown territory.

Lemay et al.[11] compared a fixed-bed reactor in the pulsing regime with a CSTR. While the former has the advantage of increased mass transfer, the latter can achieve the same result by using finely divided catalyst. The CSTR was found to be the reactor of choice.

Here there are some reservations—the following factors may reverse the above choice:

- The catalyst recovery economics of the CSTR
- The catalyst contamination of the product in the CSTR
- The requirement for high yield of reaction, which is impossible in the CSTR

The design procedure for the pulsing-flow or spray-regime fixed-bed reactor is basically the same as that for the plug-flow type of trickle-bed reactor.

NOMENCLATURE

a	External surface area of the catalyst pellets per unit bed volume, m^{-1}
C^*	Equilibrium hydrogen concentration in liquid phase, $kmol/m^3$
C_s	Hydrogen concentration in liquid phase at catalyst surface, $kmol/m^3$

E_L	Power dissipation by the liquid phase per unit packed volume, W/m^3
E_L'	Power dissipation per unit packed volume and per unit mass of liquid holdup, W/kg
H_L	Liquid column height in an FBBR, m
k_c	Catalyst surface-to-liquid mass transfer coefficient, m/s
k_L	Liquid-to-gas mass-transfer coefficient, m/s
Pe	Péclet number, dimensionless
$\mathcal{R}_c$	Global reaction rate, kmol/(s · kg) of catalyst
Re	Reynolds number, dimensionless
Sc	Schmidt number, dimensionless
u_L	Superficial liquid velocity, m/s
ε_L	Liquid holdup, dimensionless
ρ_c	Bulk density of catalyst, kg/m^3
ρ_L	Liquid density, kg/m^3
$(-\Delta P/Z)_{LG}$	Pressure drop for concurrent gas-liquid flow, Pa/m or bars/m

REFERENCES

1. K. Schoenemann, *Der chemische Umsatz bei kontinuierlich durchgeführten Reaktionen,* Dechema Monograph **21,** 1952, p. 203.
2. J. W. Snider and J. J. Perona, "Mass Transfer in a Fixed-Bed Gas-Liquid Catalytic Reactor with Concurrent Upflow," *AIChE J*. **20:**1172–1177 (1974).
3. S. Mochizuki and T. Matsui, "Selective Hydrogenation and Mass Transfer in a Fixed-Bed Catalytic Reactor with Gas-Liquid Concurrent Upflow," *AIChE J*. **22:**904–909 (1976).
4. D. F. Boucher and G. E. Alves, "Fluid and Particle Mechanics," in Perry and Chilton (eds.), *Chemical Engineering Handbook,* McGraw-Hill, New York, 1973, Sec. 5, pp. 5-47–5-48.
5. W. J. Litz, "Design of Gas Distributors," *Chem. Eng.* (Nov. 13) 162–166 (1972).
6. Hanns Hofmann, "Der derzeitige Stand bei der Vorausberechnung in technischen Reaktoren," *Chem. Eng. Sci.* **14:**193–208 (1961).
7. S. Goto, J. Levec, and J. M. Smith, "Mass Transfer in Packed Beds with Two-Phase Flow," *Ind. Eng. Chem. Process Design Develop.* **14:**473–478 (1975).
8. D. L. Johnson, H. Saito, J. D. Polejes, and Olaf A. Hougen, "Effects of Bubbling and Stirring on Mass Transfer Coefficients in Liquids," *AIChE J*. **3:**411–417 (1957).

9. B. D. Babcock, G. T. Mejdell, and Olaf A. Hougen, "Catalyzed Gas-Liquid Reactions in Trickling-Bed Reactors. Part I. Hydrogenation of α-Methylstyrene Catalyzed by Palladium," *AIChE J.* **3:**366–369 (1957).

10. T. S. Chou, F. L. Worley, Jr., and Dan Luss, "Transition to Pulsed Flow in Mixed-Phase Cocurrent Downflow through a Fixed Bed," *Ind. Eng. Chem. Process Design Develop.* **16:**424–427 (1977).

11. Y. Lemay, G. Pineault, and J. A. Ruether, "Particle-Liquid Mass Transfer in a Three-Phase Fixed-Bed Reactor with Cocurrent Flow in the Pulsing Regime," *Ind. Eng. Chem. Process Design Develop.* **14:**280–285 (1975).

12. P. H. Calderbank and M. B. Moo-Young, "The Continuous Heat and Mass Transfer Properties of Dispersions," *Chem. Eng. Sci.* **16:**39–54 (1961).

13. Vern W. Weekman, Jr. and John E. Myers, "Fluid Flow Characteristics of Concurrent Gas-Liquid Flow in Packed Beds," *AIChE J.* **10:**951–958 (1964).

14. W. E. Beimesch and D. P. Kessler, "Liquid-Gas Distribution Measurements in the Pulsing Regime of Two-Phase Concurrent Flow in Packed Beds," *AIChE J.* **17:**1160–1165 (1971).

Chapter 9 SUSPENDED-BED REACTORS

In the previous two chapters we discussed various forms of gas-liquid-phase fixed-bed reactors. In this chapter we will discuss catalytic gas-liquid-phase reactors in which the catalyst does not form a fixed bed but is suspended in the liquid by a variety of methods.

9.1 DEFINITIONS—CLASSIFICATION

Suspended-bed reactors are a class of heterogeneous gas-liquid phase reactors in which the catalyst particles are loosely supported in the liquid phase. This support is provided either by vigorous mechanical agitation as in continuous stirred-tank reactors (CSTRs), by rising gas bubbles as in slurry-bubble reactors, or by upflow of liquid as in ebullated-bed and three-phase transport reactors (3ϕTR). Let us now define and describe each reactor type before discussing the transport phenomena in each type and then their process design.

Continuous Stirred-Tank Reactor (CSTR)

Continuous stirred-tank reactors that contain finely divided heterogeneous catalyst suspended in liquid are in most ways quite similar to CSTRs in which homogeneous gas-liquid reactions take place. They basically consist of the same shape of tank with a stirrer. The main mechanical design difference is that the stirrer must keep the fine catalyst particles in suspension in addition to adequately stirring the liquid. To make this task easier the catalyst is supplied in a very fine size, preferably less than 200 μm. Figure 9-1 is a schematic representation of a typical heterogeneous CSTR. The gas feed is injected through a sparger. The

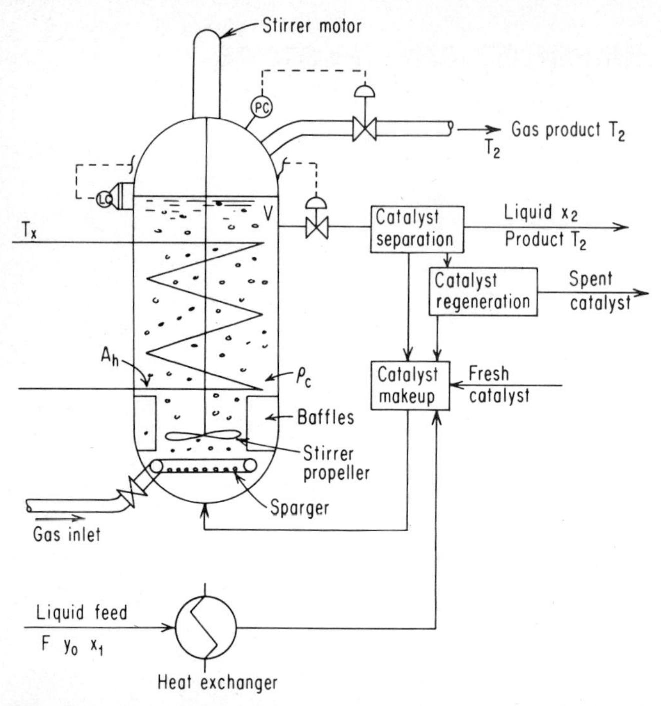

FIG. 9-1 Flow diagram of a typical continuous stirred-tank reactor system.

product gas—if there is any—is removed overhead through a back-pressure control system. The stirrer must disperse gas bubbles sufficiently to provide for adequate absorption time. If the absorption is slow, the exit gas will still be rich in the gas reactant and should be recycled to the gas inlet.

The liquid feed is first brought to the required temperature in a heat exchanger if preheating or precooling is required. The fine catalyst is blended into the liquid feed and introduced into the CSTR with the feed. The liquid product has to be removed from the CSTR together with the suspended catalyst, usually through a level-control system. The catalyst must be separated from the liquid product by filtration, centrifugation, or simple settling. Part of this catalyst might be reused while part of it might have to be regenerated or discarded.

Like the homogeneous CSTR, the heterogeneous catalytic CSTR operates fully isothermally, its contents are thoroughly mixed, and its product concentration is the same as the liquid concentration at any point of the reactor. Figure 9-1 shows only one way of (1) keeping the fine catalyst in suspension and (2) providing for an efficient gas-liquid contact. These two goals can be met in a variety of ways, some of which are schematically shown in Figs. 9-2, 9-3, and 9-4. The choice of any particular way is

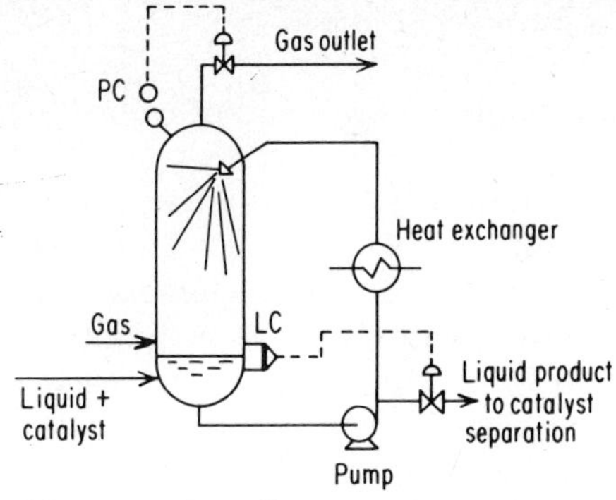

FIG. 9-2 Flow diagram of a CSTR with gas spray contact.

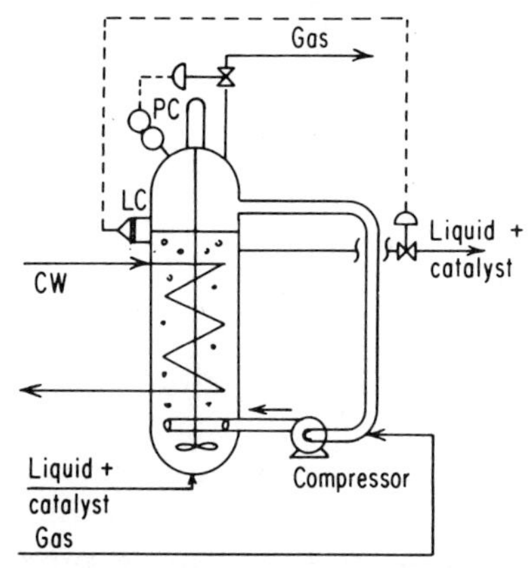

FIG. 9-3 Flow diagram of a CSTR with gas recirculation for increasing gas residence time.

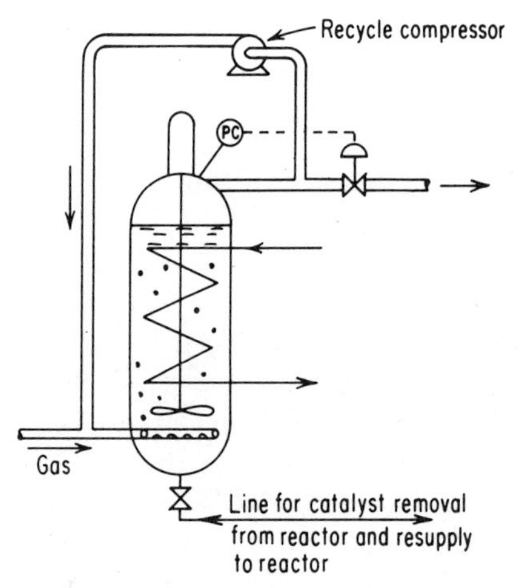

FIG. 9-4 Flow diagram of a CSTR for gas feed and gas product only.

governed by the peculiarity of the gas-liquid reaction and of course by economics.

Figure 9-2 shows a spray-type CSTR, which has the advantage of lower pressure drop for the gas flow than the bubble-type CSTR of Fig. 9-1. Also, the heat exchanger is outside of the reactor, which makes this system easier to design and operate. The stirring is done by pumping around a large amount of liquid and by spraying it into the reactor space. Thus the reactor has no moving parts, no rotating stirrer shafts, and no glands. The catalyst feed and removal are identical to those indicated in Fig. 9-1. Figure 9-3 is a gas recirculation reactor. Basically it is a reactor of the type of Fig. 9-1 with a gas recirculation system to increase the gas residence time in the CSTR. The reactor of Fig. 9-4 has only a gas feed and a gas product. The role of the liquid is simply to suspend the catalyst and to transfer the heat. The liquid is of course fully inert to the gas reactants but dissolves them easily. It is helpful if the product gas is insoluble in the liquid. The advantages and disadvantages of CSTRs are listed in Sec. 9.4.

Slurry Reactors

A *slurry reactor* is a gas-liquid reactor in which the finely divided solid catalyst is held in suspension in the liquid by rising gas bubbles. Thus the English term "slurry reactor" is only partially descriptive: it notes only the catalyst slurry in the liquid. The Germans call this type "Blasenreaktor," or *bubble reactor,* which is also only partially descriptive, since it notes only the bubbles of gas and nothing else. Although all the suspended-bed reactors have a catalyst slurry, the term "slurry reactor" will be used to denote only the particular kind of suspended-bed reactor in which the slurry is supported by an upflow of gas bubbles. Fair[1] used the term *gas-sparged reactor,* which may be justified if bubbles are generated by a sparger. Besides, a gas sparger may also be used in CSTRs and other reactors (Figs. 9-1 and 9-4).

The slurry reactor is attracting increasing attention. Sherwood and Farkas[2,3] at MIT, and especially Kölbel and his pupils[4–10] in Germany, have studied it thoroughly. However, there still is much more to learn. The various uses of the slurry reactor are illustrated in Figs. 9-5 through 9-9. Figure 9-5 shows the most general case, in which a gas and a liquid feed produce a gaseous and a liquid product. The catalyst addition, separation, and regeneration steps are identical to those already discussed for the CSTR. These steps have not been shown in Figs. 9-6 through 9-9 although they are included. The major difference from CSTRs is that the slurry is kept in suspension by rising bubbles instead of by mechanical agitation. Figure 9-6 shows a design for liquid feed and liquid product. An inert gas is recirculated over the sparger to maintain the slurry in suspension. Figure 9-7 shows a design for gaseous feed and gaseous product only. An inert liquid is used to suspend the catalyst. Figure 9-8 shows a slurry reactor for gas and liquid feed and gas products only. The liquid is recirculated until all of it is converted to gas. Figure 9-9 shows a slurry reactor for gas feed and liquid product only. No gas leaves the reactor. The gas is catalytically condensed to a liquid product.

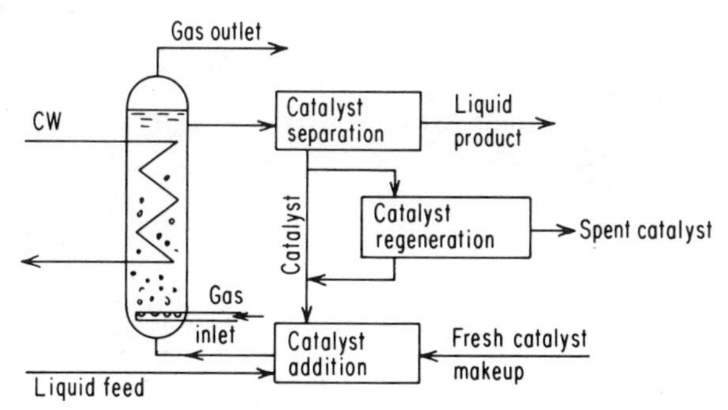

FIG. 9-5 Flow diagram of a slurry reactor system for gas and liquid reactants.

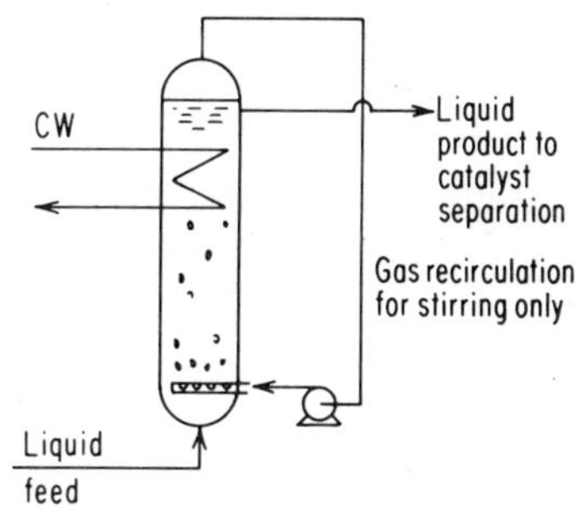

FIG. 9-6 Flow diagram of a slurry reactor for liquid feed and liquid product only.

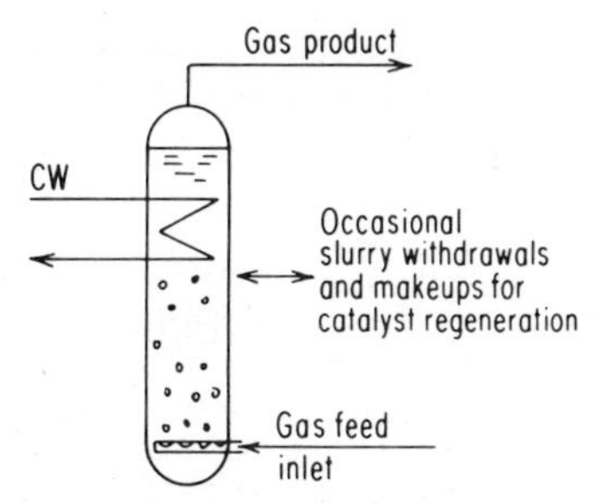

FIG. 9-7 Flow diagram of a slurry reactor for gaseous feed and gaseous product only.

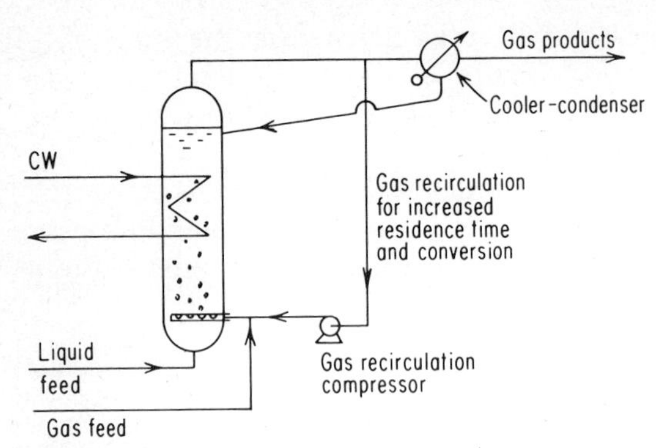

FIG. 9-8 Flow diagram of a slurry reactor for gaseous and liquid feed and gaseous products only.

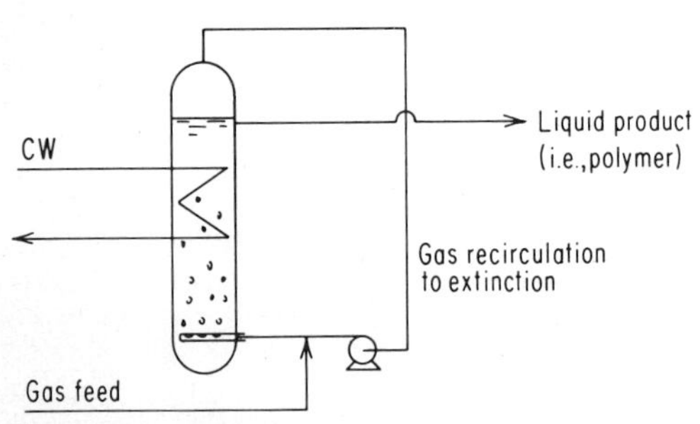

FIG. 9-9 Flow diagram of a slurry reactor for gaseous feed and liquid product only.

Slurry reactors as a rule have been used in the chemical industry only in small-scale batch hydrogenations and are not yet common in the larger operations of either the chemical or petrochemical industries. A notable exception might be the Institut Français du Pétrole's (IFP) recent development of the slurry reactor process for catalytic hydrogenation of benzene to cyclohexane.[11] The use of the slurry reactor extends beyond batch hydrogenations to some continuous operations such as the Fischer-Tropsch reaction[5,6] and various other continuous processes of possible commercial interest. Examples may be the hydrogenation of α-methylstyrene to cumene reported by Polejes,[12] oxidation of ethylene by air reported by Smidt et al.,[13,14] and hydrogenation of ethylene reported by Kölbel and Maennig.[9]

Ebullated-Bed Reactors

The *ebullated-bed reactor* is a concurrent upflow gas-liquid reactor in which a strong liquid upflow expands the bed of coarse solid catalyst up to 100% or more of the fixed-bed volume. We can also say that the ebullated-bed reactor is a three-phase fluidized-bed reactor in which fluidization is accomplished by the liquid upflow.

The ebullated bed may be best understood by watching a laboratory glass reactor filled with a bed of coarse solid catalyst when an upflow of liquid through it is slowly increased and when, in addition, a flow of gas is started and increased (Fig. 9-10). Let us assume a vertical glass reactor of 2.5 cm ID containing a 0.2-m-high bed of 3-mm extrudate of a commercial alumina-based catalyst. Let us fill the reactor with water and let us start a slow upflow of the water. At low liquid rates the fixed bed of catalyst is not disturbed. Water flows through it. At a rate of approximately 30 $m^3/(h \cdot m^2)$, or 0.00833 $m^3/(s \cdot m^2)$, the catalyst bed

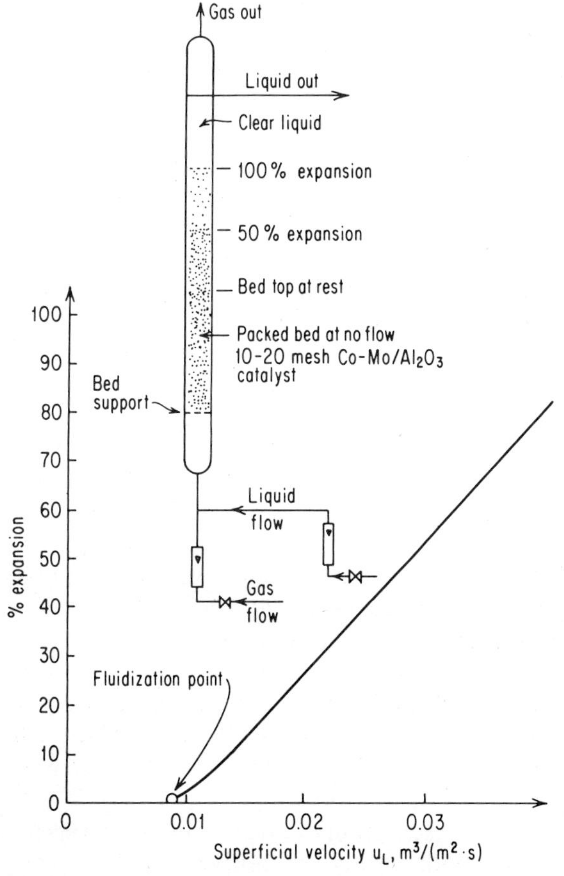

FIG. 9-10 The expansion of a catalyst bed in an ebullated-bed reactor.

starts to expand upwards in the same way that a gas-solid fluidized bed "unlocks" at the fluidization point. Each catalyst particle in the expanded bed acquires a random movement, quickly moving in all directions but still remaining in the same general location. When the liquid upflow is further increased, the now loosened bed is further expanded according to the plot shown in Fig. 9-10. This bed expansion is obviously a kind of fluidization similar to the gas-solid phenomenon known by chemical engineers for several decades. As in gas-solid fluidization, the top of the expanded liquid-solid bed is fairly well defined. The liquid layer above the bed is quite clearly distinguished.

When a concurrent gas flow is added to the liquid upflow, the bed expansion data still fall on the same curve obtained with liquid flow only. It is not possible to expand the bed by using a little liquid flow and increased gas flow. Usually the liquid is first blown over and then pistons of wet slugs of the catalyst bed are also blown over. This means that the gas upflow does not affect the fluidization significantly, at least not in the proportions of gas and liquid described above. Thus it appears that the ebullated bed is basically a liquid-solid phenomenon. The only effect of the gas flow is to make the upper boundary of the fluidized bed somewhat less well defined and to intensify the random movement of the catalyst pellets.

The catalyst size in the ebullated bed is very important. If a catalyst of relatively large particle size is used for a first reaction and a somewhat smaller-size catalyst is used for a second reaction, the coarser catalyst forms a bed at the lower part of the reactor while the finer catalyst is expanded further above the coarse bed and forms a second bed, both beds being at the same temperature. This way two consecutive reactions can be run in the same reactor.

Of course large catalyst pellets are easier to separate from the feedstock, but on the other hand such large pellets have a low effectiveness factor. In order to increase the effectiveness factor Hydrocarbon Research, Inc. (HRI) has suggested catalyst sizes as fine as 60 mesh. An important advantage of using relatively coarse catalyst pellets is the ability to treat feedstocks containing particulate materials which would plug up fixed-bed reactors. Particulate materials simply pass through the ebullated catalyst bed without plugging it. In fact, in the H-Coal process the feedstock consists of finely ground coal mixed with the product oil.

In spite of the vigorous turbulence in the ebullated bed, cylindrically shaped catalyst pellets are not degraded by abrasion, so that extruded pellets can be used.

Figure 9-11 is a schematic representation of an ebullated-bed reactor. The gas and liquid inlets are both located at the bottom. The bed is supported by a screen which permits the gas and the liquid to pass through but not the solid catalyst. There is sufficient clear liquid on top of the bed to allow the liquid product to be withdrawn without also withdrawing any catalyst particles.

The solid-liquid-gas fluidized-bed reactor was first studied by E. S. Johanson of Hydrocarbon Research, Inc., who called it an *ebullated bed* and patented it.[15] The H-Oil and H-Coal processes use such a reactor.[16–20] The H-Oil process is fully commercialized. Experience has been obtained in plants at Lake Charles, Louisiana and Shuaiba, Kuwait,[21–22] and a number of other plants have since been built.[23]

Three-Phase Transport Reactor (3φTR)

In the ebullated bed, the settling velocity of catalyst particles balances the liquid upflow velocity, and the catalyst bed as a whole does not move. When the liquid velocity is further increased, the liquid upflow entrains the catalyst particles out of the reactor. If the entrained liquid-catalyst slurry is recycled to the bottom of the reactor and if a gas is added at the bottom and separated at the top, we have a *three-phase transport* reactor (3φTR) (Fig. 9-12). This reactor type was studied by B. B. Pruden and M. E. Weber in Canada[24] and appears to have some advantages. It can be designed either as a concurrent or a countercurrent reactor. In either case, the catalyst is entrained by the liquid flow, which is up or down, respectively. The gas is, of course, always upflow. Figure 9-12 represents

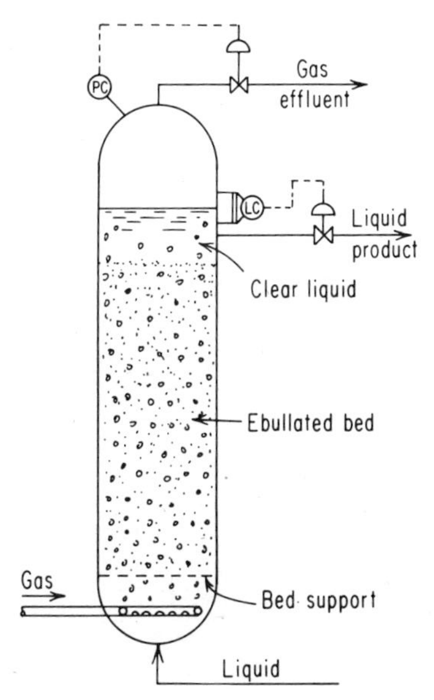

FIG. 9-11 A diagram of an ebullated-bed reactor.

a concurrent 3ϕTR. Gas and liquid feeds are injected into the outlet line of the slurry pump, which circulates the liquid-catalyst slurry at a rate greater than the fluidization velocity. Gas bubbles go straight up and reach the gas space. The liquid is strongly recirculated over the downcomer line and the slurry pump. Liquid corresponding to the feed rate leaves the top of the reactor through a liquid level control valve CV_2. The gas leaves the top of the reactor through a back-pressure control valve CV_1. The entire liquid product stream must be treated in the catalyst separation step, in which catalyst is separated from the liquid. Depending on the properties of the catalyst used, part or all of the separated catalyst pellets can be regenerated and then recycled to the process over the catalyst makeup step. The regenerated catalyst is screened to eliminate fines and conglomerates, pretreated, if necessary (e.g., presulfided), and blended into a slurry along with fresh makeup catalyst and added to the downcomer stream.

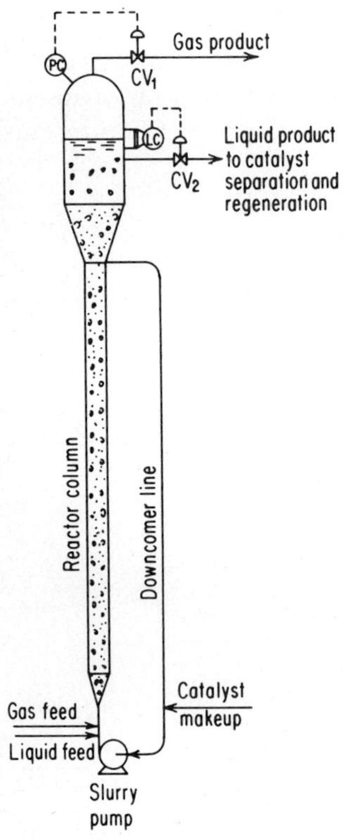

FIG. 9-12 A diagram of a three-phase concurrent transport reactor.

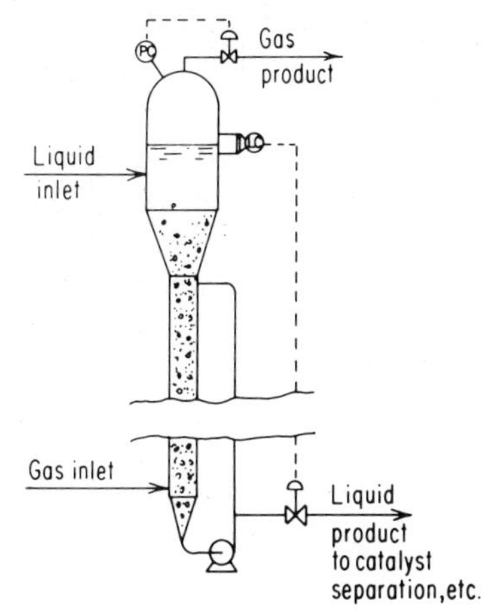

FIG. 9-13 A diagram of a three-phase countercurrent transport reactor.

The concurrent 3ϕTR is suitable for reactions that require short residence time for the gas. The main advantage of the countercurrent 3ϕTR is the long residence time it allows the gas bubbles. Figure 9-13 represents such a reactor system. Gas bubbles introduced into the catalyst slurry must rise against the down-flowing slurry. By varying this downflow velocity, it is possible to decrease the velocity of the bubbles relative to the reactor wall and hence increase the residence time of the gas in the reactor. Of course, the velocity of the bubbles in relation to the slurry is constant.

The gas flow in the 3ϕTR is plug flow, while the liquid flow is completely backmixed.

9.2
TRANSPORT PHENOMENA IN GAS-LIQUID-PHASE SUSPENDED-BED REACTORS

When designing suspended-bed reactors, the main flow dynamic concerns of the designer are:

- The pressure drop across the reactor
- The dispersion of the gas bubbles into the liquid
- Maintaining the catalyst in suspension in the liquid and the means for achieving this suspension
- Achieving adequate mass transfer between the gas and the liquid and

between the liquid and the catalyst surface

- Heat transfer to or from the suspended bed

The major task of the designer is to design for the conditions of the suspended bed. Once this is achieved, the calculation of the size of the bed is usually quite simple. In many cases it does not require the use of computers unless complex kinetic problems are involved. Thus the main problem is represented by transport phenomena.

Pressure Drop across Suspended-Bed Reactors

The pressure drop across suspended-bed reactors consists of (1) the pressure drop needed to overcome the column of liquid, gas, and catalyst, and (2) the pressure drop in the device used to inject the gas into the suspended bed, such as a sparger.

The pressure drop of ebullated-bed reactors can be calculated using relationships developed by Ergun and Orning[25] for expanding beds and gas flow. When the pressure gradient becomes equal to the buoyant weight of the packing per unit volume of the bed,

$$\frac{dP}{dZ} = (1 - \varepsilon)(\rho_s - \rho_L)g \tag{9-1}$$

the bed begins to expand. Equation (6-2) remains valid, the pressure gradient being given by Eq. (9-1). The fractional void volume ε increases with flow rate.[25] This relationship can be expressed by Eq. (9-2)

$$\frac{\varepsilon^3}{1 - \varepsilon} = \frac{4.935\, a^2\, \mu\, u_m}{\rho_s\, g} \qquad u_m > u_{m0} \tag{9-2}$$

where ρ_s = density of solid catalyst particles, kg/m^3

a = external-particle-surface/particle-volume ratio, m^{-1}

u_m = superficial liquid velocity at mean of entrance and exit pressures, m/s

u_{m0} = u_m at beginning of expansion

Z = height of bed, m

g = gravitational constant = 9.80597 m/s^2

μ = viscosity of the liquid, kg/(m · s)

The Dispersion of Gas Bubbles and Liquid in Suspended Beds

Gas bubbles are generated in suspended beds either by injecting gas through a sparger or impeller into the liquid or by stirring the liquid with a propeller near the liquid surface. Designing for the desired size and quantity of bubbles is not easy because few reliable data are available.

The bubbles play different roles in different types of suspended-bed reactors. In the CSTR, ebullated-bed reactor, and 3ϕTR, bubbles simply constitute the disperse gas phase and have no role in the support of the catalyst in the liquid. In the slurry reactor, however, the finely divided catalyst is supported in the liquid only by the effect of the rising gas bubbles. Consequently, the size and intensity of bubbles are of paramount importance for slurry reactors, not only for mass transfer but for bulk mixing as well.

Gas dispersion in the *CSTR* can be achieved by borrowing methods from other gas-liquid phase reactors, such as installing spargers in the reactors and recirculating part of the gas through the sparger. This may be the most practical solution of the gas dispersion problem in the CSTR. Another method of achieving gas dispersion might be to use dispersing turbines, which suck gas into the liquid through their shaft and disperse through the rotor. Such turbines are called *cavitators.* Power requirements for a cavitator type of gas disperser are discussed by Michel and Miller.[26] The cavitator has certain limitations: If the reactor must be deep, then the vacuum created by the impeller is not sufficient to draw sufficient gas and force it into the liquid. Also the mechanical design of impellers presents certain difficulties on scale-up.

A third method of dispersing gas into the liquid is the *surface stirring* method. Surface stirring by means of impellers is commonly practiced in waste disposal plants. A halfway-immersed impeller rotating on the surface of a liquid can disperse considerable amounts of gas into the liquid. However, in order to apply this method in a dispersed bed reactor a large gas-liquid interface is necessary.

A fourth method of dispersing gas bubbles in a liquid mass is to disperse the gas through a sparger and to stir the liquid above the sparger by an impeller. Relationships of various parameters in this method of dispersal have been discussed by Oldshue and Connelly.[27] According to these authors, the most effective sparger ring diameter is for overall mass transfer considerations 0.8 to 0.9 times the impeller diameter. Dispersal of the gas through a center inlet pipe is about 10 to 15% less effective than dispersal through a properly designed sparger, even though in both cases the mixture of liquid and gas bubbles is being stirred by a mechanical stirrer.

The dispersion of the gas in the *slurry reactor* is achieved by generating a large number of bubbles, which also support the finely divided catalyst in the slurry. The size, shape, and frequency of the bubbles are of great importance. The relationships between various bubble parameters have been reviewed by among others, Fair,[1] Calderbank et al.,[28] Argo and Cova,[29] and Kölbel et al.[7,30] At superficial velocities (of gas leaving the sparger) of $u < 0.05$ m/s the bubbles are discrete, particulate, uniform, and spherical. They are almost ordered and rise through the liquid at almost constant velocity, the upward force of the bubbles being balanced by viscous drag from the liquid. The liquid has little visually observable agitation. Bubble sizes of 0.0016 to 0.0063 m may be obtained. This bubble regime is called the *quiescent* or *laminar* regime. At superficial gas velocities higher than about 0.015 m/s, bubble size becomes independent of gas flow rate. One result of this is that the rising velocity of individual bubbles is also approximately independent of gas flow rate. Another result is that in order to increase the gas flow rate the gas holdup ε_G has to be increased.

Kölbel et al.[7] measured the liquid-phase fraction ε_L, or liquid holdup, of bubble columns of different viscosities as a function of superficial gas velocity u. They found that ε_L decreases quite sharply and at different linear rates for different viscosities up to $u \approx 0.005$ m/s, then goes through an irregular transition range up to $u \approx 0.018$ m/s, and then decreases at a constant linear rate in the practical range up to $u = 0.26$ m/s.

With further increase of the gas rate beyond 0.015 m/s, the reactor tube becomes filled with bubbles. At still higher gas flow rates, collision between bubbles causes coalescence into larger bubbles, which rise faster. At a superficial gas velocity of 0.051 m/s, the gas phase begins to slug and the liquid phase becomes violently turbulent. The bubbles become poorly defined, the contacting action is violent and erratic, and there is a high degree of bulk mixing. This bubble regime is called the *turbulent* regime. While the sparger design is very critical in the quiescent regime, it is not critical at all in the turbulent regime. However, orifices must be well distributed over the vessel cross section and emergent velocity for each orifice must not exceed 75 to 90 m/s. However, in terms of superficial velocity u, the gas velocity should not exceed 0.15 m/s, since above this limit entrainment may become excessive.[31] For deep vessels and liquids of relatively low viscosity (≈ 1 mPa · s), mean bubble diameter will be in the range of about 0.003 to 0.006 m.[31,32]

Because the aim in reactor design is to obtain maximum capacity per unit volume, one seldom needs to use the quiescent regime. In any reactor of industrial size using the quiescent regime, the bubbles would start to coalesce at some distance from the sparger, and the quiescent regime would be disturbed. Thus, one should design for the turbulent regime. However, this is easier said than done because complete reliance must be placed on empirical correlations of experimental data and most probably on the designer's own data. The few published data on the air-water system may perhaps at least guide the designer, since they are claimed to check reasonably well with systems other than air-water, according to Fair,[1] who presents these data in the form of a plot of fractional gas holdup ε_G versus superficial velocity u_{0G} with reactor length/diameter ratio as a parameter. This plot is given in Fig. 9-14.

The *mean bubble rise velocity* u_{BM} in bubble columns can be calculated according to Siemes[33] as

$$u_{BM} = \frac{u}{1 - \varepsilon_L} = \frac{-\partial u}{\partial \varepsilon_L}$$

The average bubble diameter in the air-water system increases sharply with increasing superficial gas velocity up to about 0.005 m/s and then increases very gradually up to 0.05 m/s according to Kölbel and Langemann,[30] as shown in Fig. 9-15. The rising velocity of gas bubbles in water depends on bubble diameter, as shown in Fig. 9-16.[30] The rising velocity increases linearly and very sharply up to about 0.0015 m in diameter and then suddenly begins to decline. The minimum is reached at about 0.006 m in diameter and the velocity increases slowly from there on.

Bubbles rising in a bubble reactor coalesce into larger bubbles, thus reducing the gas-liquid contact area. Bubble size and bubble coalescence are important to know because if there is excessive coalescence, it may become necessary to redistribute the gas above a certain reactor height in order to regain the lost contact area. Calderbank et al. studied bubble coalescence in viscous liquids and found that rising ellipsoidal bubbles rapidly coalesce when they come within about 1.6 mm of each other, center to center. Even when they are not that close together at the bottom of the reactor, they move toward each other and toward the center of the reactor. When the center-to-center distance between bubbles at the

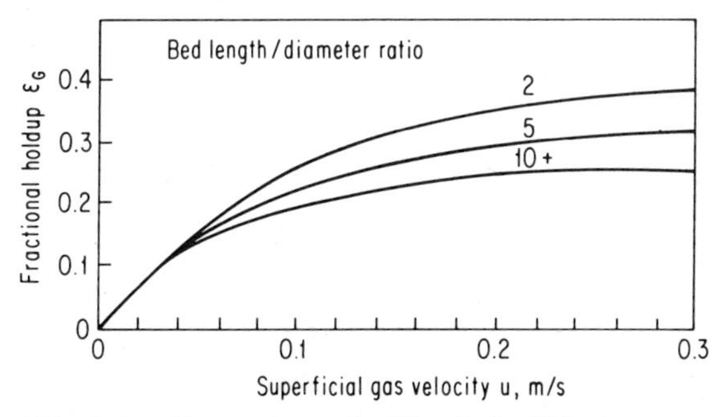

FIG. 9-14 Dynamic gas holdup in bubble reactors as a function of superficial gas velocity. (*From James R. Fair,*[1] *excerpted by special permission from Chemical Engineering*, July 3, 1967.)

reactor axis becomes less than 1.6 diameters, bubbles begin clustering and coalescing to form large spherical cap bubbles, each formed from an average of six ellipsoidal bubbles.

The coalescence of bubbles is strongly dependent on liquid viscosity. The fractional gas holdup ε_G decreases as a result of coalescence up to 0.04 Pa · s, then is constant at up to about 0.07 Pa · s, and then drops sharply and levels off again at a low value of about $\varepsilon_G = 0.007$.[28]

During simultaneous coalescence and dissolution (absorption regime), the bubble size remains substantially constant.[28]

The apparent effect of gas bubbles is to expand the liquid volume in the reactor. This expansion is important in:

- Vessel sizing
- Level control location
- Residence time determination
- Interface area determination for mass transfer and chemical reaction

If we call Z_L the height of clear liquid at no gas flow and Z_E the height of the expanded liquid, including bubbles, the gas holdup is

$$\varepsilon_G = \frac{Z_E - Z_L}{Z_E} \tag{9-3}$$

The average residence time $\bar{\theta}_G$ of the gas in the expanded liquid is:

$$\bar{\theta}_G = \int_0^{Z_E} \frac{\varepsilon_G \, dZ}{u} \tag{9-4}$$

where u is the superficial gas velocity in meters per second. As already

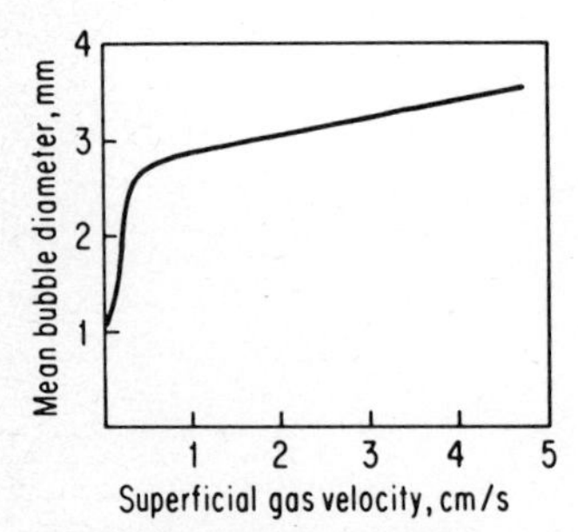

FIG. 9-15 Mean bubble diameter as a function of superficial gas velocity. Column diameter 0.092 m; mean pore diameter 25 μ; temperature 20°C; air-water system. (*From Kölbel and Langemann*[30] *by permission from Dechema.*)

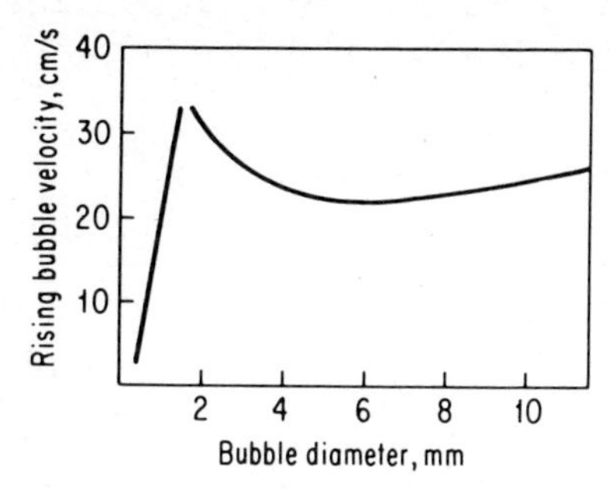

FIG. 9-16 Rising velocity of gas bubbles as a function of bubble diameter. (*From Kölbel and Langemann*[30] *by permission from Dechema.*)

mentioned, the plot of Fig. 9-14 correlates the superficial gas velocity u with the fractional gas holdup ε_G for various bed length/diameter ratios.

In the design of elevated-pressure bubble reactors, it is important to know the *effect of pressure on bubbles.* With increasing pressure, bubbles become smaller for the flow of the same gas quantity. However, in relation to the actual volume of the gas under various pressures, there is no effect of pressure on bubble size and ε_L.[7] The *specific bubble surface area* is affected by pressure. Kölbel suggests that when designing pressure columns, the superficial gas velocity, which is related to actual volume under pressure, be set above 0.006 to 0.007 m/s, since below these values the specific bubble area is reduced and the transport properties accordingly are adversely affected.

Since the main purpose of generating bubbles in suspended-bed reactors is to create a large interfacial area for mass transfer, it is also of interest to measure this *interfacial area* in any given system. The chemical method for determining the interfacial area, as discussed by Astarita,[34] consists of measuring the reaction rate under conditions such that the chemical reaction is rate-controlling and then calibrating the procedure by running it under conditions such that the interfacial area is known, as in a laminar jet or a wetted-wall column.

When the chemical reaction is rate-controlling, the mass-transfer rate is equal to the chemical reaction rate:

$$D_i = \frac{d^2C_i}{dz^2} = \Re = f(C) \tag{9-5}$$

where D_i = diffusivity of the ith component, m^2/s

C_i = concentration of the ith component, $kmol/m^3$

z = longitudinal coordinate, m

$\Re$ = chemical reaction rate function, $kmol/m^3$

and the boundary conditions at the interface are of the type:

$$C_i = C_i^0 \qquad \text{for volatile components} \tag{9-6}$$

$$\frac{dC_i}{dz} = 0 \qquad \text{for nonvolatile components} \tag{9-7}$$

$$C_i = C_{eq} \qquad \frac{dC_i}{dz} = 0 \qquad \text{for all components} \tag{9-8}$$

where C_{eq} is the equilibrium concentration in kilomoles per square meter.

The solution of Eqs. (9-5) to (9-8) is clearly independent of existing flow conditions and does not affect either the ODE or the boundary conditions. At steady state we may write:

$$\phi = -DA \left.\frac{dC_i}{dz}\right|_{\text{interface}} = AF \tag{9-9}$$

where A = total interface area, m^2

ϕ = transfer rate, kmol/s

F = parameter which is independent of flow conditions, kmol/($m^2 \cdot s$)

Hence we may determine A from the transfer rate ϕ, and F can be determined by calibration experiments, as mentioned above.

The interfacial area in gas-sparged suspended-bed reactors has been studied by I. H. Lehrer.[35] The following equations were developed to estimate this area within the right order of magnitude:

$$A = \frac{6\, V_L Q}{u_t\, D_{BM}\, A_c} \tag{9-10}$$

where A = total interfacial area of bubbles leaving the sparger, m^2

V_L = liquid volume at rest, m^3

Q = volumetric flow rate, m^3/s

u_t = terminal velocity of bubbles, m/s

D_{BM} = diameter of geometric mean bubble, m

A_c = cross-sectional flow area in reactor vessel, m^2

$$A = \frac{6\, V_L\, v_0\, A_{SPH}}{u_t\, D_{BM}\, A_B} \tag{9-11}$$

where v_0 = velocity at sparger orifice, m/s

A_{SPH} = area of oblate spheroid bubble with major-axis/minor-axis ratio ≤ 2.6 where $A_B < A_{SPH} \leq 1.2\, A_B$

A_B = area of bubble

The reactor designer needs to know, among other things, the *fractional gas holdup* ε_G in suspended beds. In bubble reactors, gas holdup ε_G has been correlated with Froude and Bodenstein numbers.[36]

$$\frac{\varepsilon_G}{1 - \varepsilon_G} = 0.65\ \mathrm{Fr} \cdot \mathrm{Bo}^{0.25} \tag{9-12}$$

where Fr = Froude number

Bo = Bodenstein number

In this study, the bubble columns were small (0.02- to 0.15-m-diameter tubes), the gas was air, and the variables had the following values: u 0.0008 to 0.02 m/s, liquid surface tension 0.022 to 0.072 N/m, ρ 795 to 1170 kg/m^3, and viscosities 0.001 to 0.022 Pa · s were used.

The gas holdup of tall industrial-size bubble columns vary with height. Deckwer et al.[37]* showed that this variation must be taken into account in designing bubble reactors. Local values of ε_G were described by a regression function of the dimensionless axial coordinate Z:

$$\varepsilon_G(Z) = \bar{\varepsilon}_G\ \varphi(Z) \tag{9-13}$$

with

$$\varphi(Z) = a_0 + a_1 Z + a_2 Z^2 \tag{9-14}$$

An integrated mean value $\bar{\varepsilon}_G$ is defined by

$$\bar{\varepsilon}_G = \sum_i \varepsilon_G(Z_i)\ \Delta Z_i \tag{9-15}$$

The mean Sauter diameter d_s of bubbles was found to be approximately independent of Z. The interfacial area a is calculated from $\bar{\varepsilon}_G$[37]:

$$a(Z) = 6\bar{\varepsilon}_G\ \varphi(Z)/d_s \tag{9-16}$$

The gas holdup ε_G increases linearly with gas throughput, reaches a maximum, and at higher gas throughput values becomes independent of gas throughput. Kölbel and Langemann[30] showed that the profile of the ε_G vs. u_G graph depends very much on the kind of liquid, as illustrated by the graphs of six liquids which they published. In these graphs ε_G passes through a maximum and then declines. The viscosity of the liquid has a strong effect on ε_G. With increasing liquid viscosity, the ε_G maxi-

*Adapted with permission from Wolf-Dieter Deckwer, I. Adler, and Ahmet Zaidi, "Detailed Analysis of CO_2-Interphase Mass Transfer in a Bubble Column to Prove the Validity of a Design Model," in Weekman and Luss (eds.) *Chemical Reaction Engineering—Houston, 5th ISCRE,* ACS Symposium Series 65, 1978, pp. 359–371. Copyright 1978 American Chemical Society.

mum is reached at a lower throughput value. The dependence of ε_G on gas throughput can be expressed by the relationship[10]:

$$\varepsilon_G = \frac{v_G}{A + Bv_G + Cv_G^2} \tag{9-17}$$

where v_G is the linear velocity of fresh gas at the reactor bottom in meters per second and A, B, and C are constants. This relationship represents most but not all of the measured data.

The dependence of ε_G on the reactor diameter has also been studied by Kölbel et al.[10] With increasing reactor diameter, the ε_G vs. v_G maximum shifts to higher ε_G and v_G values.

The *rising velocity of small bubbles* (0.003 to 0.006 m diameter) is given by[36]:

$$u_t = 1.538\,(\sigma\, g/\rho)^{0.25} \qquad \text{m/s} \tag{9-18}$$

where σ = surface tension, kg/s^2

g = gravitational acceleration = 9.80597 m/s^2

ρ = density, kg/m^3

Lehrer[35] provided a reasonable estimate of *fractional gas holdup* in a steady-state gas dispersion in a gas-agitated, water-filled batch vessel with a ratio of liquid height above the sparger to vessel diameter $\geqslant 1$ and with negligible wall effect:

$$\varepsilon_G = \frac{Q/(A_c \cdot u_t)}{1 + Q/(A_c \cdot u_t)} = \frac{(v_0/u_t)}{1 + (v_0/u_t)} \tag{9-19}$$

In this expression Q and A_c are known. The terminal bubble velocity u_t can be calculated by the relationship proposed by Mendelson[38] in 1967 for the rise velocity of a single bubble in an infinite low-viscosity liquid in the nonlaminar regime:

$$u_t = \left(\frac{2\sigma}{\rho_L D_B} + \frac{g\, D_B}{2}\right)^{0.5} \tag{9-20}$$

where σ = surface tension, kg/s^2

D_B = bubble diameter, m

ρ_L = liquid density, kg/m^3

g = gravitational acceleration = 9.80597 m/s^2

The D_B value is obtained from

$$D_B = (D_{B0} D_{BE})^{0.5} \tag{9-21}$$

where D_{BE} = minimum stable bubble diameter, m

A simplified equation for D_{BE} based on balancing surface tension and dynamic pressure effects was developed by Lehrer[35]:

$$D_{BE} = \left(\frac{8\sigma}{\rho f}\right)^{0.6} E^{-0.4} \tag{9-22}$$

where f = friction factor and drag coefficient in the nonlaminar region.

$$f = \frac{8}{3}\frac{\text{Eö}}{(4 + \text{Eö})} \quad \text{(Mendelson)}^{38} \tag{9-23}$$

$E = (w/\rho_L V_L)(0.5\ \eta v_0^2 + RT\ \ln(p_1/p_2))$

w = mass flow rate, kg/s

η = efficiency = 0.06

v_0 = velocity of gas at sparger orifice, m/s

p = pressure, bars

Eö = Eötvös number (Weber number/Froude number), dimensionless

The *backmixing of the gas and liquid phases* in bubble reactors was studied by Afschar et al.[39] If the gas phase is insoluble in the liquid phase, then the gas bubbles travel upward in plug flow. However, if the gas phase is soluble in the liquid phase, then the backmixing of the gas phase is determined by the intensity of dissolution in the liquid phase. The backmixing in the liquid phase is intermediate between plug flow and perfect mixing. In terms of Bodenstein numbers, bubble columns operate at Bo = 1 to 16. The Bodenstein number increases with increasing gas flow and decreases with increasing liquid flow. Of course, large Bodenstein numbers are desirable in certain reactions in which a high yield is needed.

The reactor designer has a great interest in knowing the degree of mixing in the reacting liquid-bubble system, which is especially needed for scale-up. Information on two extreme cases can be quite easily obtained. These are (1) perfectly mixed systems, and (2) systems in which no mixing occurs. For these extreme cases, the reactor designer requires a knowledge of the reaction kinetics and a laboratory evaluation of the relevant velocity constants. Unfortunately, it is not always known with certainty that one of these extreme cases exist. A partially mixed system introduces mathematical complexities. Even with complex mathematics it is necessary to know how much mixing occurs. Assuming that both the complex mathematics and the degree of mixing are available, the problem can be approached along the lines of either a residence time distribution or a diffusion model. The second approach is preferred[29] for designing gas-sparged reactors.

The mixing of a liquid by upflowing gas bubbles was studied by Siemes and Weiss,[40] who measured the coefficient of mixing in the range 0.0001 to 0.0075 m^2/s (1 to 75 cm^2/s), depending on the size of bubbles and gas throughput. In the laminar regime the mixing coefficient increases about linearly with increasing gas throughput, while in the turbulent regime the mixing coefficient increases progressively with throughput but then reaches a peak. At low gas rates, the viscous drag of the liquid is responsible for the formation of turbulent eddies and movement of the liquid, which constitutes axial liquid dispersion.[29]

The one-dimensional axial backmixing model for the liquid phase of bubble reactors leads to the relationship:

$$\ln \frac{C}{C_0} = -u_L z / K_L \tag{9-24}$$

where K_L = liquid-phase backmixing coefficient, m^2/s
u_L = superficial liquid velocity, m/s
z = longitudinal coordinate (distance from sparger), m

This means that if u_L/K_L is constant, the plot of $\ln(C/C_0)$ vs. z gives a straight line with the slope $-u_L/K_L$. Contrary to this model, Deckwer et al.[41] have found that over a certain range of gas throughput for concurrent and countercurrent flow, the mixing in the liquid phase of bubble columns is not uniform but splits into two different regimes:

$$K_L = (0.00012 \pm 0.000012)\, D_T^{1.5}\, u_G^{0.5} \quad m^2/s$$ in the lower region of the column

$$K_L = (0.00024 \pm 0.000018)\, D_T^{1.5}\, u_G^{0.5} \quad m^2/s$$ in the upper region of the column

and $$K_L = (0.0002 \pm 0.000015)\, D_T^{1.5}\, u_G^{0.5} \quad m^2/s$$ if a single mixing regime exists

Here, D_T is column diameter in meters.

Longitudinal mixing in gas-sparged tubular reactors has also been discussed by Argo and Cova,[29] who measured the superficial dispersion coefficient D_s of liquids as a function of superficial gas velocity. In open tubes D_s increased linearly above 0.025 m/s but was roughly constant under pressure. Their data did not lend themselves to generalized correlations.

Also, Péclet numbers based on tube diameter as a function of superficial gas velocity have been measured for turbulent flow regime.[29] This Péclet number is:

$$\mathrm{Pe}_{BT} = D_T\, v_R/D_a \tag{9-25}$$

where v_R = actual mean gas velocity *relative* to actual mean liquid velocity = $(u/\varepsilon_G) - v_L$, m/s

v_L = actual mean liquid velocity, m/s

D_a = dispersion coefficient, axial, m^2/s

For superficial gas velocities up to 0.2 m/s, Pe_{BT} varied only between 0.5 and 1.0.

Other relationships worth noting are as follows:

- Diffusivities increase with tube diameter.
- Gas holdup ε_G rises rapidly with superficial gas velocity, and then, above 0.076 m/s, levels off at about $\varepsilon_G = 0.3$ to 0.4.

A similar result was obtained by Eissa et al.[42] Afschar et al.[39] observed that ε_G varies proportionally with the superficial gas velocity up to 0.05 m/s and then, levels off.

The data of Argo and Cova[29] for axial diffusivities may be used to estimate order-of-magnitude diffusivities.

A continuous first-order reaction at steady state may be represented by the following differential equation:

$$\frac{dC}{dz} = \frac{d^2C}{dz^2} \cdot \frac{D_{aL}}{v_L} - \frac{kC}{v_L} \tag{9-26}$$

For a similar case of a packed tubular reactor, Dankwerts[43] developed the following solution:

$$\frac{C}{C_0} = \exp(v_L\, z/2\, D_{aL})\, \frac{A^*}{B^*} \tag{9-27}$$

where

$$A^* = 2(1 + \dot{a}) \exp\left[\frac{v_L \dot{a}}{2\, D_{aL}} (Z_T - z)\right] - 2(1 - \dot{a}) \exp\left[\frac{v_L \dot{a}}{2\, D_{aL}} (z - Z_T)\right]$$

$$B^* = (1 + \dot{a})^2 \exp\left(\frac{u_L \dot{a} Z_T}{2\, D_{aL}}\right) - (1 - \dot{a})^2 \exp\left(\frac{-u_L \dot{a} Z_T}{2\, D_{aL}}\right)$$

with

$$\dot{a} = \left[1 + \frac{4k\, D_{aL}}{v_L^2} \right] \tag{9-28}$$

where Z_T = reactor length, m

z = longitudinal distance in reactor, m

D_{aL} = dispersion coefficient, axial, liquid phase

v_L = actual mean liquid velocity, m/s

k = reaction rate constant

This equation is also applicable to bubble reactors. If D_{aL} is known, Eq. (9-27) can be used with the help of a computer program to calculate the reaction rate. Thus the accuracy of the reaction rate constant k depends on that of the axial dispersion coefficient D_{aL}.

Radial as well as axial dispersion in concurrent bubble columns was studied by S. H. Eissa et al.[42] by means of tracer experiments. Dispersion was found highest in the central core region with a maximum value slightly shifted from the reactor vessel center. These authors introduced an *effective local dispersion coefficient E,* which reflects the combined effect of axial and radial dispersion. However, it was understood that the radial contribution is very minor compared with the axial contribution. For further simplification, Eissa et al. developed *a uniform dispersion model* that uses mean velocities and mean dispersion coefficients instead of point properties. The *mean effective dispersion* number in the bubble-flow regime was found to increase with gas velocity up to about 0.05 m/s (which coincides with the start of the *transition regime*), to decline to a minimum value (close to the beginning of the *slugging regime*), and finally to increase again.

Axial backmixing of liquid in three-phase fluidized beds, i.e., ebullated beds, was studied by Y. K. Vail et al.[44] by a tracer technique using a relationship developed by Gilliland and Mason[45]:

$$\ln(C/C_x) = (vz/K_{aL}) + B \tag{9-29}$$

where C = concentration of the tracer at axial coordinate z, kmol/m^3

C_x = concentration of the tracer in the total flow leaving the reactor, kmol/m^3

v = velocity of the fluidized stream, m/s

K_{aL} = coefficient of axial dispersion, liquid phase, m^2/s

B = a constant

Vail et al. concluded that:

- Tracer concentrations approximately obey a logarithmic law.
- Increase of the gas velocity intensifies axial backmixing.
- Increase of the liquid velocity weakens axial backmixing.
- The presence of a solid dispersed phase considerably reduces axial backmixing.
- Radial irregularity in concentration increases with increased liquid feed and decreased gas feed.

Finally, extensive pilot-plant data are being developed on ebullated-bed fluid dynamics by Amoco Oil Company under contract with the U.S. Department of Energy[46] in order to provide design data for the H-Coal process. Relationships among several parameters such as u, u_L, ε_G, ε_L, and ε_p are already available.

Suspending the Catalyst in Suspended Beds

The maintenance of the catalyst in suspension as a slurry is achieved in different types of suspended beds by different means:

- In CSTRs, propeller agitation keeps the catalyst in suspension.
- In slurry reactors, rising bubbles create the necessary turbulence to keep the finely divided catalyst in suspension.
- In ebullated-bed reactors, the liquid upflow counterbalances the settling velocity of catalyst particles in the liquid.
- In 3ϕTRs, the liquid upflow must be much greater than the settling velocity of catalyst particles so that they are entrained with the liquid.

The terminal velocity of small spheres settling in a liquid is given by Stokes' law:

$$u_t = \frac{g d_p^2 \,\Delta\rho}{18\mu} \tag{9-30}$$

where g = acceleration due to gravity, 9.81 m/s^2

$\Delta\rho$ = difference of density between particles and the liquid, kg/m^3

μ = liquid viscosity, kg/(m · s)

In both CSTRs and slurry reactors, it is necessary to use a very fine catalyst, of particle diameter in the order of a few hundred micrometers, so that it does not settle easily. The design of mixing and stirring devices is still based on empirical knowledge. The reader is referred to the literature on mixing. Some very good annual reviews by J. Y. Oldshue are available,[47] as well as a paper on suspension of solids and dispersal of gases in mixing vessels.[48]

In geometrically similar baffled agitated vessels, the power input from the impeller is related to rotational speed by the equation:

$$N_p = K\mathrm{Re}^a = P'/(N^3 D_i^5 \rho) \tag{9-31}$$

where N_p = the power number

K, a = dimensionless constants depending on the system geometry

N = impeller speed, s^{-1}

D_i = impeller diameter, m

ρ = fluid density, kg/m^3

P' = power, W

Nienow and Miles[49] reported values of N_P for a variety of impeller-vessel geometries as a function of the Reynolds number. These values may be quite useful in designing CSTRs.

The ebullated-bed reactors operate in a relatively narrow range of solution upflow between the fluidization velocity and the total entrainment velocity. The operators must know at all times how much the catalyst bed is expanded and where the top of the bed is located. This is usually achieved by measuring the bed density across the diameter at several levels by means of commercially available instruments.

Mass Transfer in Suspended-Bed Reactors

Mass transfer in suspended-bed reactors has been fairly widely discussed by Carberry,[50] Satterfield,[31] Kölbel,[30] and Johnson et al.[51] The phenomenon is basically the same as that in fixed-bed bubble reactors except that the quantitative relationships of the various variables change depending on the choice of reactor type.

Reaction rate expressions in suspended beds affected by mass transfer can be developed as follows[31]:

Let us call N_v the molar flux in kilomoles per second per cubic meter of the key reactant in the bubble-expanded slurry. At steady state we have:

$$N_v = k_L \cdot a_b(C_e - C_L) \quad \text{(gas interface} \rightarrow \text{bulk liquid)} \tag{9-32}$$

$$= k_c \cdot a_p (C_L - C_s) \quad \text{(bulk liquid} \rightarrow \text{particle)} \tag{9-33}$$

$$= k_s \cdot a_p C_s \quad \text{(surface reaction)} \tag{9-34}$$

where k_L = gas-liquid mass-transfer coefficient, m/s
k_c = bulk liquid-to-particle mass-transfer coefficient, m/s
k_s = surface reaction rate coefficient, m/s
a_b = bubble surface area per unit volume of expanded slurry, m^2/m^3
a_p = exterior catalyst surface per unit volume of expanded slurry, m^2/m^3
C_e = equilibrium concentration of gaseous reactant in liquid, $kmol/m^3$
C_L = reactant concentration in bulk liquid, $kmol/m^3$
C_s = reactant concentration at catalyst surface, $kmol/m^3$

In the last three equations C_e can be taken from books, but C_L and C_s are difficult to obtain. Therefore the latter quantities may be eliminated from the expressions as follows.

Dividing both sides of Eq. (9-32) by N_v and rearranging gives:

$$\frac{C_e}{N_v} = \frac{1}{k_L a_b} + \frac{C_L}{N_v} \tag{9-35}$$

Similarly, Eq. (9-33) gives:

$$\frac{C_L}{N_v} = \frac{1}{k_c a_p} + \frac{C_s}{N_v} \tag{9-36}$$

And Eq. (9-34) gives:

$$\frac{C_s}{N_v} = \frac{1}{k_s a_p} \tag{9-37}$$

By combining Eqs. (9-35), (9-36), and (9-37) we obtain:

$$\frac{C_e}{N_v} = \frac{1}{k_L a_b} + \frac{1}{k_c a_p} + \frac{1}{k_s a_p} \tag{9-38}$$

If bubbles and catalyst particles are spherical:

$$a_b = \frac{6\varepsilon_G}{D_B} \tag{9-39}$$

$$a_p = \frac{6m}{\rho_s d_p} \tag{9-40}$$

where ε_G = gas holdup in the liquid, m^3 gas per m^3 expanded slurry
m = catalyst loading, kg catalyst per m^3 expanded slurry
ρ_s = catalyst particle density, kg/m^3
D_B = bubble diameter, m

Substituting Eq. (9-39) and Eq. (9-40) into Eq. (9-38) gives:

$$\frac{C_e}{N_v} = \frac{D_B}{6k_L\, \varepsilon_G} + \frac{\rho_s\, d_P}{6m}\left(\frac{1}{k_c} + \frac{1}{k_s}\right) \tag{9-41}$$

Here, we see that C_e/N_v is a linear function of $1/m$. At reasonable catalyst loadings C_e/N_v increases with $1/m$. At extremely high catalyst loadings, $1/m \to 0$, $N_v \to 6k_L\varepsilon_G C_e/d_p$, and the rate becomes controlled by the rate of gas absorption k_L.

The mass transfer from gas bubbles to liquids is relatively well known.[32,52] Small bubbles (<0.0025 m diameter) behave like rigid spheres and mass-transfer coefficients from the interface to the liquid are correlated by the same relationships that apply to small solid spheres. The mass-transfer coefficient k_c for a single sphere at rest in a large volume of stagnant fluid is given by

$$k_c = 2\, D_{1m}/d_p \tag{9-42}$$

where D_{1m} is the molecular diffusion coefficient for the species diffusing in the fluid.

Mass transfer for flow past single spheres may be correlated by[31,53]:

$$\mathrm{Sh}^2 = \left(\frac{k_c\, d_P}{D_{1m}}\right)^2 = 4.0 + 1.21\, \mathrm{Pe}^{2/3} \tag{9-43}$$

where Sh is the Sherwood number = $k_c d_p/D_{1m}$ and Pe is the Péclet number = $d_p u/D_{1m}$. Catalysts used in slurries are not always spheres, but it is convenient to use a diameter corresponding to a sphere having the same ratio of external surface to volume, and hence the same settling velocity, as the irregular particle. The terminal velocity of settling for small spheres is given by Stokes' law [Eq. (9-30)]. The corresponding Péclet number, denoted by Pe*, is:

$$\mathrm{Pe}^* = g_c d_p^3 \Delta\rho/(18\mu D_{1m}) \quad \text{at terminal velocity} \tag{9-44}$$

and the corresponding k_c^* may be estimated at settling velocities $\mathrm{Pe}^* < 500$ by combining Eqs. (9-44) and (9-43). The results are plotted in Satterfield's Fig. 2-5 (page 115 of Ref. 31). The coefficient k_c^* is the mass-transfer coefficient between bulk liquid and a particle settling quietly.

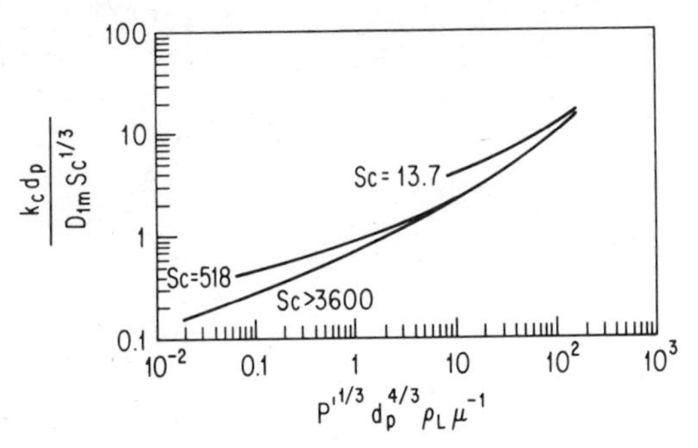

FIG. 9-17 Effect of power input on mass transfer to spheres suspended in an agitated liquid. (*From Brian and Hales,*[53,54] *by permission from the American Institute of Chemical Engineers.*)

Under turbulent conditions in a reactor the actual value of k_c is greater than k_c^*. Satterfield suggests as a first approximation taking k_c as twice the value calculated from the combination of Eqs. (9-43) and (9-44).

In mechanically stirred reactors, k_c can be calculated from the power input to the slurry according to Briand and Hales,[53,54] provided the power input is known. This relationship is presented in Fig. 9-17. Here, the ordinate is Sh/Sc$^{1/3}$ and the abscissa is $P'^{1/3} d_p^{4/3}\, \rho_L/\mu$ where P' is the power input and is expressed as power per unit mass of slurry. Both groups are dimensionless. In SI units P' must be expressed in watts per kilogram of slurry. According to Satterfield,[31] this method is the soundest way of estimating k_c, provided power input can be calculated with reasonable assurance. Calderbank[32] states that when a dispersed phase is suspended or is in free rise or in free fall and under the influence of gravity, the heat-transfer and mass-transfer coefficients are almost completely unaffected by mechanical power dissipated in the system. In other words, it does not pay to stir a catalyst suspension beyond the point at which the particles are held in suspension. Thus it can be concluded that the power input to keep suspended beds in suspension should not be used to estimate k_c unless (1) the power is computed properly, and (2) no power is wasted.

Mass transfer from large bubbles is greater than that from small spherical bubbles since the large bubbles undergo internal circulation and their shape becomes distorted as they move through the liquid. The correlation:

$$k_L\, \mathrm{Sc}^{1/2} = 0.42 \left(\frac{\mu\, g_c\, \Delta\rho}{\rho^2} \right)^{1/3} \tag{9-45}$$

applies to these large bubbles,[31,32] where Sc is the Schmidt number for the liquid, $\mu/\rho D$.

Most of these mass-transfer relationships have been developed for the air-water system. Fair has discussed[1] the extension of these relationships to other systems by using the formula:

$$\frac{(k_L a) \text{ other system}}{(k_L a) \text{ air-water}} = \frac{D(\text{other system})}{D \text{ (air-water)}} \tag{9-46}$$

in which D (air-water) $= 2.49 \times 10^{-4}$ m²/s at 25°C. Mass transfer in ebullated beds can be expressed by the relationship[55,56]

$$\text{Sh} = 2.0 + 1.5\ \text{Sc}^{1/3}\ [(1 - \varepsilon)\ \text{Re}_p]^{1/2} \tag{9-46a}$$

where $\text{Re}_p = d_p u_L \rho/\mu = 5$ to $120 \qquad \varepsilon \leq 0.84$

Here u_L is superficial liquid velocity in meters per second.

In 3ϕTRs, bubble-to-liquid mass transfer can be calculated from the relationship:

$$\text{Sh} = 2.0 + 1.04\ \text{Re}^{1/2}\ \text{Sc}^{0.33} \tag{9-47}$$

D. L. Johnson et al.[51] studied the effect of bubbling and stirring on mass transfer in suspended-bed reactors in which the major resistance is in the transfer of the gas from the bubble to the surface of the suspended catalyst. They used as an example the hydrogenation of α-methylstyrene over a powdered Pd/Al_2O_3 catalyst and showed that the mass transfer in a stirred reactor with bubbling of the gas through the liquid is given by the relation:

$$\left(\frac{D}{k_{ov} D_i^2}\right)\left(\frac{\mu}{\rho_L D}\right)^{1/3} = A\left(\frac{\sigma}{\bar{u}_G \mu}\right)^{0.75} \cdot \left(\frac{D_i^2 N \rho_L}{\mu_L}\right)^{-1.67} + B\left(\frac{\rho_s}{m}\right)\left(\frac{D_i^2 N \rho_L}{\mu_L}\right)^{-0.75} \tag{9-48}$$

where
D = diffusivity of hydrogen through liquid, m²/s
D_i = diameter swept by impeller, m
k_{ov} = overall reaction and mass transfer rate constant
μ_L = viscosity of liquid, kg/(s · m)
σ = surface tension, kg/s²
ρ_L = density of liquid, kg/m³
ρ_s = density of catalyst particles, kg/m³

$\bar{u}_G$ = average superficial gas velocity, based on inside reactor diameter and temperature and pressure of gas, m/s

N = stirring rate, r/s

m = catalyst loading, kg/m^3 of liquid

A,B = constants

The values of A and B depend on the mechanical construction of the reactor vessel, agitator, baffles, and sparger and require separate evaluation in terms of these mechanical factors. For the two-blade flat impeller used by Johnson et al.[51] the values of these constants were $A = 29.4$ and $B = 6.55 \times 10^{-4}$.

Deckwer et al. developed a model[37] of mass transfer in an industrial size bubble reactor for the absorption and desorption of CO_2 in H_2O. They started with the following assumptions:

- Validity of Henry's law
- Axial dispersion in liquid phase
- Plug flow in gas phase
- Radial dispersion neglected
- Pressure P varying linearly with z according to $P = P_T[1 + \alpha(1 - z)]$ where P_T is the pressure at the column top
- Gas holdup ε_G and interfacial area varying with z
- Variable u
- Reaction of CO_2 with H_2O (in the system of experiment) neglected; gases assumed all inert
- Gas-phase resistance to mass transfer neglected

The dispersion coefficient in the liquid phase is $D_{aL} = 2.7\, D_T^{1.4} u^{0.3}$ where D_T = reactor diameter in meters. Although ε_G varies with z, α can be taken to be almost constant:

$$\alpha = \rho g(1 - \bar{\varepsilon}_G)Z_T/P_T$$

where Z_T is the total bubble column height in meters and $u\,P(1 - x) = u_0\,P_T(1 + \alpha)(1 - x_0)$, the subscript 0 denoting the inlet of reactor. The model equation for CO_2 balance of the gas phase is:

$$\frac{dX}{dz} = -\mathrm{St}_G\varphi(z)(1 - X)^2\left(\beta(z)X - \frac{p_L}{P_T}\right) \qquad (9\text{-}49)$$

and that for CO_2 partial pressure in the liquid phase p_L is:

$$\frac{d^2p_L}{dz^2} + a \cdot \frac{\mathrm{Pe}_L}{1 - \bar{\varepsilon}_G\varphi(z)} \frac{dp_L}{dz} = \frac{\mathrm{Pe}_L \, \mathrm{St}_L\varphi(z)}{1 - \bar{\varepsilon}_G\varphi(z)} (P_T \, \beta(z) \, X - p_L) \quad (9\text{-}50)$$

where X = mole fraction of CO_2

$\varphi(z)$ = a regression function of z

p_L = partial pressure of CO_2 in liquid phase

$\mathrm{St}_G = k_L \frac{6\bar{\varepsilon}_G}{d_s} \cdot \frac{Z_T}{u_0(1 + \alpha)(1 - X_0)} \cdot \frac{RT}{H}$, dimensionless

d_s = mean Sauter diameter, m

H = Henry's constant

$\beta(z) = 1 + \alpha(1 - z)$, dimensionless

$\mathrm{Pe}_L = u_L Z_T / D_{aL}$, dimensionless

D_{aL} = axial dispersion coefficient in liquid phase

$\mathrm{St}_L = k_L \frac{6\bar{\varepsilon}_G Z_T}{d_s u_L}$, dimensionless

k_L = liquid-side mass-transfer coefficient

u_L = superficial liquid velocity

The initial condition for the gas-phase equation is

$$x(0) = x_0$$

The boundary conditions for the liquid-phase equation are, for the case of concurrent flow ($a = -1$):

$$p_L(0) = p_{Li} + \frac{1 - \bar{\varepsilon}_G\varphi(0)dp_L(0)}{\mathrm{Pe}_L \, dz}$$

$$\frac{dp_L(1)}{dz} = 0$$

and for countercurrent flow ($a = +1$):

$$\frac{dp_L(0)}{dz} = 0$$

$$p_L(1) = p_{Li} - \frac{1 - \bar{\varepsilon}_G\varphi(1)dp_L(1)}{\mathrm{Pe}_L \, dz}$$

where the subscript i denotes inlet condition.

The gas-phase and liquid-phase differential equations are nonlinear boundary-value ODEs that have nonconstant coefficients. They can be solved numerically by the method of Lee (see Chap. 2). For certain parameter combinations, the method of Lee causes problems, as reported by Deckwer et al.,[37] who explain at length how they circumvented the difficulties.

Kölbel and Langemann[30] studied the absorption of oxygen in water and the desorption of oxygen by nitrogen and found that the mass transfer coefficient increased linearly with superficial gas velocity up to about 0.05 m/s and then declined, also linearly. This bend in the curve seems to reflect the flow regime change.

The mass transfer in gas-liquid fluidized beds or ebullated beds has been studied by K. Østergaard et al.[57] They found that 6-mm spheres were characterized by 10 times higher mass transfer than 1-mm spheres. Surprisingly, no spheres at all gave mass-transfer intermediate between that of 1- and 6-mm spheres. Mass transfer increased with the gas flow rate and was approximately proportional to the gas holdup. On the other hand, variation of the liquid rate caused little change in mass transfer.

Heat Transfer in Suspended-Bed Reactors

Suspended-bed reactors have an important advantage over fixed-bed reactors in heat transfer: exothermic heat may be removed much more easily from the former by simply installing cooling coils in them. Another characteristic of the suspended-bed reactors (which may also be considered an advantage) is that they are operated isothermally and are immune to localized hot spots.

Exothermic heat can be removed from suspended-bed reactors:

- By the vaporization of reactants or products
- By the vaporization of an inert solvent
- By the recirculation of the liquid through an external cooler
- By direct heat transfer to the vessel jacket or to cooling coils installed in the reactor (only this case will be discussed below)

Heat transfer in a suspended-bed reactor can be characterized as follows:

- The liquid temperature in the reactor is quite uniform (it operates isothermally).
- For reactors larger than 0.07 to 0.10 m in diameter, there is no diameter effect on transfer rates.

- Process-side coefficients are not influenced by transfer-surface geometry (tubes vs. jackets).
- Process-side coefficients are quite high.

The heat-transfer coefficient h of various liquids in slurry reactors have been correlated with the superficial gas velocity u, as shown in Fig. 9-18.[1] The correlation equation is (in SI units):

$$h = 8.844u^{0.22} \tag{9-51}$$

where h is the heat-transfer coefficient in kilojoules per second per square meter per Kelvin and u is the superficial gas velocity in meters per second. In USCS units u is in feet per second, the coefficient of u is 1200, and h is in British thermal units per hour per square foot per degree Fahrenheit.

Data for liquids other than water were correlated by the relationship:

$$\frac{h_{\text{other liquid}}}{h_{\text{water}}} = \left(\frac{\text{Pr}_{\text{water}}}{\text{Pr}_{\text{other liquid}}}\right)^{0.5} \tag{9-52}$$

where $\text{Pr} = c_p\mu/\lambda_L$ = Prandtl number of the liquid

λ_L = liquid thermal conductivity, kJ/(m · s · K)

c_p = specific heat at constant pressure, kJ/(kg · K)

μ = viscosity, Pa · s = kg/(m · s)

Suspensions of solid catalysts tend to give higher transfer rates than liquids only because of the scouring action of the solids on the walls. Reliable correlations in this field have yet to be developed. Consequently, Fig. 9-18 and Eq. (9-51) can be used only for thin suspended beds of very finely divided catalysts.

Seth and Stahel[58] have discussed heat transfer from helical coils immersed in agitated vessels. The reader is referred to this detailed paper. Lavingia and Dickson[59] have developed the following correlation for heat transfer in an agitated vessel with coils to a two-phase liquid system for an impeller Reynolds number range of $3.7 \times 10^4 \leqslant \text{Re} \leqslant 1.1 \times 10^6$:

$$\text{Nu} = 4.04\,\text{Re}^{0.42}\text{Pr}^{0.33}(\mu/\mu_w)^{0.14} \tag{9-53}$$

where subscript w denotes "wall" and Nu is the Nusselt number. In this system both phases are liquid.

According to Kölbel et al.[10] the heat-transfer coefficient h increases very steeply with linear gas velocity v_G and asymptotically approaches a maximum value of 4500 kcal/(m^2 · h · K) or 5.23 kJ/(m^2 · s · K) at a gas flow rate of about 0.1 m/s. This maximum value of the heat-transfer coefficient cannot be exceeded by further agitation by the bubbles. This

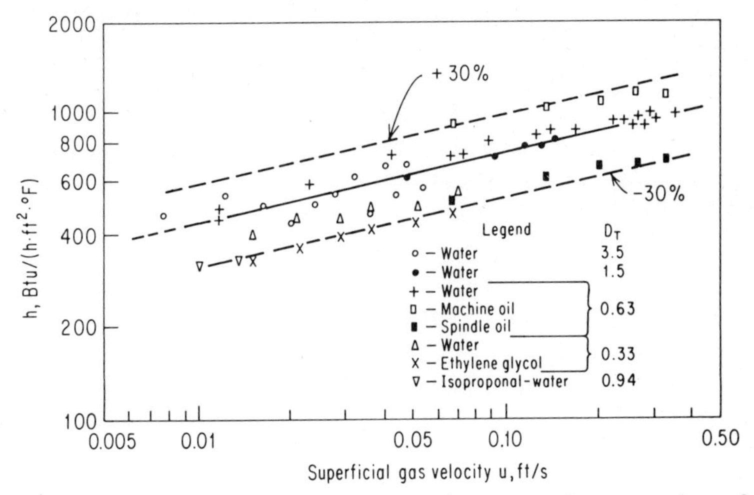

FIG. 9-18 Heat transfer in gas-sparged reactors for a number of different materials. (*Excerpted by special permission from James R. Fair,*[1] *Chemical Engineering, July 17, 1967.*)

value is considerably higher than the value of heat transfer in tubing of the same diameter in which only water is flowing. The intensive heat transfer in a bubble column is explained by the convective heat transport caused by the radial velocity component of the liquid around rising bubbles. Figure 9-19 illustrates the radial velocity component preceding and following a rising bubble.

Heat transfer in bubble reactors that have diameters much larger than the bubble diameters can be described by Kölbel et al.'s relationship[10]:

$$St = f(Re \cdot Fr \cdot Pr^2) \tag{9-54}$$

where St = Stanton number = $h/(v_G \cdot \rho \cdot c_P)$

Fr = Froude number = $v_G^2/(g \cdot D_T)$

Measured data were plotted by Kast on a double logarithmic scale with St as ordinate and $\sqrt[3]{ReFrPr^{2.5}}$ as abscissa (Fig. 9-20).

The heat transfer coefficient decreases with increasing viscosity of the liquid phase.[10]

9.3 ADVANTAGES AND DRAWBACKS OF VARIOUS SUSPENDED-BED REACTORS

Suspended-bed reactors have a number of interesting advantages over fixed-bed reactors. Of course, they also have some drawbacks. These advantages and drawbacks have been summarized on Table 9-1, where an x in a given box means "yes, that is true." For example, it is stated on the first line that "diffusion of reactant through bulk liquid is minimized by intensive agitation." This is true for CSTR and 3ϕTR but not true for slurry and ebullated-bed reactors. Thus in the first line an x denotes an advantage. However, in the bottom three lines, where disadvantages are mentioned, an x denotes a drawback.

9.4 PROCESS DESIGN OF SUSPENDED-BED REACTORS

The strategy in designing any type of suspended-bed reactor is to first design the method of catalyst suspension and the gas-liquid contact—the rest is then relatively simple.

Process Design of CSTRs

In the CSTR the method of catalyst suspension is some kind of mechanical stirring. Thus the main strategy is to design the stirrers and the gas-liquid contact.

General Procedure

Let us develop the design equations for the CSTR. The characteristic property of the CSTR is that the composition at any point of the expanded liquid phase is the same. Referring to Fig. 9-1, let us specify:

V = volume of expanded liquid, m^3 (net reactor volume)

ρ_c = mass of catalyst per unit volume of expanded liquid, kg/m^3

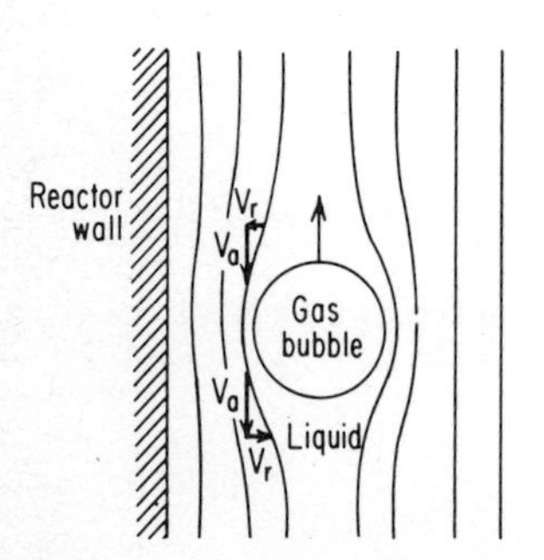

FIG. 9-19 Liquid flow around a bubble near the wall of the slurry reactor: v_a = axial component of the flow velocity; v_r = radial component of the flow velocity. (*From Kölbel, Hammer, and Langemann*[10] *by permission from Chemiker Zeitung.*)

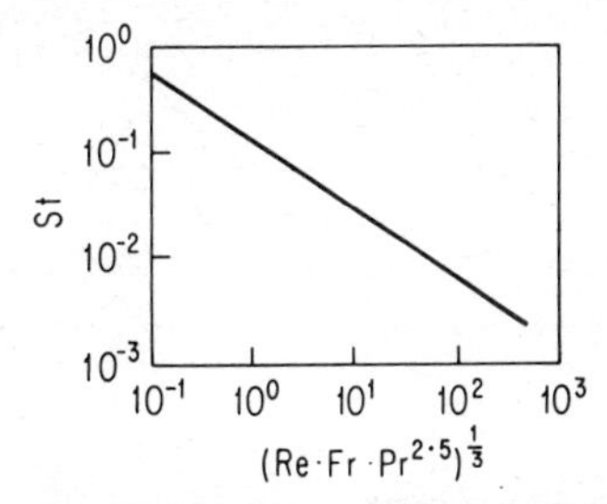

FIG. 9-20 Heat transfer in bubble column in dimensionless presentation. (*From W. Kast, "Untersuchungen zur Wärmeübergang in Blasensäulen," Chem. Ingr. Tech.* 35(*11*)*:787* (*1963*), *by permission from Dechema.*)

x_1 = fractional conversion of the critical reactant at inlet to the reactor (assuming the reaction is run in more than one reactor in series), dimensionless

x_2 = fractional conversion of the critical reactant at outlet from the reactor, dimensionless

r_w = reaction rate, amount of critical reactant converted per second and per kilogram of catalyst in suspension, kmol/(s · kg)

The molar balance for a time element $\Delta\theta$ and a volume element ΔV can be written:

(Moles of reactant fed to volume ΔV)
− (moles of reactant leaving volume ΔV)
− (moles of reactant converted in volume ΔV)
= (accumulation of reactant in ΔV) (9-55)

At steady-state operation in a CSTR, the accumulation term is zero. In a CSTR with constant concentration throughout the expanded liquid volume, the element ΔV could be easily integrated to obtain the whole volume of expanded liquid, which we may call the *net reactor volume V.*

Moles of reactant fed in time $\Delta\theta$ is $Fy_0(1 - x_1)\Delta\theta$

Moles of reactant in outlet stream in time $\Delta\theta$ is $Fy_0(1 - x_2)\Delta\theta$

Moles of reactant converted in volume V and time $\Delta\theta$ is $r_w \eta V \rho_c \Delta\theta$

Substituting these expressions into Eq. (9-55) gives:

$$Fy_0(1 - x_1)\Delta\theta - Fy_0(1 - x_2)\Delta\theta - \eta r_w V \rho_c \,\Delta\theta = 0$$

We can divide all the terms by $\Delta\theta$, simplify, and rearrange:

$$V = \frac{Fy_0}{\rho_c} \cdot \frac{(x_2 - x_1)}{\eta r_w} \tag{9-56}$$

TABLE 9-1
Advantages and Drawbacks of Suspended-Bed Reactors

	CSTR	Slurry	Ebullated bed	3ϕTR
Diffusion of reactant through bulk liquid is minimized by intensive agitation	x			x
Intraphase diffusion is minimized by using finely divided catalysts	x	x		
Catalyst stays in reactor, no catalyst-product separation step necessary			x	
Catalyst can be constantly withdrawn, regenerated, and made up without shutting down reactor	x	x	x	x
Removal of exothermic heat is easy, high h	x	x	x	x
Isothermality favors aiming at a given selectivity	x	x	x	x
Pelleting cost for the catalyst can be avoided	x	x		
Higher rates of reaction per unit weight of catalyst	x	x		
Catalyst must be added to fresh liquid flow and removed from liquid product. Handling of slurries requires special techniques	x	x		
High conversion requires several reactors in series	x	x	x	x
Design data generally not available	x	x	x	x

It is important to exactly define F. We will define it as the flow of liquid feed per unit time, kmol/s, not the reactant flow!

The average residence time in the reactor can be calculated as follows. First multiply both sides of Eq. (9-56) by $\overline{M}/\rho_L$, where $\overline{M}$ is the average molecular weight of the liquid feedstock in kilograms per kilomole and ρ_L is the density of the liquid feed in kilograms per cubic meter.

$$\frac{V\overline{M}}{\rho_L} = \frac{F\overline{M}\, y_0}{\rho_L \rho_c \eta} \frac{(x_2 - x_1)}{r_w} \tag{9-57}$$

Here $F\overline{M}/\rho_L$ is the volume feed flow and has the dimensions of cubic meters per second, while V represents the expanded liquid volume of the reactor and can be written as

$$V = \frac{V_L}{\varepsilon_L}$$

where V_L is the nonexpanded actual liquid volume in the reactor in cubic meters and ε_L is the liquid holdup (dimensionless). Equation (9-57) can be written as:

$$\frac{V_L \overline{M}}{\varepsilon_L \rho_L} = \frac{F\overline{M}\, y_0 (x_2 - x_1)}{\rho_L \rho_c r_w}$$

or

$$\frac{V_L}{F\overline{M}/\rho_L} = \frac{\rho_L \varepsilon_L\, y_0 (x_2 - x_1)}{\overline{M}\, \rho_c\, \eta r_w} \tag{9-58}$$

The left-hand side of Eq. (9-58) represents the average residence time $\bar{\theta}$ in the reactor and we write:

$$\bar{\theta} = \frac{\rho_L \varepsilon_L\, y_0 (x_2 - x_1)}{\rho_c\, \overline{M}\, \eta r_w} \tag{9-59}$$

The heat balance equation for the steady-state CSTR (without the accumulation term) can be written as:

$$\begin{pmatrix}\text{Heat in streams}\\ \text{fed to volume } \Delta V\end{pmatrix} - \begin{pmatrix}\text{heat in streams}\\ \text{leaving volume } \Delta V\end{pmatrix} + \begin{pmatrix}\text{heat transferred from}\\ \text{surroundings to } \Delta V\end{pmatrix} = 0 \tag{9-60}$$

We must choose a base state (temperature, pressure, and composition) from which to evaluate the energy. Let us assume that the enthalpy per mole above the base state of the feed streams is H_1 and that of the product stream is H_2. If F_T is the total molar feed rate, including both the liquid and the gas, the first and second terms in Eq. (9-60) are $F_T H_1\, \Delta\theta$ and $F_{T2} H_2\, \Delta\theta$, respectively. After dividing all terms by $\Delta\theta$, the balance becomes:

$$F_T H_1 - F_{T2} H_2 + h\, A_h (T_x - T_2) = 0 \tag{9-61}$$

where h = overall heat-transfer coefficient, $kJ/(s \cdot m^2 \cdot K)$

A_h = effective area of heat transfer, m^2

T_x = temperature of the exterior or surroundings or of the cooling medium in the jacket or the cooling coil, K

T_2 = reactor exit temperature

In Eq. (9-61) the difference between $H_1 - H_2$ must be replaced by a function of T, r_w, and ΔH. This is accomplished by considering the enthalpy change when feed at T_1 is first heated to T_2 and then changed in composition to that of the product:

$$H_2 - H_1 = C_p(T_2 - T_1) + (x_2 - x_1)\,\Delta H\,\frac{Fy_0}{F_T} \tag{9-62}$$

where C_p is molar heat capacity in kilojoules per kilomole per Kelvin and ΔH is heat of reaction per mole of limiting (key) reactant in kilojoules per kilomole. The combination of Eqs. (9-61) and (9-62) gives:

$$F_T C_p(T_1 - T_2) - (x_2 - x_1)\Delta H\, Fy_0 + hA_h(T_x - T_2) = 0 \tag{9-63}$$

Now we can replace $(x_2 - x_1)$ from Eq. (9-56) and simplify:

$$F_T C_p(T_1 - T_2) - \eta r_w\, V\, \rho_c \Delta H + hA_h(T_x - T_2) = 0 \tag{9-64}$$

In case more than one reaction takes place in the reactor, Eq. (9-64) must be written as:

$$F_T C_p(T_1 - T_2) - V\rho_c \Sigma \mathcal{R}_{wi}\,\Delta H_i + hA_h(T_x - T_2) = 0 \tag{9-65}$$

Finally, we need the rate equation in form of the Arrhenius expression:

$$\mathcal{R}_w = \eta r_w = \eta A \exp(-E/RT)\, C_a^{\alpha} C_b^{\beta} \tag{9-66}$$

In most cases of liquid phase reactions the kinetic expression becomes much more complex because of the additional involvement of intra- and interparticle transport phenomena. Thus the design procedure consists in calculating the transport conditions to create the desired gas-liquid-catalyst mixture, to solving Eqs. (9-66) and (9-56) for V, and from the V value calculating the necessary heat-transfer surface A_h. From V the amount of catalyst can be easily calculated.

Example of CSTR Design

The example for CSTR design will be the same hydrodesulfurization process used in Chap. 7 for trickle-bed reactors. Let us assume that we want to build the same 250,000-t/yr plant, but with the trickle-bed reactor replaced by a CSTR of the type shown in Fig. 9-3. The following aspects of the process will differ from the trickle-bed case:

- The catalyst will be smaller, ½-mm-diameter ($d_p = 0.0005$ m) spheres, which gives an effectiveness factor of 0.99.[60]
- A liquid/solid volume ratio of 10 : 1 will be assumed in the slurry.
- A gas circulation rate twice the fresh gas rate will be assumed.
- A conversion of $x = 0.65$ is aimed at.

Let us now calculate the total volume of expanded bed per cubic meter of liquid feed:

$$\varepsilon_p = 0.1\ \varepsilon_L \qquad \varepsilon_p + \varepsilon_G + \varepsilon_L = 1 \qquad \varepsilon_L = \frac{1 - \varepsilon_G}{1.1}$$

The amount of gas recirculated is twice the amount of fresh gas dictated by the H_2/oil mole ratio. For each cubic meter of pure liquid we will have:

$$\frac{(569.3\ \text{kg/m}^3)(0.5\ \text{m}^3\ H_2(\text{NTP})/\text{kg oil})(2.)(648.2\ \text{K})(1.01325\ \text{bars})}{(55\ \text{bars})(273.2\ \text{K})}$$
$$= 22.88\ \text{m}^3\ H_2\ \text{per m}^3\ \text{oil}$$

The dynamic holdup ε_G can be calculated from Fig. 9-14 as $\varepsilon_G = 0.26$ for a maximum gas velocity. Then we will have:

$$\varepsilon_L = \frac{1 - 0.26}{1.1} = 0.6727 \qquad \varepsilon_p = 0.1\ \varepsilon_L = 0.06727$$

and for the catalyst density (including pores)

$$\rho_p = \frac{\rho_B}{1 - \varepsilon} = \frac{950\ \text{kg/m}^3}{1 - 0.36} = 1484\ \text{kg/m}^3$$

The catalyst density in the slurry is

$$\rho_c = \rho_p \varepsilon_p = (1484\ \text{kg/m}^3)(0.06727)$$
$$= 99.86\ \text{kg/m}^3$$

The design equations are:

$$V = \frac{F y_0}{\rho_c} \frac{(x_2 - x_1)}{\eta r_w} = \frac{(9.3339\ \text{kg/s})(0.8358)(0.65)}{(670\ \text{kg/kmol})(0.99)\ \rho_c r_w}$$

The key reaction rate is:

$$r_w = 2.8 \times 10^4 \exp(-82{,}060/RT) C_{L0} C_r / \rho_c \qquad (7\text{-}28)$$

Other side-reaction rates are:

$$\mathcal{R}_3 = \eta_3\ 1.8 \times 10^3 \exp(-72{,}060/RT)\ C_{rN} C_{N0}/\rho_c \qquad (7\text{-}30)$$
$$\mathcal{R}_4 = \eta_4\ 2.5 \times 10^{15} \exp(-243{,}000/RT)\ C_{rhy} C_{hy0}/\rho_c \qquad (7\text{-}31)$$
$$\mathcal{R}_5 = \eta_5\ 1.0 \times 10^3 \exp(-46{,}860/RT)\ C_{rhc} C_{hc0}/\rho_c \qquad (7\text{-}32)$$

We will assume that all effectiveness factors are equal to 0.99, and we express the activity of the catalyst in the slurry reactor by the same kinetic equation, Eq. (7-28), that expresses the activity in the trickle-bed regime, taking in consideration that

$$r_v = r_w \cdot \rho_c$$

This is a pure assumption for purposes of comparison of the slurry and trickle-bed regimes and does not reflect the facts. With these assumptions the reactor volume is calculated to be

$$V = 1.577 \text{ m}^3$$

This is, of course, the expanded liquid volume only. The total volume of the tank must also include the gas volume and the volume of the cooling coils installed in the reactor. Thus we can select a diameter of 1.0 m for a reactor of the type of Fig. 9-1. Then the hemispherical bottom part will have a volume of:

$$0.5\ (\pi/6)\ D_T^3 = 0.2618 \text{ m}^3$$

The cylindrical part will have the volume of:

$$1.577 - 0.2618 = 1.3152 \text{ m}^3$$

The height of that section without considering the coil volume will be:

$$(1.3152/0.5^2\pi) = 1.675 \text{ m}$$

We will probably have to design the cylindrical part of the reactor for a height of 2.0 m to accommodate the coils and other internals, e.g., the sparger and the total reactor volume will be:

$$(2.0)(0.5^2\pi) + (2)(0.2618) = 2.094 \text{ m}^3$$

In comparison with this CSTR reactor size, the plug-flow trickle-bed reactor had a 1.5-m diameter, and a conversion of 65% was reached at a length of 11.21 m, indicating a volume of 19.81 m^3.

What this example shows is simply that catalysts having the same activity in the trickle bed and the CSTR need a trickle-bed volume 12.5 times as large than the CSTR volume. The catch is that the same catalyst has a much lower activity in a submerged reaction than in a trickle-bed regime—otherwise all trickle beds would be replaced by CSTRs having about 8% of the volume of the trickle beds. This is not being done.

Let us notice that we did not need a computer to calculate the volume of our CSTR. However we might have needed a computer if the reaction kinetics and transport phenomena had resulted in messy mathematics.

Once the volume of a CSTR is determined for the key reactant, the conversions of other reactants, e.g., nitrogen, hydrocrackables, and unsaturates, can be calculated by using the already known reactor volume and the design equations for each reactant, i.e., Eqs. (7-30) to (7-32).

The heat of reaction can be removed through cooling jackets or cooling coils in accordance with Eq. (9-65). Also part of the reaction heat can be removed by supplying the feed at a temperature below the reaction temperature. Jacket cooling is unattractive in high-pressure reactions such as hydrodesulfurization of petroleum oils at 55 bars because the reactor wall is made of thick plate, which has a poor heat transfer coefficient.

Finally the stirrer of the CSTR must be designed. In the United States we have companies specializing in the design and fabrication of all sorts of mixing and stirring equipment. Since these companies will supply the actual stirrer anyway, the reactor designer might just as well let them size and specify the stirrer. These vendors must be given data such as catalyst particle size consist, concentration, density, liquid composition, density, viscosity, and temperature, and of course reactor dimensions and corrosion requirements. In places where the services of specialized companies are not available, stirrer design becomes a joint task for the mechanical designer and the reactor designer.

Scale-up of a Gas-Liquid CSTR

The scale-up of a catalytic gas-liquid CSTR in which the chemical reaction is controlling from laboratory experiments to full scale has been discussed by M. Nadler.[61] Nadler also modeled the CSTR and concluded that the scale-up of the chemical reaction-controlled reactor "was no problem."

The theoretical bases for dynamic similarity of CSTRs were laid down quantitatively by Dankwerts.[43] Three conditions that must be fulfilled are: (1) the model must be geometrically similar to the prototype; (2) the Reynolds number must be the same in both the model and the prototype; and (3) gravity waves, density differences, surface tension, and other influences apart from inertia and viscosity must not strongly affect the behavior of the fluid in both model and prototype. Cerro and Parera[62] showed experimentally that if Dankwert's three conditions are fulfilled, the CSTR's behavior can be described as a function of Reynolds number only. Here the Reynolds number is defined as:

$$\mathrm{Re} = \frac{D_i^2 N \rho_L}{60\ \mu_L} \tag{9-67}$$

where D_i = diameter of agitator blades, m

N = agitator speed, r/min

ρ_L = density of fluid, kg/m^3

μ_L = viscosity of fluid, kg/(m · s) or Pa · s

R. R. Corpstein et al.[63] recently discussed the problems of CSTR scale-up from bench scale to pilot scale and further to industrial scale and concluded that in many aspects of scale-up, dynamic similarity is not adequate—equality is necessary. For example, "when heat-transfer and temperature control are involved in scaleup, a *similar* convective temperature gradient (i.e., equal Nusselt number) is of little value when the desired result is *equal* temperature for the process." The paper also contains many useful references.

CSTRs in Series

The design of several CSTRs in series has been discussed by K. Schoenemann,[64] who listed several formulas for the residence time. Here are some of them:

$$C_{tn} = C_0 \left[1 + \sum_{m=1}^{m=n-1} \frac{1}{m!} \left(\frac{\theta}{\tau} \right)^m \right] \exp(-\theta/\tau) \qquad (9\text{-}68)$$

$$C_{t1} = C_0 \exp(-\theta/\tau) \qquad (9\text{-}69)$$

$$C_{t1} = C_0'(1 - \exp(-\theta/\tau)) \qquad (9\text{-}70)$$

where C_t = concentration of the tracer substance of the effluent stream or (in our case) concentration of key reactant at time θ, mole %.

C_{tn} = C_t for the nth reactor

C_{t1} = C_t for a single reactor

C_0' = reference concentration of the consumed component in the feed, mole %

n = number of CSTRs in series

C_0 = initial concentration of the tracer substance at time $\theta = 0$ in a CSTR, mole %

m = variable to indicate the limits for the summations in the formulas

τ = average residence time = (V/q), s

θ = time, s

V = reaction volume, m^3

q = throughput, m^3/s

Eldridge and Piret also developed equations for CSTRs in series at steady state for a variety of kinetics.[65] Mason and Piret[66] extended these equations to systems of CSTRs in series during transient periods of operation. Eldridge and Piret give the following design equations for a series of steady-state CSTRs:

$$\frac{C_{n-1}}{C_n} = 1 - \left(\frac{dC}{d\theta} \right)_n \frac{t_n}{C_n} \qquad (9\text{-}71)$$

where $t_n = V_n/F_n$ = nominal holding time in nth reactor

C = molar concentration

V_n = volume occupied by reaction medium in nth vessel

F_n = volumetric effluent rate from nth reactor

A single CSTR is the perfect model for the ideally mixed reactor. However by connecting a large number of CSTRs in series, it is possible to approach the unmixed state of the plug-flow reactor. Thus a CSTR cascade with n individual CSTRs has become a model for the degree of backmixing in a reactor. The alternate model is the well-known dispersion model in the second derivative of concentration and the Péclet number.

L. S. Kowalczyk[67] has shown the similarity between batch reactors, CSTRs in series, and plug-flow tubular reactors. Assuming first-order chemical reactions, the product distribution equations are as follows:

Batch $\quad C_A = C_{A0} \exp(-k\theta)$

CSTR cascade $\quad C_A = C_{A0}\,(1 + k\theta)^{-n}$

Plug flow $\quad C_A = C_{A0} \exp(-kV/F_v)$

where θ = residence time in a single reactor at steady state, s

V = reactor volume, m^3

F_v = volumetric rate of flow, m^3/s

n = number of CSTRs in series

k = first-order reaction rate constant, s^{-1}

Process Design of Slurry Reactor

We will first discuss the general method of attacking the design of slurry reactors and then review the application of an example from the literature.

General Procedure

The process design of slurry reactors consists in:

- Designing the gas and liquid transport conditions to create the gas-liquid-catalyst mixture
- Setting up the reaction rate equation(s)
- Setting up the design equation or mass balance equation
- Setting up the heat balance equation
- Solving these equations simultaneously

The design of slurry reactors in which the liquid is fully backmixed is similar to the design of CSTRs. Sherwood and Farkas[3] have shown that the liquid in bubble reactors is always backmixed with respect to both mass transfer and heat transfer. Thus the only reactions that are plug flow or partially backmixed are gas reactions with the liquid as catalyst carrier, as in the reactor type of Fig. 9-7.

In most cases gas and liquid transport conditions lead to the development of relationships that modify the design equations in unpredictable ways. Thus no "typical design equation" can be given except in the most generalized terms:

$$Z_T = \int_0^z dz = \int_0^{x_D} f\,(\mathcal{R}, x, dx, Fy_0, A_c, \rho_c, \ldots)dx \tag{9-72}$$

Such equations can be either initial-value or boundary-condition types. The reactor designer must develop the appropriate algorithm to integrate them, using techniques presented in Chap. 2.

Slurry reactors are usually isothermally operated. Heat is continuously supplied to or removed from them by means of a heat-exchange coil installed in the reactor shell.

The heat balance equation equates the heat produced or absorbed by the reaction with the heat transferred through the coil to the heat-exchange medium flowing in the coil. As long as the reaction temperature can be maintained constant, the reaction rate and the conversion are not affected. For this reason the heat balance equation must be used to calculate the required heat transfer surface area and the flow rate of the heat-exchange medium.

The simple look of the slurry reactor hardware is quite misleading. Actually the process design is quite involved and complex and is difficult to model, to scale up, to obtain parameter values for, and to compute. Deckwer has recently discussed some of these difficulties in an excellent paper.[68]

The design example selected for this book is a relatively simple one. Still, it is quite involved, as will be seen below.

Example of Slurry Reactor Design

The methanation of carbon monoxide in an isobaric-isothermal slurry reactor according to the reaction

$$3\,H_2 + CO \rightarrow CH_4 + H_2O \tag{9-73}$$

was selected as a relatively simple calculation example. A set of data was obtained from literature[8,10,59,69] and from private communications.

The reaction is known to proceed at 230 to 270°C and 1 to 10 bars pressure, using a catalyst concentration of up to 10% and catalyst particle sizes of 5 to 60 μm. Paraffin hydrocarbons melting at 100 to 110°C were used to suspend the fine catalyst. Gas flowed at 1 to 23 cm/s. The slurry bed was about 3 m high and had a diameter of 38 mm. The gas distributor at the bottom of the reactor was a metallic fritte of 75- to 100-μm pore diameter.

The feed gas ($3H_2 + CO$) moved through the slurry as bubbles, dissolved in the paraffin liquid, diffused to catalyst particles, and reacted on the catalyst surface, and the product gas ($CH_4 + H_2O$) diffused back to and desorbed into other rising bubbles. Kölbel, Hammer, and Langemann[10] assumed that the reaction rate on the catalyst surface is equal to the mass-transfer rate from the bubble to the solution. At low temperatures, low catalyst concentrations, and high gas holdups, the chemical reaction is the controlling resistance.

The intrinsic reaction under these conditions and at steady state is:

$$u_{CO}(dx/dz) = \varepsilon_L k\, c_c C_H^{\alpha} \qquad \text{kmol CH}_4/(\text{m}^3\cdot\text{s}) \tag{9-74}$$

where x = conversion of CO, dimensionless

z = height of the reactor bed above the gas distributor, m

ε_L = liquid holdup, dimensionless

u_{CO} = superficial CO loading, kmol CO/($m^2 \cdot s$)

k = reaction rate constant

c_c = catalyst concentration of nonexpanded slurry, kg/m^3

C_H = concentration of dissolved H_2 in position z, kmol/m^3

α = fractional exponent, approximately = 0.5

The CO loading u_{CO} is given by:

$$u_{CO} = 1.60614\, v\, X_{CO}^0\, (T_0/T)(P/P_0) \qquad \text{kmol CO}/(\text{m}^2 \cdot \text{s}) \tag{9-75}$$

where v = gas flow rate, m/s

X_{CO}^0 = mole fraction of CO in feed gas, dimensionless

T = temperature, K

P = pressure, bars

Subscript 0 denotes NTP conditions.

Under experimental conditions in which the mass transfer of hydrogen from the gas phase to the liquid phase is exclusively rate-determining, i.e., at higher temperatures, higher catalyst concentrations, and low gas holdups, the following mass transfer equation applies:

$$r = u_{CO}(dx/dz) = (k_L a/3)(HPX_H - C_H) \qquad \text{kmol CO/m}^2 \cdot \text{s} \qquad (9\text{-}76)$$

where k_L = mass transfer coefficient for H_2 from the gas bubble into the liquid phase, m/s

a = specific phase boundary area per unit volume of expanded suspension, m^2/m^3

H = Henry constant, kmol/($m^3 \cdot$ bar)

X_H = mole fraction of H_2 in gas at position z

The variations of X_H, ε_L, and a with z as a result of conversion x can be handled by the following equations:

$$X_H(x) = \frac{X_H^0 - 3\,X_{CO}^0 x}{1 - 2\,X_{CO}^0 x} \qquad (9\text{-}77)$$

$$\varepsilon_L(x) = \varepsilon_L^0 + 2\,X_{CO}^0 x(1 - \varepsilon_L^0) \qquad (9\text{-}78)$$

$$a(x) = a^0(1 - 2\,X_{CO}^0 x)^{2/3} \qquad (9\text{-}79)$$

The superscript 0 means at position $z = 0$.

At steady state, the rates of reaction and mass transfer are equal. Equations (9-74) and (9-76) to (9-79) can be combined as follows:

$$\frac{dx}{dz} = \frac{k_L a^0}{3u_{CO}}(1 - 2X_{CO}^0\,x)^{2/3}\left[HP\frac{X_H^0 - 3X_{CO}^0\,x}{1 - 2X_{CO}^0\,x} - \left(\frac{dx/dz \cdot u_{CO}}{kc_c(\varepsilon_L^0 + 2X_{CO}^0 x(1 - \varepsilon_L^0))}\right)^{1/\alpha}\right] \qquad (9\text{-}80)$$

Equation (9-80) cannot be solved analytically. Kölbel et al.[10] solved and optimized Eq. (9-80) by means of an analog computer. More recently, a digital solution was obtained by Hammer and Schmal,[70] who also optimized the reactor. This latter study is a good example of how involved slurry reactor design can really be. The integration of Eq. (9-80) gives the reactor height Z_D for the desired conversion x_D when the reactor is assumed to have no backmixing. In order to allow for backmixing, a residence time distribution function $\varphi(z,N)$ is superimposed on the integration of Eq. (9-80)

$$x_D = \int_0^{x_D} x(z)dz \qquad (9\text{-}81)$$

in the form

$$x_{DB} = \int_0^{\infty} x(z)\varphi(z,N)dz \qquad (9\text{-}82)$$

where N is the stirred tank equivalent number for the degree of backmixing in the slurry reactor. This is quite a different way of expressing backmixing in reactor design equations than is used in this book and is due to studies by K. Schönemann[64] and H. Hofmann.[71] Thus, the numerical computations of Hammer and Schmal will not be repeated here. The interested reader is referred to the paper of these authors.[70]

Other Examples

Perhaps the most important industrial application of the slurry reactor concept is the Fischer-Tropsch synthesis. There is now considerable literature on the so-called liquid-phase Fischer-Tropsch synthesis. Let us mention only a few papers by Kölbel, Ackermann, and Engelhardt,[72] Kölbel and Ackermann,[6] Zaidi et al.,[69] and Hubert.[73]

The hydrogenation of ethylene over Raney nickel is of interest for modeling studies of slurry reactors. A paper of Kölbel and Maennig[9] reports on experimental data development to verify various process models.

In the past, slurry reactors have as a rule been used in the chemical industry only in small-scale batch hydrogenations and have not been common in the larger-scale operations of either the chemical or petrochemical industry. Recently the Institut Français du Pétrole (IFP) developed a slurry reactor process for the catalytic hydrogenation of benzene to cyclohexane.[11] Besides the IFP and the Fischer-Tropsch processes, an increasing number of new processes are emerging through various stages of development.

Process Design of Ebullated-Bed Reactors

The first task of the designer is to determine the ebullated bed conditions of the process:

- The ebullating (fluidizing) liquid velocity of the particular liquid and the catalyst material, shape, and size must be known from laboratory experiments.
- The mean residence time of the liquid in the bed, which corresponds to the desired product yield, must be known. This information may be empirical.
- The transport phenomena between gas and liquid and between liquid and catalyst must be known.

The actual design equation depends upon the way the ebullated bed is operated. If a high space velocity is used in a slender reactor and no product is recirculated, then the ebullated bed can be treated like a plug-flow reactor with some axial dispersion and a Péclet number can be determined.

$$\frac{dC_r}{dZ} = \frac{1}{\text{Pe}_{mal}} \cdot \frac{d^2C_r}{dZ^2} - \frac{\mathcal{R}\, d_p}{u_L\, C_{L0}} \tag{9-83}$$

where $C_r = C_L/C_{L0}$

$Z = z/d_p$

z = axial coordinate in the expanded bed

The gas flow can be definitely plug flow, and if the gas effluent is the main product, the design equation for it is:

$$\frac{dC_{Gr}}{dZ} = \frac{-\mathcal{R}d_p}{u\, C_{G0}} \tag{9-84}$$

where $C_{Gr} = C_G/C_{G0}$.

If, however, the ebullated bed is operated with liquid recycle, as in most cases, then the liquid phase is for all practical purposes a CSTR and the design equation is:

$$V = \frac{F y_0\, x}{\rho_c \mathcal{R}_w} \tag{9-85}$$

where V = volume of expanded liquid-gas-catalyst mixture, excluding the volume needed for internal or external recirculation, m^3

F = feed rate, kmol/s of total feedstock, liquid and gas

y_0 = mole fraction of the critical reactant in the total feedstock, dimensionless

ρ_c = mass of catalyst per unit volume of expanded bed, kg/m^3

$\mathcal{R}_w$ = reaction rate function = $\eta\, r_w$

r_w = intrinsic reaction rate, kmol of critical reactant converted per second and per kilogram of catalyst in suspension, kmol/(kg · s)

x = fractional conversion of the key reactant, assuming that the reaction starts at the inlet of the reactor or that $x_0 = 0$

The heat balance equations also depend upon conditions at which the reactor is operated. Generally, they parallel the mass balance equation. At high liquid space velocity, in tall and narrow reactors, and when no liquid is recirculated, equations developed for trickle beds can be used

[Eq. (7-39)]. In case of low space velocity, large diameter/height ratio, and liquid recirculation, Eq. (9-65), developed for CSTRs, can be used.

Process Design of Three-Phase Transport Reactors (3φTR)

The process design of three-phase transport reactors is one of the least known. The paper of Pruden et al.[24] gives only some clues. These authors studied a countercurrent 3φTR with a simple model reaction, the hydrogenation of α-methylstyrene (AMS) to cumene in the presence of a palladium black catalyst at ambient temperature and atmospheric pressure.

$$\underset{\alpha\text{-methylstyrene}}{C_6H_5C(CH_3){=}CH_2} + H_2 \xrightarrow{Pd} \underset{\text{cumene}}{C_6H_5CH(CH_3)_2}$$

This reaction had been used in studies of trickle beds[74] and slurry reactors.[3] Cumene is the only product and AMS and cumene have low vapor pressures.

The design equation is based on integrating a differential equation that describes the reaction of individual gas bubbles as they rise upward in the reactor. The following assumptions were made:

- The gas upflow is plug flow.
- The gas-side resistance to mass transfer can be neglected.
- The rate-controlling steps are: dissolution of H_2 from the gas bubbles, mass transfer of H_2 from bulk liquid to the surface of the catalyst, and the reaction of H_2 with AMS on the surface of the catalyst, which is first-order in H_2.
- Gas bubbles are spherical in shape.
- Catalyst particles are spherical in shape.

The differential equation is:

$$\frac{dx}{dz} = \left[\frac{F_1}{(1 - x)^{2/3}} + \frac{F_2}{\rho_c} + \frac{F_3}{\rho_c}\right]^{-1} \qquad \text{(9-83)}$$

where x = gas conversion per pass, dimensionless

z = reactor height, measured from the bottom of the reactor, m

ρ_c = catalyst loading, kg/m^3 of reactor volume

The term $F_1/(1 - x)^{2/3}$ describes the mass transfer from bubbles to liquid. The term $(1 - x)^{2/3}$ corrects for the decrease in bubble surface area as the reaction proceeds.

$$F_1 = \frac{D_{B0}}{k_G \cdot 6RT} \left[\frac{P_0}{P}\right]^{1/3} \frac{v_b}{H} \tag{9-84}$$

where D_{B0} = initial bubble diameter, m

k_G = gas-liquid mass-transfer coefficient, m/s

R = gas constant, $m^3 \cdot$ bars/(kmol $\cdot$ K) = 0.08314

T = absolute temperature, K

v_b = bubble velocity with respect to liquid, m/s

H = Henry's law constant defined by $C^* = HP$, in which H has the dimensions kmol/($m^3 \cdot$ bars)

C^* = saturation concentration of hydrogen in bulk liquid, kmol/m^3

P = pressure at height z, bars

P_0 = pressure at bottom of reactor, bars

The F_2/ρ_c term accounts for mass transfer from the bulk liquid to the catalyst surface:

$$F_2 = n_{b0}\, f_b/(C^*\, k_c\, S_p\, A_c) \tag{9-85}$$

where n_{b0} = initial number of moles per bubble, kmol

f_b = frequency of bubble formation, s^{-1}

k_c = liquid-to-catalyst mass-transfer coefficient, m/s

S_p = specific mass transfer surface, $6/\rho_s d_p$, m^2/kg

ρ_s = particle density, kg/m^3

A_c = cross-sectional area of reactor column, m^2

The F_3/ρ_c term describes the chemical reaction:

$$F_3 = n_{b0} f_b/(C^* k\, S_p'\, A_c\, C_{AMS}) \tag{9-86}$$

where k = reaction rate constant for first-order surface reaction, m^4/(kmol $\cdot$ s)

S_p' = specific reaction surface, m^2/kg

C_{AMS} = α-methylstyrene concentration in bulk liquid, kmol/m^3

The chemical reaction rate is very rapid, and thus the reaction term F_3 might become negligible. Equation (9-83) can be integrated by assuming that F_1 and F_2 are constant:

$$Z_T = 3\,K_1\,[1 - (1 - x)^{1/3}] + \frac{K_2\,x}{0.001\,\rho_c} \tag{9-87}$$

where Z_T is total reactor height in meters and K_1 and K_2 are constants.

The values of K_1 and K_2 can be obtained from Pruden et al.'s paper.[24] Figure 5 in that paper plots conversion x vs. $0.001\,\rho_c$ for two values of Z_T. By substituting two sets of values of x vs. Z_T in Eq. (9-87), we can obtain two simultaneous equations containing K_1 and K_2, from which these constants can be calculated.

Alternatively, it is possible to numerically integrate Eq. (9-83) provided various parameters are known. These parameters and the means of evaluating them are:

- A form of the Frössling equations can be used instead of k_G:

$$\text{Sh} = (2.)(1.04)\text{Re}^{0.50}\,\text{Sc}^{0.33} \tag{9-88}$$

- Bubble diameters can be measured from high-speed motion pictures.
- Particle diameters can be measured by a settling velocity technique.
- The gas bubble velocity v_b can be calculated from

$$v_b = u/\varepsilon_G \tag{9-89}$$

where u is superficial gas velocity in meters per second and ε_G is gas holdup in cubic meters of gas per cubic meter of reactor volume, giving

$$v_b = \frac{9.94}{\varepsilon_G^{0.234}} - \frac{u_L}{1 - \varepsilon_G} \tag{9-90}$$

where u_L = superficial liquid velocity, m/s.

- $D_B = D_{B0}\,(P_0/P)^{1/3}\,(1 - x)^{1/3}$ (9-91)
- $P = P_0 - z(P_0 - P_A)/Z_T$ (9-92)
- $u = u_0\,(1 - x)(P_0/P)$ (9-93)

where D_B = bubble diameter, m

P_A = pressure at top of reactor, bar

u_0 = initial gas superficial velocity, m/s

The 3ϕTR appears to be advantageous as compared with the slurry reactor: at similar conditions, the conversion in the 3ϕTR is much higher than that in the slurry reactor because:

The gas bubbles in the 3ϕTR have lower velocity in relation to the reactor and thus longer contact time. However, the bubble velocity with respect to the liquid, which is the important velocity for mass transfer, is the same in both types of reactor.

- The catalyst tends to agglomerate in both reactors. In the slurry reactor this results in decreasing area and poor catalyst distribution. In the 3ϕTR the agglomerates are broken down in the pump, and recirculation promotes good catalyst distribution.

NOMENCLATURE

a	External particle-surface/particle-volume ratio, m,$^{-1}$ or Interfacial area in bubbles [Eq. (9-16)], or Specific phase boundary area per unit volume of expanding suspension, m^{-1}
a_b	Bubble surface area per unit volume of expanded slurry, m^{-1}
A	Total interface area, m^2
A_h	Effective area of heat transfer, m^2
A_B	Area of bubble, m^2
A_c	Cross-sectional area in reactor vessel, m^2
A_{sph}	Area of oblate spheroid bubble with major-axis/minor-axis ratio $\leqslant 2.6$, where $A_B < A_{sph} \leqslant 1.2\ A_B$
Bo	Bodenstein number, dimensionless
c_c	Catalyst concentration of nonexpanded slurry, kg/m^3
C	Concentration, kmol/m^3 or In Eq. (9-29), concentration of tracer at axial coordinate z, kmol/m^3
C^*	Saturation concentration of hydrogen in bulk liquid, kmol/m^3
C_A	Molar concentration of species A, kmol/m^3
C_{A0}	C_A at inlet
C_{AMS}	α-methylstyrene concentration in bulk liquid, kmol/m^3
C_H	Concentration of dissolved H_2 in position z, kmol/m^3
C_e	Equilibrium concentration in bulk liquid, kmol/m^3
C_{G0}	Molar concentration of critical reactant in gas phase at inlet, kmol/m^3
C_{Gr}	Dimensionless molar concentration of critical reactant in gas phase
C_L	Critical reactant concentration in bulk liquid, kmol/m^3
C_{L0}	C_L at inlet

C_0	Initial concentration at time $\theta = 0$ in a CSTR, mole %
C'_0	Reference concentration of the consumed component in the feed, mole %
C_p	Molar heat capacity, kJ/(kmol · K)
C_r	Dimensionless concentration of key reactant in liquid phase
C_s	Reactant concentration at catalyst surface, kmol/m^3
C_{t1}	Concentration of key reactant in the effluent of a single CSTR at time θ, mole %
C_{tn}	Concentration of key reactant in the effluent of the *n*th CSTR in series at time θ, mole %
C_x	Concentration of the tracer in the total flow leaving the reactor, kmol/m^3
d_p	Particle diameter, m
d_s	Mean Sauter diameter, m
D	Diffusivity, m^2/s
D_{1m}	Molecular diffusion coefficient for the species diffusing in the fluid, m^2/s
D_a	Axial dispersion coefficient, m^2/s
D_{aL}	Liquid-phase axial dispersion coefficient, m^2/s
D_B	Bubble diameter, m
D_{B0}	Initial D_B
D_{BE}	Minimum stable bubble diameter, m
D_{BM}	Diameter of geometric mean bubble, m
D_i	Impeller diameter, m
D_T	Reactor diameter, m
D_s	Superficial dispersion coefficient of liquid, m^2/s
E	Effective local dispersion coefficient
Eö	Eötvös number, dimensionless
f	Friction factor and drag coefficient in nonlaminar region
f_b	Frequency of bubble formation, s^{-1}
F	Parameter independent of flow conditions, kmol/(m^2 · s), or flow of liquid feed, kmol/s (in Sec. 9.3)
F_v	Volumetric rate of flow, m^3/s
F_T	Total molar feed rate, kmol/s

H_1	Enthalpy of feed stream, kJ/kg
H_2	Enthalpy of products, kJ/kg
Fr	Froude number, dimensionless
g	Gravitational acceleration = 9.80597 m/s^2
h	Heat transfer coefficient
H	Henry's constant, kmol/(m^3 · bar)
k	Reaction rate constant
k_c	Bulk liquid-to-particle mass transfer coefficient, m/s
k_c^*	k_c corresponding to terminal settling velocity, m/s
k_G	Gas-to-liquid mass-transfer coefficient, m/s
k_L	Liquid-to-gas mass-transfer coefficient, m/s
k_{ov}	Overall reaction and mass-transfer rate constant
k_s	Surface reaction rate coefficient, m/s
K_{aL}	Coefficient of liquid-phase axial dispersion, m^2/s
K_L	Liquid-phase backmixing coefficient, m^2/s
m	Catalyst loading, kg/m^3
$\overline{M}$	Average molecular weight of the liquid feedstock, kg/kmol
n	Number of CSTRs in series
n_{b0}	Initial number of moles per bubble, kmol
N	Impeller speed, s^{-1}
N_p	The power number or the power input from the impeller
N_v	Molar flux of key reactant in the bubble-expanded slurry
p_L	Partial pressure (of CO_2) in liquid phase, bars
P	Pressure, bars
P_0	Pressure at the inlet (bottom) of reactor, bars
P'	Power, W
Pe_{BT}	Péclet number based on reactor diameter, dimensionless
Pe_{mal}	Péclet number for mass, axial dispersion in liquid phase, dimensionless
Pe*	Péclet number corresponding to terminal settling velocity, dimensionless
Q	Volumetric flow rate, m^3/s

r_w	Reaction rate related to weight of catalyst in suspension, kmol/(s · kg)
R	Gas constant = 0.08314 m^3 bar/(kmol · K)
$\mathcal{R}$	Global rate of reaction, kmol/(s · m^3)
$\mathcal{R}_w$	Global rate of reaction related to weight of catalyst in suspension, kmol/(s · kg)
$\mathcal{R}_{wi}$	$\mathcal{R}_w$ of the *i*th reactant species
Sc	Schmidt number, dimensionless
Sh	Sherwood number, dimensionless
S_p	Specific mass-transfer surface, m^2/kg
S'_p	Specific reaction surface, m^2/kg
St_L	Liquid-phase Stanton number, dimensionless
t_n	Nominal holding time in the *n*th CSTR reactor, s
T	Absolute temperature, K
T_x	Temperature of the surroundings or cooling medium, K
T_2	Exit temperature, K
u	Superficial gas velocity, m/s
u_{CO}	Superficial CO loading, kmol CO/(m^2 · s)
$\overline{u}_G$	Average superficial gas velocity, based on inside reactor diameter and temperature and pressure, m/s
u_m	Superficial liquid velocity at mean of inlet and exit pressures, m/s
u_{m0}	u_m at beginning of expansion, m/s
u_{BM}	Mean bubble rise velocity, m/s
u_t	Terminal velocity of bubbles, m/s
v	Velocity of the fluidized stream, m/s or Gas flow rate in Eq. (9-75), cm/s
v_b	Bubble velocity with respect to liquid, m/s
v_G	Linear velocity of fresh gas at reactor bottom, m/s
v_L	Actual mean liquid velocity, m/s
v_0	Velocity of gas at sparger orifice (reactor inlet), m/s
v_R	Actual mean gas velocity relative to actual mean liquid velocity, m/s

V	Volume of expanded liquid + gas + catalyst mixture, m^3
V_L	Liquid volume at rest or nonexpanded liquid volume in reactor, m^3
w	Mass flow rate, kg/s
x	Fractional conversion of CO, dimensionless
x_D	Desired x
X	Fractional conversion, dimensionless
X_1	X at inlet
X_2	X at outlet
X_H	Mole fraction of H_2 in gas at position z [Eq. (9-76)], dimensionless
y_0	Mole fraction of key reactant in feed stream, dimensionless
z	Longitudinal coordinate, m
Z	Dimensionless axial (longitudinal) coordinate
Z_E	Height of the expanded liquid, including bubbles, m
Z_L	Height of clear liquid at no gas flow or zero expansion, m
Z_T	Total bubble column height, m
$\Delta\theta$	Time increment, s
$\Delta\rho$	Difference of density between particles and the liquid, kg/m^3
ε	Void fraction, dimensionless
ε_G	Fractional gas holdup, dimensionless
$\bar{\varepsilon}_G$	Integrated mean value of ϵ_G
ε_L	Fractional liquid holdup, dimensionless
ε_p	Catalyst particle phase fraction, dimensionless
θ	Residence time in a single CSTR at steady state, s
$\bar{\theta}$	Average residence time in the reactor, s
$\bar{\theta}_G$	Average residence time of the gas in the expanded liquid, s
θ_n	Nominal holding time in nth reactor (CSTR in series), s
μ	Viscosity of the liquid, Pa · s
ρ	Density, kg/m^3
ρ_c	Mass of catalyst per unit volume of expanded liquid, kg/m^3
ρ_L	Liquid density, kg/m^3
ρ_s	Density of solid catalyst particle, kg/m^3

σ	Surface tension, kg/s^2
ϕ	Transfer rate, kmol/s

Subscripts

eq	Equilibrium
f	Final
F	Frictional
G	Gas phase
i	ith component
L	Liquid phase
LG	Two-phase
0	Initial or inlet
T	Total
w	Wall

REFERENCES

1. James R. Fair, "Designing Gas-Sparged Reactors," *Chem. Eng.* **74,** July 3, 1967, pp. 67–74; July 17, 1967, pp. 207–214.
2. Edward J. Farkas, "A Study of the Slurry Reactor," Ph.D. thesis, MIT, 1964.
3. Thomas K. Sherwood and Edward J. Farkas, "Studies of the Slurry Reactor," *Chem. Eng. Sci.* **21:**573–582 (1966).
4. Hans Hammer, "Zur Reaktionstechnik von Blasensäulenreaktoren mit suspendiertem Katalysator," Habilitationsschrift [dissertation], Technische Universität Berlin, 1968.
5. Herbert Kölbel and P. Ackermann, "Grosstechnische Versuche zur Fischer-Tropsch-Synthese in der Flüssigphase," *Brennstoff-Chem.* **36:**347 (1955).
6. Herbert Kölbel and P. Ackermann, "Grosstechnische Versuche zur Fischer-Tropsch-Synthese in flüssigem Medium," *Chem.-Ingr. Tech.* **28:**381–388 (1956).
7. Herbert Kölbel, E. Borchers, and Horst Langemann, "Grössenverteilung der Gasblasen in Blasensäulen. Teil I. Einflüsse von Flüssigkeitsviskosität und Säuleninnendruck," *Chem.-Ingr. Tech.* **33:**668–675 (1961).
8. Herbert Kölbel, Hans Hammer, and U. Meisl, "Hydrierung und Oxydation in Gas-Flüssigphase-Reaktoren mit suspendiertem Katalysator," *Proc. 3d European Symp. Chem. Reaction Eng.; Chem. Eng. Sci.* **20** (suppl.):115–123 (1965).
9. Herbert Kölbel and H.-H. Maennig, "Heterogen-Katalytische Gasreaktionen im Blasensäulenreaktor," *Z. Elektrochem.* **66:**744–754 (1962).

10. Herbert Kölbel, Hans Hammer, and Horst Langemann, "Zur Reaktionstechnik von Blasensäulenreaktoren," *Chem. Ztg./Chem. Apparatur* **92**(16):581–90 (1968). (Copyright permission from *Chemiker Zeitung*.)

11. Andre F. Dufau, F. Eschard, A. C. Haddad, and C. H. Thonon, "High-Purity Cyclohexane," *Chem. Eng. Progr.* **60**(9): 43–47 (1964).

12. J. D. Polejes, Ph.D. thesis, University of Wisconsin, 1959.

13. Jürgen Smidt, W. Hafner, R. Jira, R. Sieber, J. Sedlmeir, and A. Sabel, "Olefinoxydation mit Palladiumchlorid-Katalysatoren," *Angew. Chem.* **74**(3):93–102 (1962).

14. Jürgen Smidt, W. Hafner, R. Jira, J. Sedlmeir, R. Sieber, R. Rüttinger, and H. Kojer, "Katalytische Umsetzungen von Olefinen an Platinmetall-Verbindungen—Das Consortium Verfahren zur Herstellung von Acetaldehyd," *Angew. Chem.* **71**(5):176–182 (1959).

15. Edwin S. Johanson, Gas-liquid Contacting Process, U.S. Patent 2,987,465, 1961; reissued Apr. 27, 1965 as RE 25,770.

16. Robert C. Ewing, "Advances Made in H-Oil Process," *Oil Gas J.*, May 12, 1969, pp. 213–215.

17. Anonymous, "Project Gasoline in Final Development Stage," *Chem. Eng. News* **45,** June 12, 1967, pp. 96–98, 102, 104.

18. Hydrocarbon Research, Inc., *Commercial Process Evaluation of the H-Coal Hydrogenation Process,* prepared for the Office of Coal Research, U.S. Dept. of the Interior, U.S. Dept. of Commerce Publication PB174696, 1965.

19. Hydrocarbon Research, Inc. *Project H-Coal Report on Process Development,* prepared for the Office of Coal Research, Dept. of the Interior, R&D Report no. 26, 1968.

20. I. A. Vasalos et al., *Study of Ebullated Bed Fluid Dynamics for H-Coal,* U.S. Dept. of Energy, Report FE-2588-15, 1978, and Report FE-2588-18, 1979.

21. "Shuaiba All-Hydrogen Refinery," *Petroleum Times,* Dec. 8, 1967, pp. 1763–1770.

22. Fernand Moreau, Jr., "Key Unit in World's First All-Hydrogen Refinery. Kuwait National to Put 28,800 B/D H-Oil Unit On-Stream," *Petro/Chem. Eng.*, no. 6, pp. 52, 54.

23. Clarence A. Johnson, Katherine C. Hellwig, Edwin S. Johanson, Roland H. Wolk, and Harold H. Stotler: "H-Coal: Conversion of Western Coals," *Trans. AIME* **254:**235–238 (1973).

24. B. B. Pruden and M. E. Weber, "Evaluation of the 3-Phase Transport Reactor," *Can. J. Chem. Eng.* **48:**162–167 (1970). (Special copyright permission from the *Canadian Journal of Chemical Engineering*.)

25. Sabri Ergun and A. A. Orning, "Fluid Flow through Randomly Packed Columns and Fluidized Beds," *Ind. Eng. Chem.* **41:**1179–1184 (1949).

26. B. J. Michel and S. A. Miller, "Power Requirements of Gas-Liquid Agitated Systems," *AIChE J.* **8:**262–266 (1962).

27. J. Y. Oldshue and F. L. Connelly, "Gas-Liquid Contacting with Impeller Mixers," *Chem. Eng. Progr.* **73**(3):85–89 (1977).

28. P. H. Calderbank, M. B. Moo-Young, and R. Bibby, "Coalescence in Bubble Reactors and Absorbers," *Proceedings of the 3d European Symposium on Chemical Reaction Engineering (ESCRE 3), Amsterdam, Sept. 15–17, 1964, Chem. Eng. Sci.*, suppl. 91–113 (1964).

29. Wesley B. Argo and D. R. Cova, "Longitudinal Mixing in Gas-Sparged Tubular Vessels," *Ind. Eng. Chem. Process Design Develop.* **4**:352–359 (1965).

30. Herbert Kölbel and Horst Langemann, "Der Stoffübergang in Gas-Flussigkeitsreaktoren bei verschiedenen Strömungsformen," in *Dechema Monograph* 49, 1964, pp. 253–275.

31. Charles N. Satterfield, *Mass Transfer in Heterogeneous Catalysis*, MIT Press, Cambridge, 1970. (Special copyright permission from the MIT Press.)

32. P. H. Calderbank, in Uhl and Gray (eds.), *Mixing*, vol. 2, Academic Press, New York, 1967, Chap. 6.

33. W. Siemes, "Gasblasen in Flüssigkeiten. I. Entstehung von Gasblasen an nach oben gerichteten kreisförmigen Düsen," *Chem.-Ingr. Tech.* **26**:479–496 (1954): "II: Der Aufstieg von Gasblasen in Flüssigkeiten," *Chem.-Ingr. Tech.* **26**:614–630 (1954).

34. Giovanni Astarita, "Two-Phase and Slurry Reactors," in *Chemical Reaction Engineering*, American Chemical Society, Advances in Chemistry Ser. 109, 1972. pp. 223–236.

35. Isaac H. Lehrer, "Gas Hold-Up and Interfacial Area in Sparged Vessels," *Ind. Eng. Chem. Process Design Develop.* **10**:37–40 (1971).

36. M. Roustan, L. Gbahoue, and H. Roques, "Study of the Retention of Gases in Bubble Columns with Free Ascension," *Chem. Eng. J. (Lausanne)* **13**(1):1–5(1977) (French).

37. Wolf-Dieter Deckwer, I. Adler, and Ahmed Zaidi, "Detailed Analysis of CO_2-Interphase Mass Transfer in a Bubble Column to Prove the Validity of a Design Model," in Weekman and Luss (eds.), *Chemical Reaction Engineering–Houston 5th ISCRE*, American Chemical Society Symposium Ser. 65, 1978, pp. 359–371.

38. H. D. Mendelson, "The Prediction of Bubble Terminal Velocities from Wave Theory," *AIChE J.* **13**:250–252 (1967).

39. A. S. Afschar, M. Diboun, and K. Schügerl, "Eine Blasensäule mit Gleichstrom von Wasser und Luft. III. Wechselwirkung zwischen den Phasen," *Chem. Eng. Sci.* **23**:253–265 (1968).

40. W. Siemes and W. Weiss, "Flüssigkeitsdurchmischung in engen Blasensäulen," *Chem.-Ingr. Tech.* **29**:727–732 (1957).

41. Wolf-Dieter Deckwer, U. Graeser, Horst Langemann, and Yalçin Serpemen, "Zones of Different Mixing in the Liquid Phase of Bubble Columns," *Chem. Eng. Sci.* **28**:1223–1225 (1973).

42. Sherif H. Eissa, Mohamed M. El-Halwagi, and Mohamed A. Saleh, "Axial and Radial Mixing in a Cocurrent Bubble Column," *Ind. Eng. Chem. Process Design Develop.* **10:**31–36 (1971).

43. P. V. Dankwerts, "Continuous Flow Systems—Distribution of Residence Times," *Chem. Eng. Sci.* **2:**1–13 (1953).

44. Y. K. Vail, N. Kh. Manakov, and V. V. Manshilin, "Turbulent Mixing in a 3-Phase Fluidized Bed," *Intern. Chem. Eng.* **8**(2):293–296 (1968).

45. Edwin R. Gilliland and E. A. Mason, "Gas Mixing in Beds of Fluidized Solids," *Ind. Eng. Chem.* **44:**218–224 (1952).

46. E. M. Vasalos, E. M. Bild, and D. E. Tatterson, *Study of Ebullated-Bed Fluid Dynamics for H-Coal,* Quarterly Progress Report No. 4 for Sept. 1 to Nov. 30, 1978, no. FE-2588-15. U.S. Department of Energy.

47. J. Y. Oldshue, "Mixing, Annual Review," *Ind. Eng. Chem.* **58**(11):50–57 (1966); **59**(11):58–70 (1967); **60**(11):24–35 (1968); **61**(11):121–127 (1969).

48. J. Y. Oldshue, "Suspending Solids and Dispersing Gases in Mixing Vessels," *Ind. Eng. Chem.* **61**(9):79–89 (1969).

49. Alvin W. Nienow and David Miles, "Impeller Power Numbers in Closed Vessels," *Ind. Eng. Chem. Process Design Develop.* **10:**41–43 (1971).

50. James J. Carberry, "Heat and Mass Diffusional Intrusions in Catalytic Reactor Behavior," *Catalysis Rev.* **3**(1):61–91 (1969).

51. D. L. Johnson, Hirotaro Saito, J. D. Polejes, and Olaf A. Hougen, "Effects of Bubbling and Stirring on Mass Transfer Coefficients in Liquids," *AIChE J.* **3:**401–417 (1957).

52. Thomas K. Sherwood and Robert L. Pigford, *Absorption and Extraction,* McGraw-Hill, New York, 1952.

53. P. L. T. Brian and H. B. Hales, "Effects of Transpirating and Changing Diameters on Heat and Mass Transfer to Spheres," *AIChE J.* **15:**419–425 1969.

54. P. L. T. Brian, H. B. Hales, and Thomas K. Sherwood, "Transport of Heat and Mass between Liquid and Spherical Particles in an Agitated Tank," *AIChE J.* **15:**727–733 (1969).

55. Daizo Kunii and Octave Levenspiel, *Fluidization Engineering,* John Wiley, New York, 1969, p. 197.

56. Liang-Tseng Fan, Y. C. Yang, and Ching-Yung Wen, "Mass Transfer in Semi-fluidized Beds for a Solid-Liquid System," *AIChE J.* **6:**482–487 (1960).

57. Knut Østergaard and W. Suchozebrski, "Gas-Liquid Mass Transfer in Gas-Liquid Fluidized Beds," *Proc. 4th European Symp. Chemical Reaction Engineering* Brussels, 1968, pp. 21–29.

58. K. K. Seth and E. P. Stahel, "Heat Transfer from Helical Coils Immersed in Agitated Vessels," *Ind. Eng. Chem.* **61**(6):39–49 (1969).

59. Pramod Lavingia and P. F. Dickson, "Heat Transfer to a Two-Phase Liquid System in an Agitated Vessel with Coils," *Ind. Eng. Chem. Process Design Develop.* **10:**206–209 (1971).

60. J. J. Van Deemter, "Trickle Hydrodesulfurization—A Case History," *Proceedings* 3d *European Symposium Chemical Reaction Engineering Amsterdam,* Sept. 15–17, 1964, pp. 215–223.

61. Murray Nadler, "Scaleup of a Liquid-Gas Stirred Tank (LGST) Reactor," Paper 44*b* presented at the 57th Am. Inst. Chem. Engrs. Annual Meeting, Boston, Dec. 6–10, 1964.

62. Ramon L. Cerro and José M. Parera, "Dynamic Similarity in Continuous Stirred Tank Reactors," *Ind. Eng. Chem. Fundamentals* **9:**181–183 (1970).

63. R. R. Corpstein, R. A. Dove, and D. S. Dickey, "Stirred Tank Reactor Design," *Chem. Eng. Progr.* **75**(2):66–74 (1979).

64. K. Schoenemann, "Der chemische Umsatz bei kontinuierlich durchgeführten Reaktionen," in *Dechema Monograph* 21, 1952 pp. 203–236.

65. John W. Eldridge and Edgar L. Piret, "Continuous Flow Stirred Tank Reactor Systems. I. Design Equations for Homogeneous Liquid Phase Reactions. Experimental Data," *Chem. Eng. Progr.* **46**(6):290–299 (1950).

66. Donald R. Mason and Edgar L. Piret, "Continuous Flow Stirred Tank Reactor Systems—Development of Transient Equations," *Ind. Eng. Chem.* **42:**817–825 (1950).

67. Leon S. Kowalczyk, "Application of Difference Equations in Design of CSTR's in Series," paper 55*d* at the Am. Inst. Chem. Engrs. 62d Annual Meeting, Washington, Nov. 16–20, 1969.

68. Wolf-Dieter Deckwer, "Blasensäulen-Reaktoren: ihre modelmässige Erfassung und Berechnung," *Chem.-Ingr. Tech.* **49:**213–223 (1977).

69. Ahmed Zaidi, Youssef Louisi, Milos Ralek, and Wolf-Dieter Deckwer, "Ermittlung von Stoffübergangszahlen für die Fischer-Tropsch-Flüssigphase-Synthese," *Chem.-Ingr. Tech.* **50:**628–629 (1978).

70. Hans Hammer and Martin Schmal, "Zur Optimierung von Gas-Flüssigphase-Reaktoren mit suspendiertem Katalysator," *Brennstoff-Chem.* **49:**225–228 (1968).

71. Hanns Hofmann, Dissertation, Technische Hochschule Darmstadt, 1955.

72. Herbert Kölbel, P. Ackermann, and F. Engelhardt, "Neue Entwicklungen zur Kohlenwasserstoffsynthese," *Erdöl Kohle* **9**(3):153–156; **9**(4):225–228; **9**(5):303–307 (1956).

73. Hans-Jürgen Hubert, "Bau und Betrieb einer Fischer-Tropsch-Laboranlage mit Flüssigphase Reaktor," NTIS Report BMFT-FB-T 80-033, 1980.

74. Charles N. Satterfield, A. A. Pelosof, and Thomas K. Sherwood, "Mass Transfer Limitations in a Trickle-Bed Reactor," *AIChE J.* **15:**226–234 (1969).

Chapter **10**

DESIGN OF LABORATORY AND PILOT-PLANT REACTORS

This chapter covers laboratory and pilot reactors, including their mechanical design. The sizing of laboratory reactors is almost always made approximately and does not require the tedious process design necessary for full-scale reactors.

10.1 DEFINITIONS AND GENERALITIES

Laboratory reactors are small-size exploratory or experimental reactors that can be set up on a laboratory bench. There is really no definite size limit which would distinguish laboratory reactors from pilot reactors. Laboratory reactors are normally used to determine whether a given reaction does or does not occur or whether a catalyst shows sufficient activity, sufficient life, the desired selectivity, or the like. Most investigators use laboratory reactors for exploratory work and once they have a promising reaction, they immediately build a small-scale pilot reactor, on which they begin to measure the specific properties of that reaction.

We can distinguish between general-purpose and special-purpose laboratory reactors. Exploratory bench-scale reactors are examples of the former. There also are special-purpose laboratory reactors that are designed only to determine certain kinetic properties of reactions. Both categories will be discussed below.

Most often a laboratory reactor is designed with very little knowledge of the reaction on which one wants to experiment. Therefore, it makes sense to be cautious and to carry out the preliminary experiments safely in strong reactors, if necessary behind safe barricades.

On the other hand, if one is absolutely certain that no pressure is needed and will not be developed during the reaction, it is practical to design a simple glass reactor in order to see what is happening inside. It is still advisable to place a strong Plexiglas shield between the apparatus and the experimenter. A laboratory reactor must either be so easy to change or so cheap that it can be thrown away and another one built, or be universally useful and versatile, like an autoclave. With the advent of gas chromatography, it has become possible to work with very small amounts of reactants, and consequently one can design and build very small continuous reactors which are easy to modify or replace if they plug up.

The laboratory reactor should not take too long to put together. A chemist or chemical engineer who has an idea should be able to try it immediately. Some questions just cannot wait too long to be answered. If a good batch autoclave is available, it may be extremely convenient to try pressure reactions in batch operation. Also, if a simple bench-scale continuous microreactor system is available, many fixed-bed catalytic reactions may be tried without much preliminary preparation. Some people try to foresee reaction results by elaborate calculations, but since their input never contains unforseen factors, these people will always be open to surprises until they actually run an experiment, which, by the way, can be much faster than most elaborate computations.

Pilot reactors are intermediate reactor stages between the experimental or explorative bench-scale size and the full-scale commercial size. The function of the pilot reactor is to obtain:

- Process information such as effects of various parameters on yields or selectivity
- Transport information for scale-up
- Data to fit process models

The commercial function of the pilot plant resides in the fact that we try to make all our mistakes with it so that we can make all our profits with the commercial plant.

Pilot-plant reactors are designed on the basis of fairly good knowledge of the nature of the reaction or reactions to be studied in them. A thorough experimental design scheme is worked out and a pressure-temperature tolerance of the reactor is specified accordingly. Consequently, a pilot plant is always designed for considerably greater severity than a plant reactor.

Sizewise, pilot reactors can span the range from large bench reactors to small commercial reactors. The nature of the process and the extent of prevailing ignorance and caution determine how closely pilot reactor design approaches full scale. Of course, there are compelling economic reasons to keep the number of pilot stages and the reactor sizes small.

However, the minimum size of the last pilot stage is dictated by the suitability of the reactor to clearly and reliably show the full effect of transport phenomena on various process parameters.

10.2 LABORATORY REACTORS

Most heterogeneous catalytic reactions that involve gases also require elevated pressures to enhance catalyst surface concentrations and elevated temperatures to improve reaction rates. Thus, in the majority of cases laboratory reactors are designed to withstand both pressure and heat.

General-Purpose Laboratory Reactors

The chemical reaction engineer must have universal tools to explore ideas without too much fuss and red tape. For heterogeneous catalytic reactions that can be studied in the batch mode, one generally uses either a shaking autoclave or an upright stirred reactor when dealing with liquids. Basically, both types are designed quite similarly except that the stirred reactor has a built-in stirrer, frequently of the magnetic type. Both do about the same thing except that the shaking autoclave is simpler and has no moving parts inside the reactor. Thus, what one may say of the construction of the shaking autoclave is also true of that of the stirred reactor.

The Shaking Autoclave

The shaking autoclave is a pressure vessel that is attached to a shaking mechanism. It is standard equipment in any petroleum or hydrocarbon research laboratory and is a practical tool for testing gas-liquid-phase reactions. Results obtained in a shaking autoclave may be used to build a pilot unit to measure specific parameters.

Shaking autoclaves are built for volumes of 100 to 1000 cm^3 and can be pressurized to 1700 bars at 200°C or heated up to 650°C at somewhat lower pressure. They are quite useful to have at one's disposal. If one does not know what is going to happen, one can always place the reactants into such an autoclave and run the reaction behind a sturdy barricade.

The mechanical design of the autoclave reactor is tricky. Of course, what we will say about the shaking autoclave also applies to any other autoclave. Many types of autoclave closures develop leaks when heated above 300 to 350°C. In some cases a new reactor does not leak, but as one goes through several heating and cooling cycles, the leakage becomes intolerable and nothing helps. There is one type of autoclave closure

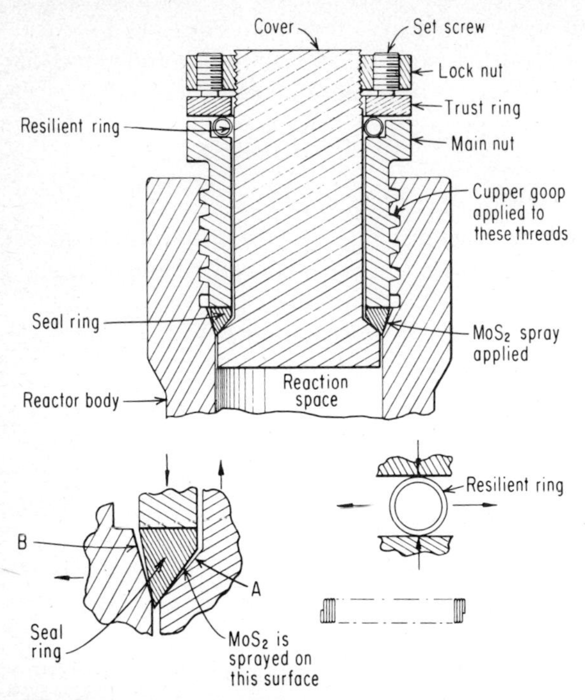

FIG. 10-1 Gasche closure with resilient ring.[1] (*Courtesy Autoclave Engineers, Inc.*)

design that does not have this drawback. This design is shown in Fig. 10-1. It was invented by Gasche[1] by modifying the old Bridgeman closure.[2] An earlier design by Gasche,[3] shown in Fig. 10-2, can also be used satisfactorily. The properties for both closure designs are given in detail in the respective U.S. patents. The common characteristic of both designs is a seal ring as shown in detail in Fig. 10-1. Increased pressure in the reactor makes the reactor closure tighter. The resilient ring in Fig. 10-1 takes up some of the slack during the differential expansion of the closure on heating and keeps the closure tight. Also, the opening of the set screws is considerably simpler and easier with the closure of Fig. 10-1 than with that of Fig. 10-2.

The Gasche closures are the best ones known, but still they can be very troublesome if not used properly. The main problem with these closures is that they gall. *Galling* is the sticking together of metal surfaces at high temperatures and pressures. Sometimes even at room temperature, closures gall when subjected to high pressures. Galling is the fusion of the surface molecules of two identical or similar metal surfaces that are pressed together. In the Gasche closure the lower side surfaces of the seal ring tend to gall either with the surface A of the so-called dead man (Fig. 10-1), or with the inside reactor wall at B. It is known that galling does not occur between dissimilar surfaces. Therefore, when the reaction chemistry permits it, one of the surfaces, for example the seal ring, is made from a different material. In high-pressure reactors used for hydrocarbon reactions such as those involving coal tar, coal, or petroleum products, one must use highly alloyed stainless steels to withstand hydrogen and hydrogen sulfide at high pressures and temperatures. A slight modification of this composition is not enough to prevent galling. The only working solution in hydrogenation reactions is to spray a thin film of MoS_2 on the surface edges that are prone to gall.[4] On heating, this sulfide film sufficiently changes the metal surfaces to prevent them from galling. Such sprays are commercially available.

An absolute necessity for successful operation of autoclaves is that closures and closure surfaces must be handled with great care. Laboratory personnel handling autoclaves must be properly trained, well supervised, and kept on the job.

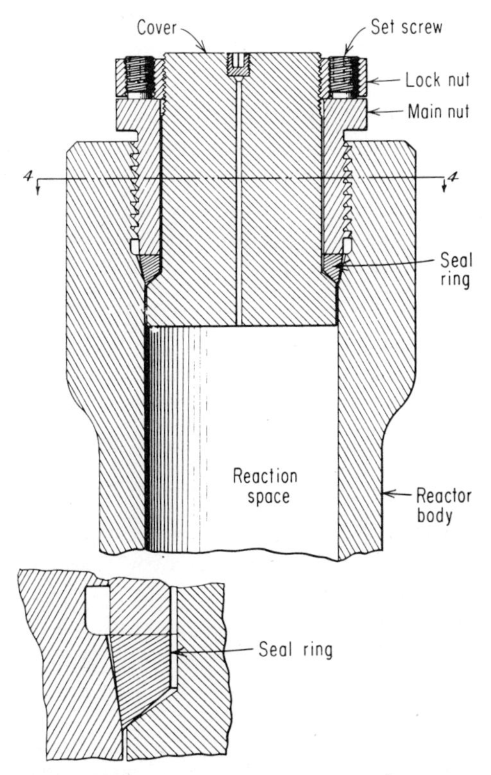

FIG. 10-2 Earlier Gasche closure.[3] ***(Courtesy Autoclave Engineers, Inc.)***

When similar materials are used on the seal ring and on the touching reactor surfaces, keeping the reactor closure under 1700 bars nitrogen pressure at room temperature for several hours can cause severe galling.

Figure 10-3 shows the general arrangement of a shaking autoclave, both from the front (*a*) and from the back (*b*).

The Swagelok Reactor

Home-made reactors can be put together quite easily by using stainless steel tubing lengths and swagelok fittings.* If the ends of the tubing pieces are well prepared by filing them properly and annealing them, the swagelok reactor is a very safe pressure reactor and does not need any state inspection or any code stamps. A very elaborate microreactor system using such a swagelok reactor has been described by Harrison et al.[5] A considerably simpler, and of course less costly, microreactor system is shown in Fig. 10-4. Such a system can be assembled in a relatively short time for use, for example, in hydrocarbon hydrogenation reactions. Product samples are collected and analyzed elsewhere by specialized gas chromatographers. The microreactor itself has a reaction volume of 8 cm^3. It is assembled from ½-in (0.0127-m)-OD tubing as the reactor wall and ⅛-in- (0.0031-m)-OD tubing as the inlet and outlet pipes. Reactor and tubing are immersed in a fluidized-bed sand bath. Tiny rounds of wire screen are installed on both ends of the microreactor to prevent the catalyst charge from plugging the inlet or the outlet pipe. The fluidized sand bath is a very satisfactory method of uniformly heating the reactor. The feed can be preheated in the same sand bath by passing it through a coil before it enters the microreactor.

It should be emphasized that this simplified version of the microreactor system is only suitable for quick exploratory work. Anyone who expects to do frequent exploratory investigations would do well to set up an elaborate microreactor system with automatic sampling, on-line analysis, and automatic computer processing of the results. The development of analytical techniques useful in automatic microreactor systems is presently expanding at an explosive rate.

Larger versions of the swagelok reactor, up to 1-in (0.0254-m) OD by over 1 m long, can be assembled by using special-order swagelok reducing fittings to connect the 1-in-OD reactor tubing to ¼-in- (0.00635-m)-OD inlet and outlet tubings. Such reactors can be heated by placing them in special electric furnaces or by wrapping them with electrical heat-tracing wire units.

*Swagelok fittings are pressure fittings manufactured by Crawford Fitting Company, 29500 Solon Road, Solon, Ohio 44139.

FIG. 10-3 **A rocker-shaker autoclave assembly: (*a*) front view, (*b*) rear view.** ***(Courtesy Autoclave Engineers, Inc.)***

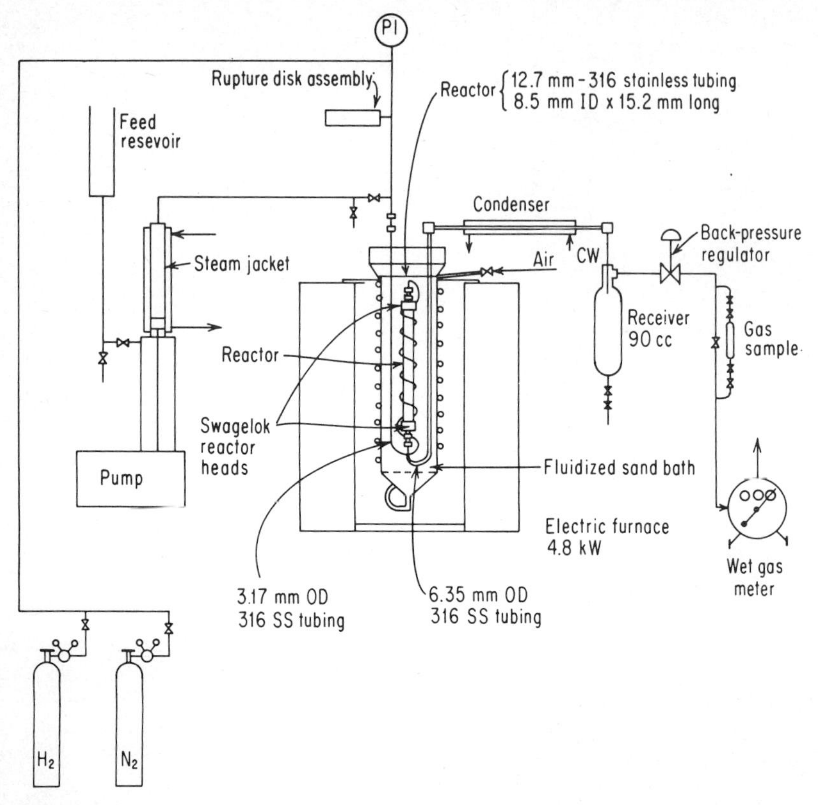

FIG. 10-4 A microreactor system.

The temperatures can be sensed at the outside of the reactor skin by means of thermocouples wrapped together with the reactor with asbestos tape. While this is not an accurate temperature measurement, it may be close enough for exploratory purposes. Surprisingly enough, these homemade reactors can be operated leak-free above 300 to 350°C. However, they do gall and are difficult to open after use. Depending on the wall thickness and the material of the tubing, a 25-mm-OD swagelok reactor can be used at severities as high as 500°C at 100 bars.

Again, it should be emphasized that these larger versions of the swagelok reactor are no substitutes for properly designed flow reactors that are used in well-planned bench-scale or pilot programs. They do however fulfill a definite purpose: that of quickly improvising a catalytic reactor for a brief exploratory study that requires substantial quantities of samples.

Reactions that do not require high pressures and elevated temperatures can be explored in simpler microreactor systems built of plastic swageloks and tubing, which are much easier to assemble and operate.

Special-Purpose Laboratory Reactors

There are quite a number of special-purpose laboratory reactors that serve to determine the kinetics of catalytic reactions. The advantages and disadvantages of these reactors have been discussed by Weekman[6] and by Carberry.[7]

Differential Flow Reactor

The differential flow reactor (see Sec. 3.3, Fig. 3-7) is a long, thin tubing containing a small amount of catalyst that causes a differential conversion in a flow reaction. Depending on the temperature and pressure of the reaction, the tubing is of either glass or metal. In any case it must be run absolutely isothermally. For this purpose, the reactor tubing is contained in a cooling jacket or a heating jacket as the case may be. The accuracy of the analysis of the converted reaction products determine how small a differential catalyst bed is used.

Integral Flow Reactor

The integral flow reactor (see Sec. 3.3) is a long, thin tubing that is filled with catalyst. The major problem is again isothermality, which is obtained in much the same way as in the differential flow reactor. Because a sizable fraction of the feed is converted, analytical problems are easier.

The Continuous Stirred-Tank Reactor (CSTR)

A continuous autoclave can be used for liquid reactions. Actually, any continuous-flow stirred pot can be used for gas-liquid reactions if pressure-temperature conditions are met (see Fig. 3-12 and Sec. 3.3). For solid-catalyzed gas reactions Carberry introduced the *continuous-stirred-tank catalytic reactor* (CSTCR), which consists of a rotating basket of catalyst particles (Fig. 10-5).[8] This CSTCR reactor operates isothermally and delivers integral reactor conversions. It accommodates commercial-size pellets and extruded catalysts. It is now available commercially. Ross and Calderbank[9] used the CSTCR in the study of naphthalene oxidation over V_2O_5.

Numerous variations of the CSTCR idea have been proposed. One that claims to enhance "uniformity of composition of both gas and liquid phases with independent control of individual film resistances and interfacial area" has been published by Levenspiel and Godfrey[10] who call the apparatus a "double mixed contactor." It extends the concept of gradientless reactors for heterogeneous catalysis to two-fluid systems.

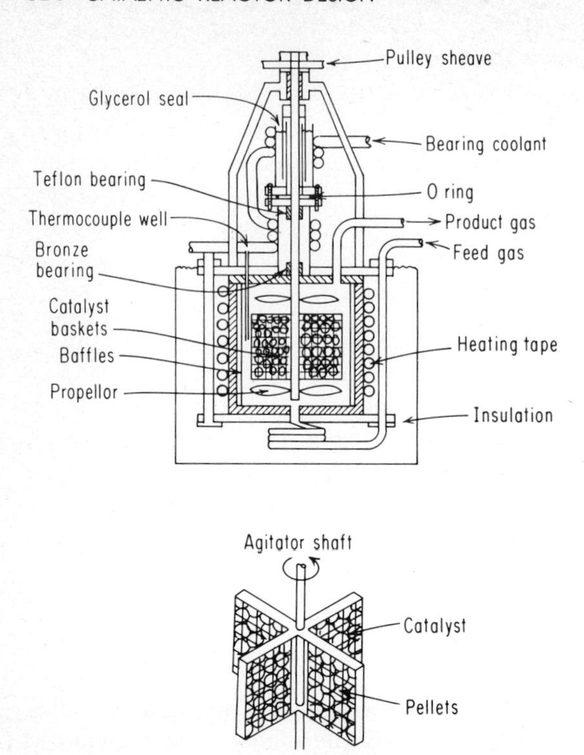

FIG. 10-5 Continuous stirred-tank catalytic reactor of J. J. Carberry (From *D. G. Tajbl, J. B. Simons, and James J. Carberry, "Heterogeneous Catlysis in a Continuous Stirred Tank Reactor," Ind. Eng. Chem. Fundamentals,* 5:*172 (1966), by permission from the American Chemical Society.*)

The Recycle Reactor

The recycle reactor (see Fig. 3-13), like the CSTCR, combines the advantage of isothermal operation with delivery of integral reactor conversions. The original recycle reactor, which consists of a small packed-bed reactor with an external loop and pump, is quite tricky to operate. The external loop is plagued by mechanical pump problems, which require cooling and subsequent reheating of the recycle stream.[11] A number of variations of the recycle reactor have been developed which use a packed bed with an internal recycle. Bennett et al.,[12] Livbjerg et al.,[13] and J. M. Berty[14,15] describe such reactors. The Berty reactor is now being commercially produced and appears to be widely used. Although it was originally designed for gas reactions, it is now being adapted to gas-liquid reactions as well.[11] Figure 10-6 shows a Berty reactor.

The design of any of the above-mentioned laboratory reactors requires hardly any computation for process sizing. Most of the design problems are of a mechanical nature.

10.3
PILOT REACTORS

Pilot reactors can be as varied as plant reactors. They can be built from standard Pyrex glass pipes and fittings, from ordinary pipes and fittings, or if intended for high-pressure use, they can be built from high-strength steels or stainless steels. For quick and inexpensive experiments one can use large swagelok reactors similar to those discussed above for laboratory reactors.

The recommended closure for an elevated-temperature, elevated-pressure pilot reactor is the Gasche closure with the resilient ring. This is true both for fixed-bed service or suspended-bed service. These closures are costly and usually have a long delivery time. However, once

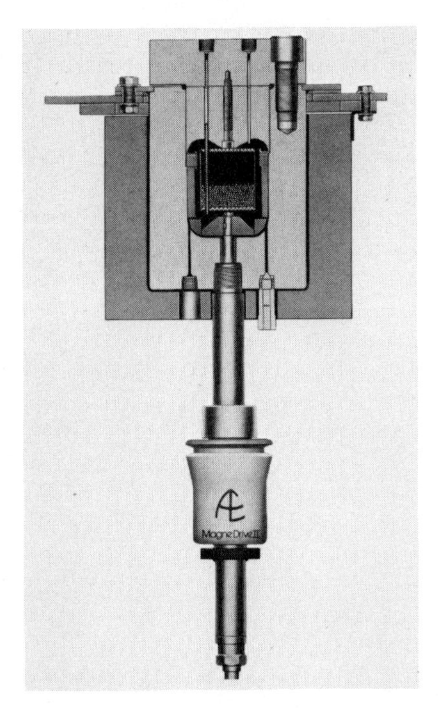

FIG. 10-6 The Berty reactor. (*Courtesy Autoclave Engineers, Inc.*)

one good reactor has been purchased, it can be used for many process development studies.

The mechanical design of pilot reactors is based on the same principles as the design of commercial-size reactors, as discussed in Chap. 12. However, it is much easier to design a small-diameter pilot reactor than a full-scale reactor because for a given temperature-pressure severity the wall thickness is proportional to the inside radius of the reactor. Thus, a high-severity reaction that can easily be contained in a 5-cm-diameter pilot reactor with a thick wall may become a really difficult design problem for a 2-m-diameter commercial reactor. Such problems are discussed in Chap. 12.

Because of the high cost and long delivery time of properly designed pilot reactors, from time to time many researchers have to resort to homemade reactors that can be quickly assembled when an urgent and unforseen need arises. Figure 10-7 shows a cold-sealing closure. The principle of this design is to keep the sealing part of the closure far from the high-temperature zone of the reactor furnace. Then the closure can be designed for temperatures below 300°C. A metal block called the *dead man* is used to fill the reactor space outside the heating zone. Such a reactor should have no leakage problem since it avoids the critical differential expansion problem.

Finally, Fig. 10-8 shows an old type of reactor closure that is relatively inexpensive to fabricate and to maintain. However, it is recommended

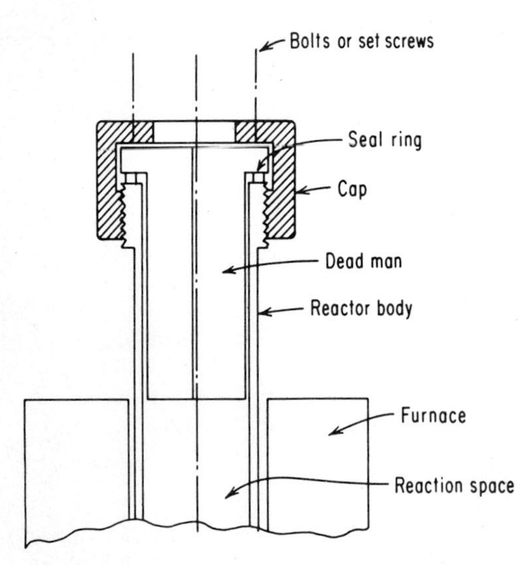

FIG. 10-7 A cold-sealing reactor closure with "dead man."

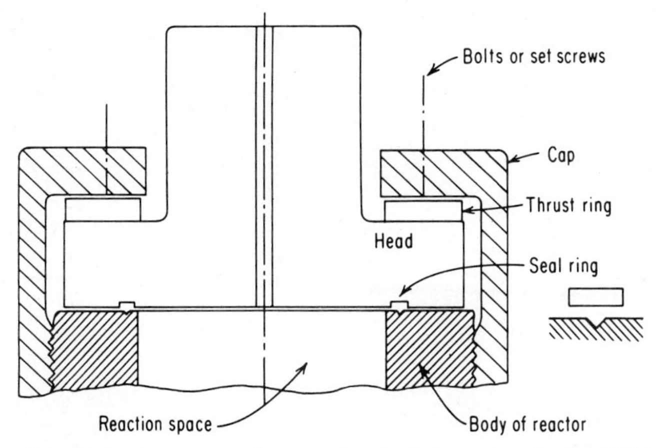

FIG. 10-8 A reactor closure that is tight up to about 300°C.

only for reactions below 300°C, where it can be operated without serious leakage problems.

The following criteria must be met in designing pilot reactors:

- The reactor must be easily removed from its location. Unlike a plant reactor, a pilot reactor is frequently opened.
- The closure must be easy to open, clean, and reuse.
- It should be possible to remove the catalyst from the reactor easily and completely.
- The reactor must be easily cleanable.

The design of reactor internals must also follow the same concern for ease of removal and cleaning. The inlets and outlets of many fixed-bed reactors are filled with inert alumina balls because the ends are not heated to preserve the closures. Alumina balls filled unused reactor volume in very much the same way a dead man does. Stainless steel screens are used to prevent these balls from blocking reactor inlet or outlet pipes.

REFERENCES

1. Fred Gasche, "Seal," U.S. Patent 3,144,163, Aug. 11, 1964.
2. Fred Gasche, "Design of Reactors and Closures," *Ind. Eng. Chem.* **48:**838–840 (1956).
3. Fred Gasche, "Closure for High-Pressure Vessel," U.S. Patent 2,424,449, July 22, 1947.

4. E. S. Hodge, C. B. Boyer, and F. D. Orcutt, "Gas Pressure Bonding," *Ind. Eng. Chem.* **54**(1):31–35 (1962).
5. D. P. Harrison, J. W. Hall, and H. F. Rase, "An Automatic Precision Microreactor," *Ind. Eng. Chem.* **57**(1):18–25 (1965).
6. Vern W. Weekman, Jr., "Laboratory Reactors and Their Limitations," *AIChE J.* **20:**833–840 (1974).
7. James J. Carberry, *Chemical & Catalytic Reaction Engineering,* McGraw-Hill, New York, 1976.
8. D. G. Tajbl, J. B. Simons, and James J. Carberry, "Heterogeneous Catalysis in a Continuous Stirred Tank Reactor," *Ind. Eng. Chem. Fundamentals* **5:**171–175 (1966).
9. G. L. Ross and P. H. Calderbank, "Kinetics of the Catalytic Oxidation of Naphthalene over V_2O_5 Using a Spinning Catalyst Basket Reactor," *Chem. Eng. Sci.* **26:**2003–2008 (1971).
10. Octave Levenspiel and J. H. Godfrey, "A Gradientless Contactor for Experimental Study of Interphase Mass Transfer with/without Reaction," paper presented at the 66th Am. Inst. Chem. Engrs. Annual Meeting, Philadelphia, Nov. 11–15, 1973.
11. J. A. Mahoney, "The Use of a Gradientless Reactor in Petroleum Reaction Engineering Studies," paper presented at the 74th National Am. Inst. Chem. Engrs. Meeting, New Orleans, March 13, 1973.
12. C. O. Bennett, M. B. Cutlip, and C. C. Yang, "Gradientless Reactors and Transient Methods of Heterogeneous Catalysis," *Chem. Eng. Sci.* **27:**2255–2263 (1972).
13. Hans Livbjerg and John Villadsen, "Internal Recirculation Reactor for the Oxidation of Sulfur Dioxide on Vanadium Catalyst," *Chem. Eng. Sci.* **26:**1495–1503 (1971).
14. J. M. Berty, "Reactor for Vapor-Phase Catalytic Studies," *Chem. Eng. Progr.* **70**(5):78–84 (1974).
15. J. M. Berty, J. O. Hambrick, T. R. Malone, and D. S. Ullock, "Reactor for Vapor-Phase Catalytic Studies," paper presented at the 64th National Meeting of the AIChE at New Orleans, Mar. 16–20, 1969.

Chapter 11 REACTOR SAFETY AND STABILITY

Every reactor designer, and of course every chemical plant operator, is highly concerned about the safety of reactors. Most catalytic reactors keep operating smoothly in the way they are designed to operate and never cause any insurmountable problems. Only a few reactors malfunction seriously, in which case they may cause many deaths. While safely operating reactors are hardly ever remembered, the bitter memory of exploding ones lingers even long after their scrap has been reprocessed into a new generation of reactors. Thus it is the duty of the reactor designer to check and make sure that the reactor will operate smoothly and safely.

A thorough and complete discussion of this subject would require far more space than is available in this book. Because of this space limitation, this chapter is presented as an overview of the field to briefly acquaint the reader with the subject and to point out major problems and pitfalls in reactor safety and stability.

11.1 VARIOUS CAUSES OF REACTOR MISHAPS

Catalytic reactor mishaps may have a variety of causes. The most common of them will be briefly discussed here.

Defects in Mechanical Fabrication

There have been cases of reactor failure due to weak welding seams because some careless welder used the wrong electrode and the error remained undetected because of poor supervision and inspection. Such reactors usually fail without warning. This kind of mistake can be avoided if the company that is going to operate the reactor sends in its own inspector to continuously observe and check everything during the fabrication of the pressure vessel.

Excessive Thermal Excursion during Catalyst Regeneration

Catalysts that are regenerated in situ require that the reactor vessel be designed for two sets of conditions: (1) the temperature and pressure of the steady-state process and (2) the temperature and pressure of the catalyst regeneration step (see Sec. 1.5). Usually the catalyst is regenerated by burning off carbon deposits with oxygen diluted in nitrogen or steam. Oxygen is used at a concentration of about 0.5%. The combustion reaction progresses as a hot front from the inlet of the reactor to the outlet. This reaction must be carefully controlled so that the front does not become too hot. If the catalyst is in direct contact with the reactor vessel, the reactor wall must be designed to withstand the expected temperature of the traveling hot front. Once in a while, because of poor control and surveillance the combustion temperature may rise far above the permissible limits and this might not be noticed by the operators. The temperature excursion might weaken the welds, and shortly after the reactor is put back in normal operation, the pressure vessel might burst open. This kind of catastrophe can be prevented by designing the reactor vessel to withstand higher temperatures during regeneration and by controlling the regeneration extremely closely. Recording the regeneration temperature will ensure that excessive temperatures will be noticed in time to avoid putting the reactor back on stream with a weakened shell. Of course, the problem can be entirely circumvented by avoiding in situ regeneration altogether. In this case the catalyst is simply stripped and dropped from the reactor, to be immediately replaced by a second batch of catalyst. Operation can be resumed with little loss of time while the dropped catalyst can be conveniently regenerated somewhere else and recharged when the second batch requires regeneration. When in situ regeneration is not practiced, the reactor can be designed only for one set of conditions, those of the steady-state process. However, a second vessel must be designed to regenerate the fouled or coked catalyst. That vessel is designed to withstand only high temperatures but not high pressures. Even in case of severe temperature excursions, the regeneration vessel will in all probability not fail at its seams because there will be no pressure to cause such a failure.

Catalyst Failure during Regeneration

Certain regeneration procedures are known to affect the mechanical strength of some catalysts and result in the formation of dust in the catalyst bed. During the following on-stream period, the dust might catalyze some unsuspected exothermic side reaction and lead to strong exotherms and sometimes to reactor failure. Such catastrophes can be avoided by carefully checking for dust formation during regeneration as early as the bench-scale studies. Usually modifications in regeneration procedures can prevent dust formation. If this is not possible, the catalyst can be sieved after each regeneration and the reactive dust kept away from the reactor.

Dangerous Reactions

Some catalytic reactions are inherently and notoriously dangerous. Some are sensitive to temperatures, others are prone to develop dangerous side reactions, and some cause occasional explosions without apparent cause. If the products of such reactions are industrially important, someone will have the unpleasant job of designing reactors to contain these dangerous reactions. The best thing this person can do is to make sure that no problems occur that are related to pressure vessel design, fabrications, or catalyst regeneration. Then the reactor is safely placed behind barricades or reinforced concrete walls. Everything in the reactor is designed to be remotely operated and controlled. Thus if the reactor still explodes, at least people are protected. The probability of explosion simply increases the cost of the chemical product because of high insurance rates.

Process Control Problems

Sometimes even a perfectly well-designed and fabricated reactor can fail because of inadequate process control systems. In most exothermic processes certain parameters such as reactant ratio, heat-exchange conditions, and the like have to be very tightly controlled (see below on parametric sensitivity). If this control is insufficient or simply not well conceived, then serious temperature excursions, which can lead to reactor failure, can occur.

For example, in hydrogen generation from natural gas, the feed is treated with steam over a first catalyst to partially convert it to $CO + H_2$. Then the CO is further treated with steam over a CO shift catalyst to form CO_2 and more H_2. The CO_2 is absorbed by monoethanolamine washing and finally the last traces of $CO + CO_2$ are removed in a methanator by conversion to $CH_4 + H_2O$. Methanation is a highly exothermic reaction. If for any reason at all, such as a power failure that would shut down the monoethanolamine pumps, the CO_2 content of the methanator stream should appreciably increase, the control system should immediately act to by-pass the methanator. Any failure of the control system to do so would, if nothing else, cause the loss of the methanation catalyst by overheating. If the hydrogen process is designed for elevated pressures, it is quite likely that the reactor vessel would fail as well. Thus, in certain reaction systems safety depends primarily on process control.

In general it is highly desirable to analyze and model the reaction system at hand before the design task begins. Any good simulation is likely to pinpoint potential thermal excursions and weaknesses in dynamic process control and prevent the occurrence of control problems. Modeling can also bring to light problems in parametric sensitivity.

11.2 PARAMETRIC SENSITIVITY

When a small change in one parameter of a reactor system causes a big change in another parameter of that reactor, the phenomenon is called *parametric sensitivity*. For example, if we make a small increase in the coolant temperature of a NINAF reactor and observe a large increase in the temperature maximum, or *hot spot*, of the catalyst bed, we say that the hot spot temperature is very sensitive to the coolant temperature. This subject has recently been discussed by Lopez et al.[1] The NINAF reactor has a number of other parametric sensitivities such as inlet temperature and concentration. Welsenaere and Froment[2] calculated the sensitivities of an ideal one-dimensional NINAF reactor with constant

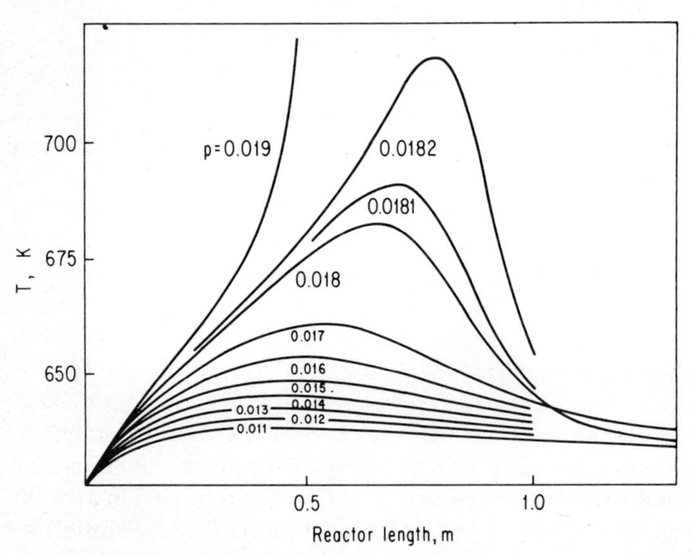

FIG. 11-1 Temperature profiles in a NINAF reactor showing the sensitivity with respect to partial pressure of reactant. (*From R. J. van Welsenaere and G. F. Froment, "Parametric Sensitivity and Runaway in Fixed-Bed Catalytic Reactors," Chem. Eng. Sci.* 25:*1505 (1970), reprinted with permission from Pergamon Press, Ltd.*)

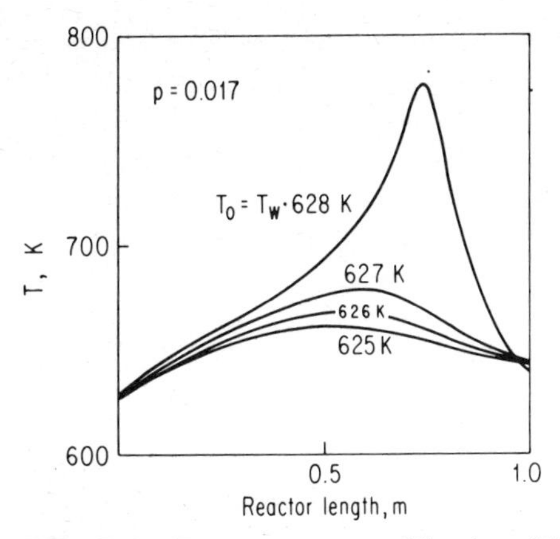

FIG. 11-2 Temperature profiles in a NINAF reactor showing the sensitivity with respect to the inlet temperature T_0; T_w = wall temperature. (*From R. J. van Welsenaere and G. F. Froment, "Parametric Sensitivity and Runaway in Fixed-Bed Catalytic Reactors," Chem. Eng. Sci.* 25:*1505 (1970), reprinted with permission from Pergamon Press, Ltd.*)

wall temperature for a single reaction, constant fluid density, and no difference in temperature and partial pressure between fluid and solid. The sensitivity of the reaction temperature T to partial pressure p is shown in Fig. 11-1. We can see that there is hardly any hot spot at low p values. As p increases above 0.016, the temperature begins to exceed 650 K. At $p = 0.018$ a hot spot of about 680 K develops at 0.7 reactor length. Here the sensitivity is sharpened. For an additional increase of the p value of only 0.0002, the hot spot increases by about 37 K, and finally when p reaches 0.019, the temperature gets out of control and runs away. The sensitivity of the reaction temperature T to inlet temperature T_0 (which is set equal to the wall temperature T_w) is shown in Fig. 11-2. Here again we can see that from 625 to 627 K we cannot discern any large increases in the hot spot temperature. However, a sudden additional increase of only 1 K causes the formation of a sharp hot spot peak of about 766 K. When designing this or any other type of reactor, the designer must first study all such sensitivities, preferably by thorough simulation and modeling.[3] The process designer must try to minimize these sensitivities by judiciously manipulating various parameters and in addition must use proper process controls to prevent runaway temperature. It follows from the foregoing that parametric sensitivity and reactor safety are very closely related.

Of course NINAF reactors are not the only types of reactors that display the kind of problems discussed above. Other types of reactors display similar sensitivities and there is a fairly large literature on the subject. Perhaps one paper by Hlavacek[4] should be mentioned in particular in this connection. That paper discusses, among other things, a method for rapid testing of parametric sensitivity in a NINAF reactor system. A calculation procedure can determine whether any such sensitivity exists. This book will not go any further into this subject. Instead, interested readers are referred to a number of good papers.[1–6]

11.3 REACTOR STABILITY

The term *stability* in general usage denotes stableness, lack of change, and durability. However, in chemical reaction engineering *reactor stability* is concerned with the existence of more than one steady state for a reactor.

Definition and Description of Multiple Steady States

Let us assume a reaction run in a NINAF reactor which produces a certain quantity of heat. Let us plot in Fig. 11-3 the total heat content Q of the reacting system against the reaction temperature T. We have an S-shaped curve P showing a very slight reaction rate, and hence very low heat production at low temperatures. Then as the temperature increases, Q increases exponentially, converting most of the reactants. At still higher temperatures the rate of increase of Q slows down because the reactants are substantially depleted. Finally, when everything has been converted, Q reaches its maximum value, i.e., it remains constant from there on. Thus curve P becomes parallel to the temperature axis OT at very high temperatures. The heat consumption curve C is a straight line because heat transfer across the sidewalls of the NINAF reactor is linear with temperature, everything else being constant. Curves P and C intersect at S_1, M, and S_2, at which points the production and removal of heat are equal. These three points are steady-state positions.

Let us first assume that the system is at point S_1. Any perturbation that would heat the system slightly above the temperature of S_1 would increase the heat removal much above the heat production. Thus the system would soon cool down and return to S_1. On the other hand, any perturbation that would cool the system slightly below S_1 would decrease the heat removal much below heat production. Thus the system would soon heat up and return to S_1. The same situation exists at S_2.

Let us assume that the system is at point M and its temperature is M'. Any perturbation that heats the system slightly above M' will increase heat production much more than heat consumption. Thus, the system will tend to heat up further and move toward S_2. If on the other hand, the perturbation is such as to cool the system slightly below M', heat

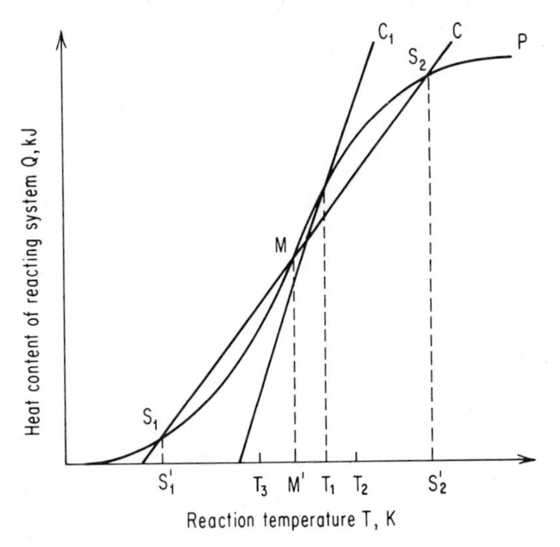

FIG. 11-3 Schematic diagram of total heat content Q of a NINAF reactor as a function of reaction temperature T. Curve P is the heat generation curve, while Curve C is the heat consumption curve.

production will be reduced much more than heat removal. Thus the system will tend to cool down further and move toward S_1.

While the system seems always to return to points S_1 and S_2 after any perturbation, it is displaced from point M by the slightest perturbation. Points S_1 and S_2 are called *stable steady states,* while point M is called a *metastable steady state.* Studies have shown that when a system has three steady states, the outer ones are generally stable and the middle one metastable.

What has just been described above is the classical example of steady-state multiplicity that was first brought to the attention of the scientific community by van Heerden in 1953.[7] For some obscure reason, a 1918 publication by F. G. Liljenroth[8] on very much the same subject failed to attract attention.[9]

Obviously, it becomes extremely important to know whether a reacting system has one or three steady states. Suppose someone designs a NINAF reactor for this system without being aware of its stability problems. Suppose this reactor is designed to be operated at temperature T_1 and the pressure vessel is designed to withstand 100 bars pressure at temperature T_2, which is below S_2'. As soon as the new reactor is put on stream with the reactant preheated to T_1, the temperature will keep on increasing by itself and swiftly go toward S_2'. Of course the reaction will not proceed at S_2 for very long because soon after the reactor vessel exceeds the temperature T_2, it will explode. Let us assume now that the

NINAF reactor was designed to be operated at a temperature T_3, which is slightly below M', again without the designer being aware of the stability problems. As soon as the new reactor is put on stream with the reactant preheated to T_3, the temperature will decrease steadily by itself and swiftly drop to S_1', at which point hardly any product will be obtained.

Once the multiplicity of steady states is known and established, there are a number of things that can be done to locate the design at a stable point in Fig. 11-3. One option is to change the intensity of heat removal, e.g., by installing a larger surface area per unit volume of catalyst and thereby bringing S_2 to a lower temperature T_1. In practice, this would mean a smaller-diameter reactor tube and more tubes. A good solution of this problem would be to intensify the heat removal to such an extent that the line C is moved into position C'. In that case, curves P and C_1 have only one intersection, which is a stable steady state, and the instability has been removed. This result might also be achieved by a somewhat different manipulation of parameters. We are not going to discuss this problem further.

In cases in which it is not possible, practical, or economically desirable to get rid of multiple steady states, the line C may be moved just enough to bring M' and T_1 together and the process then is operated at the metastable steady state M by providing it with powerful process controls. In cases where the process can be designed to operate either around S_1 or S_2 by slight manipulation of line C, the existence of multiple steady states might not be any reason for concern at all because the reactor would run at a stable steady state.

For further enlightenment, the reader is referred to two books[10,11] and three selected papers[7,12,13] on reactor stability.

Varieties of Steady-State Multiplicity

We have described multiple steady states by taking a NINAF reactor as an example. It must be said immediately that this phenomenon is not limited to NINAF reactors. Any type of reactor must be suspected of potential steady-state multiplicity. To avoid a steady-state multiplicity caused by heat transfer problems, the heat production curve must be obtained and a heat removal curve must be developed that places the operating conditions of the reactor on a stable-steady-state basis.

Among gas-phase reactor types discussed in previous chapters, only the NINAF reactor can have heat transfer of the multiple-steady-state type. Among gas-liquid-phase fixed-bed reactors, trickle beds are always designed adiabatically and consequently should not be afflicted with this type of multiplicity. However, FBBRs might conceivably have heat-exchange coils installed in the flooded catalyst beds to handle highly exothermic reactions and then should be classified as nonadiabatic. Thus nonadiabatic FBBRs and all types of suspended-bed reactors should be suspected of having multiple steady states caused by heat-transfer problems.

Unfortunately, it cannot be stated that any reactor that does not exchange heat with its surroundings is immune to stability problems. It is not. Adiabatic CSTRs can have multiple steady states.[9,14,15] Actually adiabatic CSTRs, like gas-phase adiabatic reactors, can absorb the generated exothermic heat by simply heating the reacting mixture to a temperature above the feed temperature. The conditions under which adiabatic CSTRs display a steady-state multiplicity have been analyzed and discussed by Aris[9] and others.

If the generated heat cannot be fully absorbed by the reactants, the CSTR must be cooled. Then we have a nonadiabatic CSTR at hand. The stability problems of these reactors have been analyzed quite intensively by many investigators. Under certain conditions nonadiabatic CSTRs can display more than three steady states and can oscillate.[6,15,16]

Actually the stability problem goes even deeper than that. Irrespective of reactor types or adiabaticity, some types of heterogeneous catalytic reactions can have stability problems at the catalyst pellet level.[17,18] Beusch, Fieguth, and Wicke[18] report on a reaction in which H_2 was oxidized over a 0.4% Pt-on-silica-alumina catalyst at 139°C. When the H_2 content of the gas stream was gradually increased, the temperature difference Δt between the catalyst surface and the bulk flow slowly increased to 20°C (Fig. 11-4). However, at 5.5% H_2 content of the gas Δt suddenly jumped to 185°C. When H_2 content was decreased again, Δt did not drop to 5.5% but fell somewhat gradually, forming a hysteresis loop. This loop represents the range of multiple steady states. When gas flow was increased, temperature "ignition" occurred at lower H_2 content and the area of the hysteresis loop was decreased.

When the same reaction was run at fixed flow rates and at 30 to 80°C, it was observed that the particle temperature and effluent composition (reaction rate) were oscillating (Fig. 11-5). These oscillations had a period of 1 h.

Why these oscillations occur and what their mechanism is is not quite understood. One could suspect, however, that they might have some relation to the adsorption of the catalyst surface of certain species, which then react and vacate the active sites. Then the cycle would start all over again. Recently Takoudis, Schmidt, and Aris[19] studied a case in which "the kinetics of the surface is controlling, i.e., where heat and mass transfer and reactor flow effects are absent so that the temperature and pressure at the surface are constant." The study is of a purely theoretical nature and applies to a chemical reaction of the type $A \rightarrow B + C$, where only reactant A is strongly adsorbed. Calculations show the existence of

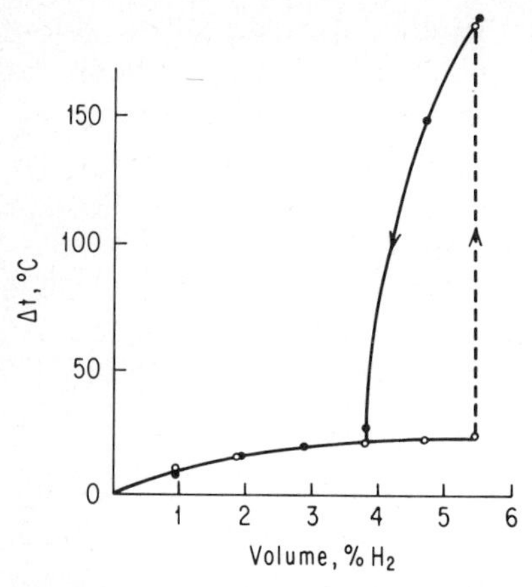

FIG. 11-4 **Stepwise transitions between lower and upper stable states of H_2 oxidation on a single catalyst particle in a packed bed of inactive pellets. Linear gas flow rate (standard conditions, empty tube): v = 1.7 cm/s; H_2 percentage increasing: ○, decreasing: ●. Temperature of furnace and gas flow is 139°C. (*From Beusch, Fieguth, and Wicke,*[18] *with permission from the American Chemical Society.*)**

multiple steady states under certain conditions. Although these results have not yet been confirmed by experiments, the experimental work by Wicke and coworkers[18] suggests that eventual confirmation should not surprise us.

11.4 DISCUSSION AND CONCLUSION

In the foregoing the reader was strongly warned of the existence of a number of reactor safety and stability problems, so that all potential sources of danger may be checked before beginning the design work. It is of course impossible to list here all potential sources of reactor failure. The designer must thoroughly study the literature, use some established techniques along with intuition to list as many of such sources as possible, and then check them all and make sure that they will not plague the design.

Reactor stability is a relatively new branch of chemical reaction engineering. Many predictions of steady-state multiplicity are based on certain reactor models that simulate reality with various degrees of success. The degree of success determines to a great extent whether the steady-state multiplicity indicated is real or not. It also determines whether reactors that are indicated to be stable are really so. This dilemma is best illustrated with the help of Fig. 11-6, published by Froment,[20] where each curve represents the temperature profile in a NINAF reactor according to a different model of the reactor. Let us assume that the designer's model gave Curve 6, but that in actual plant operation one would obtain Curve 7, which is a runaway. The designer and the plant operators would be in serious trouble. On the other hand, the reverse may happen: the designer may use a model from which Curve 7 is calculated, while actual plant operation produces Curve 6 or 1. The designer would certainly be overcautious and the resulting reactor design would be unnecessarily conservative and costly.

Consequently, it is difficult not to conclude that a wise catalytic reactor designer should insist on receiving adequate experimental data before beginning the design work. Properly performed bench-scale tests should certainly detect whether any steady-state multiplicity exists on the catalyst particle level. NINAF reactors can easily be checked by piloting a single reactor tube under various conditions. Similarly, any reactor type suspected of instability should be investigated experimentally to back up stability calculations derived from mathematical models. Granted, models are indispensable and wonderful tools for reactor design. However, when confronted with the possibilities of parametric sensitivity and instability, nothing is as reassuring to a concerned designer as *good* experimental data.

The most ambitious goal of chemical reaction engineering is to enable a designer to make an *a priori design* of any type of reactor for any set

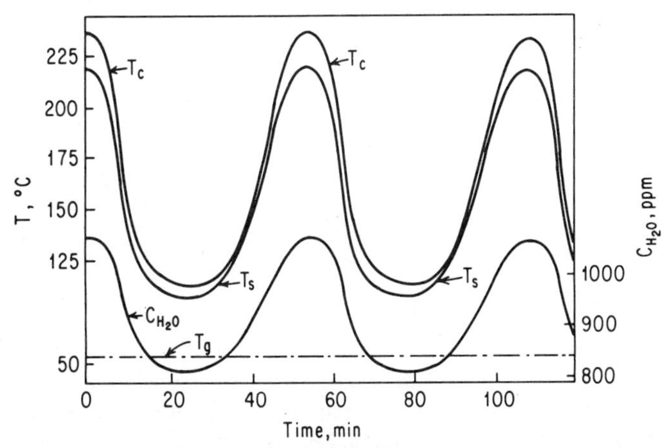

FIG. 11-5 Oscillations of temperatures of a single catalyst particle (T_c center, T_s surface) and of reaction rate (C_{H_2O} in the effluent). Gas temperature T_g = 70°C; 3.14 vol% H_2; v = 36 cm/s. (*From Beusch, Fieguth, and Wicke*[18] *with permission from the American Chemical Society*.)

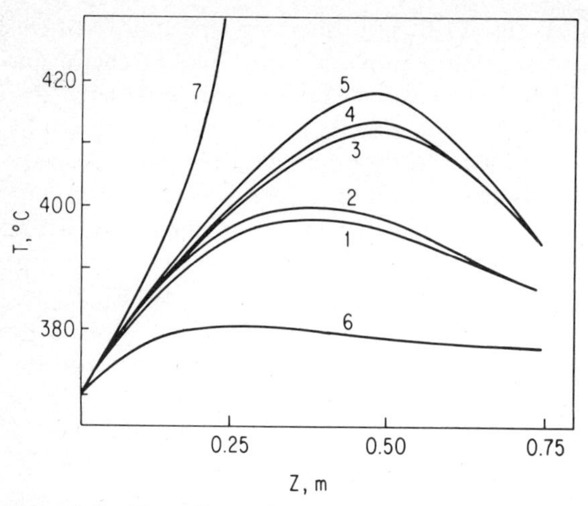

FIG. 11-6 Two-dimensional heterogeneous model. Radial mean temperature as a function of bed length. Comparison with other models. Curve 1: Basic one-dimensional pseudohomogeneous model; Curve 2: One-dimensional heterogeneous model with interfacial gradients; Curve 3: Two-dimensional pseudohomogeneous model; Curve 4: Two-dimensional heterogeneous model; Curve 5: Two-dimensional heterogeneous model. Boundary condition at the wall: $\partial^2 T_s/\partial r^2 = 0$; Curve 6: Two-dimensional heterogeneous model. Boundary condition at the wall $T_s = T_w$; Curve 7: Two-dimensional heterogeneous model. Radial heat transfer only through the fluid. (*From G. F. Froment*[20] *with the permission of the American Chemical Society.*)

of reactions of any imaginable complexity. Such a dream could only be realized if we could know everything about nature. Since this does not seem likely to happen, at least in the foreseeable future, the wise designer will always try first to mentally model nature and attempt to predict how nature is going to behave. However, the designer will not trust these predictions until nature is actually observed to behave in the predicted way.

REFERENCES

1. A. S. Lopez, H. I. DeLasa, and J. A. Porras, "Parametric Sensitivity of a Fixed-Bed Catalytic Reactor—Cooling Fluid Flow Influence," *Chem. Eng. Sci.* **36:**285–291 (1981).
2. R. J. Welsenaere and Gilbert F. Froment, "Parametric Sensitivity and Runaway in Fixed-Bed Catalytic Reactors," *Chem. Eng. Sci.* **25:**1503–1516 (1970).
3. E. D. Gilles and H. Schuler, "Zur frühzeitigen Erkennung gefährlicher Reaktionszustände in chemischen Reaktoren," *Chem.-Ingr. Tech.* **53:**673–682 (1981).
4. V. Hlavacek, "Aspects in Design of Packed Catalytic Reactors," *Ind. Eng. Chem.* **62**(7):8–26 (1970).

5. Gilbert F. Froment, "Some Aspects of the Design of Fixed-Bed Reactors for Hydrocarbon Oxidation," *Period. Polytech.* **15**(3):219–244 (1971).

6. K. R. Westerterp, "Maximum Allowable Temperatures in Chemical Reactors," *Chem. Eng. Sci.* **17:**423–433 (1962).

7. C. van Heerden, "Autothermic Processes—Properties and Reactor Design," *Ind. Eng. Chem.* **45:**1242–1247 (1953).

8. F. G. Liljenroth, "Starting and Stability Phenomena of Ammonia Oxidation and Similar Reactions," *Chem. Met. Eng.* **19:**287–293 (1918).

9. Rutherford Aris, "Some Problems in the Analysis of Transient Behavior and Stability of Chemical Reactors," in *Chemical Reaction Engineering,* Advances in Chemistry Series 109, American Chemical Society, 1972, pp. 578–604.

10. Daniel D. Perlmutter, *Stability of Chemical Reactors,* Prentice-Hall, Englewood Cliffs, N.J., 1972.

11. James M. Douglas, *Process Dynamics and Control,* vol. 1: *Analysis of Dynamic Systems,* vol. 2: *Control System Synthesis,* Prentice-Hall, Englewood Cliffs, N.J., 1972.

12. C. van Heerden, "The Character of the Stationary State of Exothermic Processes," *Chem. Eng. Sci.* **8:**133–145 (1958).

13. E. Wicke, "Über die stationären Zustände exothermer Gasreaktionen an porösen Katalysatoren," *Chem.-Ingr. Tech.* **29:**305–311 (1957).

14. Rutherford Aris, *Elementary Chemical Reactor Analysis,* Prentice-Hall, Englewood Cliffs, N.J., 1969, p. 252.

15. J. C. Charpentier, "Gas-Liquid Reactors," in *Chemical Reaction Engineering Reviews—Houston,* Symposium Series 72, American Chemical Society, 1978, pp. 223–261.

16. Peter Hugo and H.-P. Wirges, "Theoretical and Experimental Study of Self-Sustained Oscillations in a Stirred Tank Reactor," in *Chemical Reaction Engineering Reviews—Houston,* Symposium Series 65, American Chemical Society, 1978, pp. 498–511.

17. C. McGreavy and J. M. Thornton, "Stability Studies of Single Catalyst Particles," in *Chemical Reaction Engineering,* Advances in Chemistry Series 109, American Chemical Society, 1972, pp. 607–609.

18. H. Beusch, P. Fieguth, and E. Wicke, "Unstable Behavior of Chemical Reactions at Single Catalyst Particles," in *Chemical Reaction Engineering,* Advances in Chemistry Series 109, American Chemical Society, 1972, pp. 615–621.

19. C. G. Takoudis, L. D. Schmidt, and Rutherford Aris, "Multiple Steady States in Reaction Controlled Surface Catalyzed Reactions," *Chem. Eng. Sci.* **36:**377–386 (1981).

20. Gilbert F. Froment, "Analysis and Design of Fixed Bed Catalytic Reactors," in *Chemical Reaction Engineering,* Advances in Chemistry Series 109, American Chemical Society, 1972, p. 30.

Chapter 12 THE MECHANICAL DESIGN OF COMMERCIAL REACTORS

The mechanical design of commercial-size reactors is considerably more difficult than that of laboratory or pilot-scale reactors. Many sets of temperature-pressure conditions, which would be easy to meet on the pilot-scale reactors, present formidable problems in commercial scale.

The purpose of this chapter is not to teach the mechanical design of catalytic reactors but simply to give the reader an overview and understanding of the major problems and their solutions in this discipline. The catalytic reactor designer must acquire a thorough understanding of these problems because they are intimately connected with the process design. Even the most elegant process design of a reactor is worthless unless a corresponding workable mechanical design can be developed. Sometimes high pressures set the limit, at other times corrosion problems cause the difficulties. While the catalytic reactor designer must be quite knowledgeable in mechanical design, a sound and safe mechanical design by an up-to-date and experienced mechanical engineer is still essential. As a matter of fact, designing reactors is not a routine job that any mechanical engineer can tackle. It is a very special field that has to be learned and mastered.

Since most catalytic reactions are run at elevated pressures and temperatures, the first problem of the mechanical engineer is designing vessels that can safely contain the particular combination of temperature and pressure.

12.1 DESIGNING FOR PRESSURE

Designing pressure vessels is not a pure engineering task. It also has a legal aspect.

Design Codes

The pressure design of reactors is carried out in conformity with the pressure vessel code of the country where the reactor will be erected and operated. In the United States, we have the Pressure Vessel Code of the American Society of Mechanical Engineers (ASME),[1] which has been adopted into law by all states in the United States, all provinces of Canada, and a number of municipalities in both these countries. The ASME code, and with it the states' codes, are amended from time to time to conform with progress in pressure vessel technology.[2] The state codes sometimes differ slightly from each other. Other industrial countries have, of course, their own codes.[2–8] Some developing countries would probably accept a pressure vessel design if it conforms to the code of one of the foremost industrial nations, such as the United States or the Federal Republic of Germany. Although an international code of pressure vessel design is reported to be in the works,[4] American designers are still using the ASME Code. While code data may somewhat differ from country to country, the codes all follow the same principles, which the catalytic reactor designer must understand.

The Strength of the Reactor Wall

Mechanically, all catalytic reactors are metallic vessels with walls that can resist the pressure of the reacting mixture at the temperature of the reaction. Figure 12-1 schematically shows a section of a reactor wall on which the internal pressure is exerted. As a result of this force, the material of the wall is pulled apart. Any point A inside the wall is subjected to tension in two directions: the first is circumferential or perpendicular to P and in the plane of the figure; the second is longitudinal or perpendicular to the plane of the figure at A. The longitudinal tension is caused by the heads of the cylindrical reactor. The property of a metal to resist these tensile forces is called *tensile strength* and the test that measures this strength is called the *tensile test.* At no time should the pressure-induced tensions in a reactor wall exceed the tensile strength of the wall metal at that temperature or the wall may fail, i.e., crack or burst open.

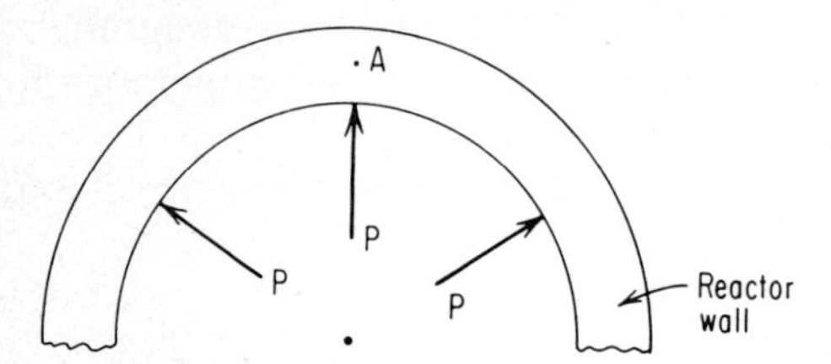

FIG. 12-1 Forces on the inside wall of a reactor.

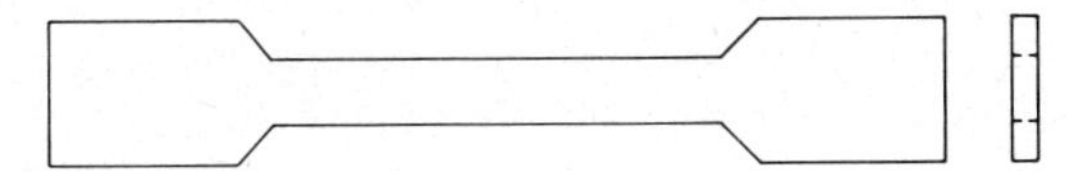

FIG. 12-2 General shape of tensile specimen of metal.

Basically, in the tensile test a specimen of standard size and shape (Fig. 12-2) is stretched in a special testing machine until it breaks. The applied load is expressed as the *stress* σ, which is defined as the load per unit of original cross-sectional area of the specimen and is expressed in pascals or newtons per square meter. The elongation of the specimen per unit of original length (a dimensionless quantity) is called *strain* ϵ. Figure 12-3 shows a curve recorded by a stress-test machine. The tested material was ASTM A588 Grade B steel, a high-strength, low-alloy structural steel. The ordinate represents load in pounds and the abscissa indicates the elongation. The shape of the curve of Fig. 12-3 is typical of low-alloy carbon steels. Normally, the data obtained from the test machine are plotted in a graph with stress σ in pascals as ordinate and strain ϵ as abscissa. Figure 12-4 represents such a typical graph (it is not a plot of Fig. 12-3 data).

The section *OA* in Figs. 12-3 aand 12-4 represents the proportional region. The elongation resulting from any load in this region disappears as soon as the load is removed and the specimen returns to its original size. This is expressed by *Hooke's law,*[9] which states that the strain in proportional to the stress applied:

$$\sigma = E \epsilon \tag{12-1}$$

and the proportionality factor E is called the *modulus of elasticity.*[10,11] In other words, the steel behaves as an elastic material in this region. For carbon steels E is in the order of 2.07×10^5 MPa.

If the stress is increased beyond the point A, the *proportional limit,* the steel no longer follows Hooke's law and one obtains an appreciable amount of elongation without increasing the load. This is called *yielding.* The stress corresponding to the point B is called the *yield point.* Upon further stretching of the specimen the steel recovers its resistance and the tensile force increase results in additional elongation up to point C, where the force reaches a maximum. The stress that corresponds to this maximum force is called the *ultimate strength* of the material. Beyond C, the bar is stretched even if the load is decreased, and it finally fractures at D. Unlike the proportional region OA, any elongation beyond A is irreversible.

When the specimen stretches under the influence of a load, it also shrinks in cross section. This lateral contraction in the OA region is elastic and reversible. The ratio of this lateral contraction to the axial elongation, expressed by the same unit, is constant inside the elastic limit for

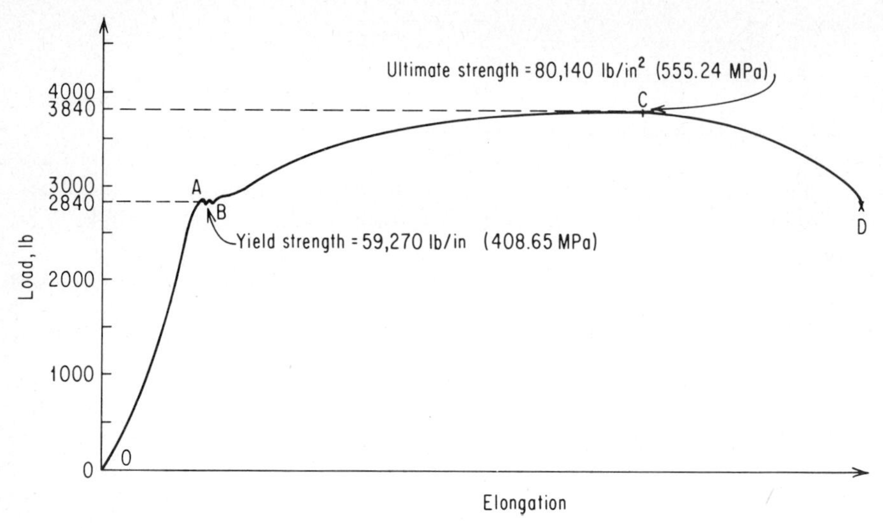

FIG. 12-3 Load-elongation diagram of a normalized ASTM A588 Grade B steel. (*Courtesy Fazil Erdogan, Lehigh University.*)

any given material. This law is called *Poisson's law,* the ratio is known as *Poisson's ratio*, and its constant value will be designated by μ. In case of ordinary structural steel μ can be taken as 0.30.

Poisson's law can be expressed as

$$\epsilon_x = \mu \, \epsilon_y \tag{12-2}$$

where ϵ_y is the strain (unit elongation) obtained in the direction y of the load and ϵ_x is the strain (unit contraction) obtained in the direction x perpendicular to the direction y of the load.

Beyond the proportionality limit, the lateral contraction of the specimen is also irreversible.

There are big differences among the stress-strain diagrams of various materials. Figure 12-5 is the load vs. elongation diagram recorded by a test machine for a tempered bainitic steel that contains Cr, Mo, and V. While this material has a very distinct proportional region, its yield point is not visible. In this diagram it was determined by convention as the intersection at 0.02% elongation, of a line parallel to the proportional line with the nonelastic part of the curve. The curve of Fig. 12-5 is of interest mostly because of its different shape.

Figure 12-6 shows a typical stress-strain diagram for cast iron. Cast iron has a very low proportionality limit, which is very difficult to determine. It has no definite yield point. The stress-strain diagrams for brass and aluminum also look quite similar to that of cast iron.

The tensile test gives very important information on the mechanical properties of a construction material. All construction materials such as beams, rods, sheets, etc., are used well below their proportionality limit. It is usually tricky to measure the exact point at which proportionality ends. In order to circumvent this difficulty, it is customary in mechanical design to calculate a *working stress* σ_w by dividing the yield stress σ_y by a *safety factor* n.

$$\sigma_w = \sigma_y/n \tag{12-3}$$

or by dividing the ultimate strength σ_u by a different safety factor n_1

$$\sigma_w = \sigma_u/n_1 \tag{12-4}$$

When designing with structural steel, Eq. (12-3) is used and a safety factor of $n = 2$ gives a conservative value for the working stress, provided that only constant or static loads have to be handled. For machine parts exposed to variable loads, larger factors of safety are necessary.

In pressure vessel design the ASME code gives *maximum allowable stress* data for each material at various temperatures. These data include the necessary safety factors and can be used as is. Such data can be found in the ASME Boiler and Pressure Vessel Code[1] and also in the *Chemical Engineers' Handbook.*[12]

The maximum allowable stress of steels is almost constant up to 350 to 450°C, above which it declines quite rapidly. Figure 12-7 shows the plots of the maximum allowable stress data for three types of steel as a function of temperature. It can be seen that the simple carbon steel begins to weaken at 340°C. The low-alloy steel containing 2.5% Cr and 1% Mo is unchanged up to 440°C, while the weakening of type 316 austenitic steel with 18% Cr, 10% Ni, and 2% Mo does not occur until 475°C. It is possible to increase the strength of the steels by properly adding alloying components such as Cr, Ni, Mo, and some other elements. Alloying also affects the corrosion resistance of steels.

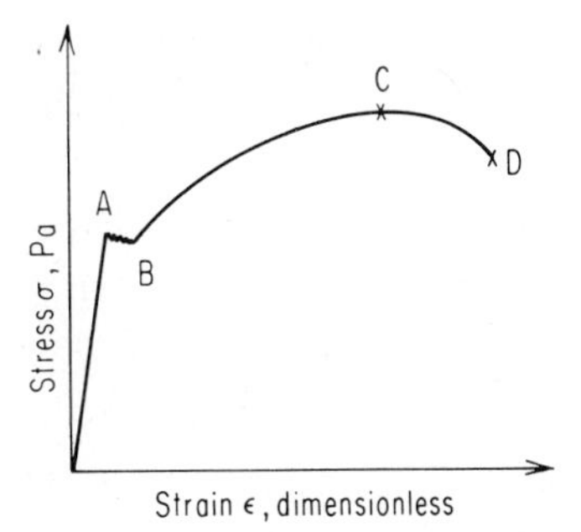

FIG. 12-4 Typical shape of a stress-strain diagram of ordinary carbon steel.

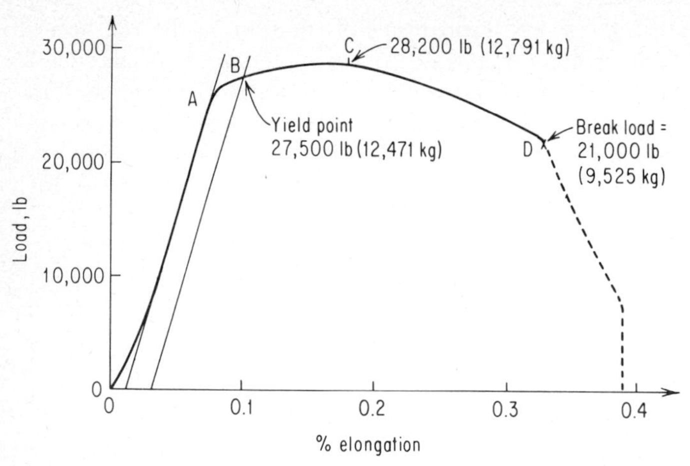

FIG. 12-5 Load-elongation diagram of a tempered bainitic steel containing Cr, Mo, and V. (*Courtesy Fazil Erdogan, Lehigh University.*)

In addition to losing their strengths, some steels also creep at temperatures above 370°C. *Creep* is very slow flow under stress. It is of course very important that creep be kept to a minimum in reactor design. The *creep test* measures the rate of elongation of a specimen under constant tension and gives the temperature at which 1% creep occurs in 10,000 h or in 100,000 h. Thus high-temperature properties of metals are just as important as their ambient-temperature properties when selecting a reactor plate steel.

Most reactor vessels are cylindrical. If a relatively low to moderate pressure is to be handled, the reactor wall does not have to be very thick and the tensile stress does not vary appreciably between the inside and outside surfaces of the wall. However, if high pressures have to be contained in the reactor, the wall thickness has to be increased, the distribution of the stress inside the thick wall becomes nonuniform, and design calculations become quite complicated. Thus we will discuss the design of thin-walled reactors separately from that of thick-walled reactors.

Design of Thin-Walled Reactors

If uniformly distributed radial forces are applied to the inside of a thin circular ring in the form of fluid pressure, as seen in Fig. 12-8*a*, the ring will be enlarged uniformly. In order to be able to size the wall thickness to contain the radial forces, we must calculate the tensile force F_T in the ring. Let us assume that the ring has a radial thickness t and a longitudinal thickness l. Let us cut it into two halves at the horizontal diameter section so that the upper half-circle behaves as a free body (Fig. 12-8*b*). Let us consider a section of the circular ring of central angle α with the horizontal, and a differential section of angle $d\alpha$. Let us calculate the forces that act upon this differential portion of the ring. The main internal force is the pressure P (force per unit area). The internal surface area of the differential ring section is $rld\alpha$, where r is the inside radius of the ring. Thus the force that acts upon this differential surface is $Prld\alpha$. The vertical component of this force acting upon the horizontal centerline is $Prld\alpha \cdot \sin\alpha$ and is directed upwards. We can take the sum of the vertical components of all the forces acting on the half-ring and balance them with a downward directed force F_T at each end of the half-ring. These balancing forces are the tensile forces:

$$2F_T = \int_0^\pi Prl \cdot \sin\alpha \cdot d\alpha = Prl\,[-\cos\alpha + \text{const}]_0^\pi$$

$$= Prl\,[1.0 + \text{const}] - [-1.0 + \text{const}] = 2Prl$$

$$F_T = Prl$$

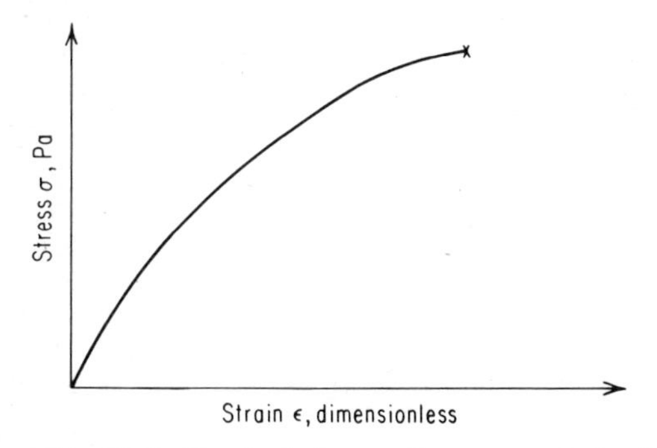

FIG. 12-6 Typical shape of a stress-strain diagram of cast iron.

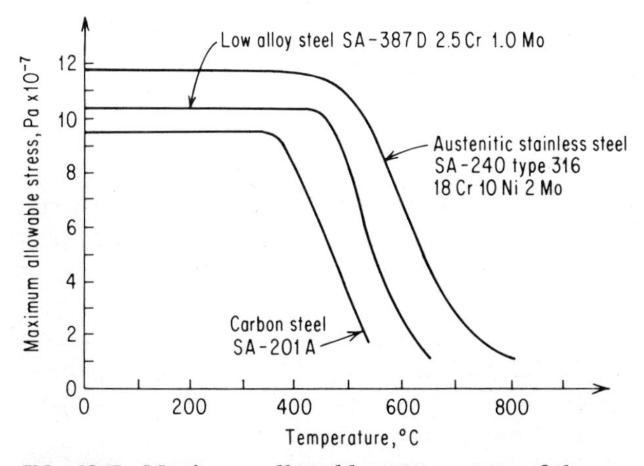

FIG. 12-7 Maximum allowable stress curves of three types of steel as a function of temperature, plotted from data in the ASME Boiler and Pressure Vessel Code.[1] By permission.

The tensile stress in the ring may now be obtained by dividing the force F_T by the cross-sectional area tl of the ring:

$$\sigma = F_T/tl = Pr/t \tag{12-5}$$

When designing according to the ASME code,[1] one uses the following formula for thin-walled pressure vessels:

$$t = Pr/(SE - 0.6P) \tag{12-6}$$

where t = minimum required thickness of shell or head after forming, exclusive of corrosion allowance, m

P = design pressure, Pa

r = inside radius of shell course under consideration, m

S = maximum allowable stress, Pa

E = lowest efficiency of any joint in the head, dimensionless

In USCS units, t and r are given in inches and P and S are given in pounds per square inch.

The parameter E expresses the confidence in the quality of a seam. Its maximum value is 1.0, which is its value for a seamless head. The efficiency of welded or riveted joints can be obtained from the ASME code.[1]

If the wall thickness of a reactor is already given, the maximum pressure it can withstand can be calculated from the formula[1]:

$$P = SEt/(r + 0.6\,t) \tag{12-7}$$

Other formulas are available for designing thin-wall reactor heads.[1,12]

Design of Thick-Walled Reactors

For a constant internal radius and construction material, we can increase the internal pressure P if the wall thickness t is also increased proportionally, as per Eq. (12-6). Beyond a certain point, a further increase in t causes the distribution of the tensile stress throughout the wall to become nonuniform. Thus the wall thickness must be increased more than in proportion to the pressure. As long as the deformation of the thick-wall reactor remains below the elastic limit of the steel, we can calculate its thickness as a function of the internal pressure.

Comings[10] used a development somewhat similar to that we used for

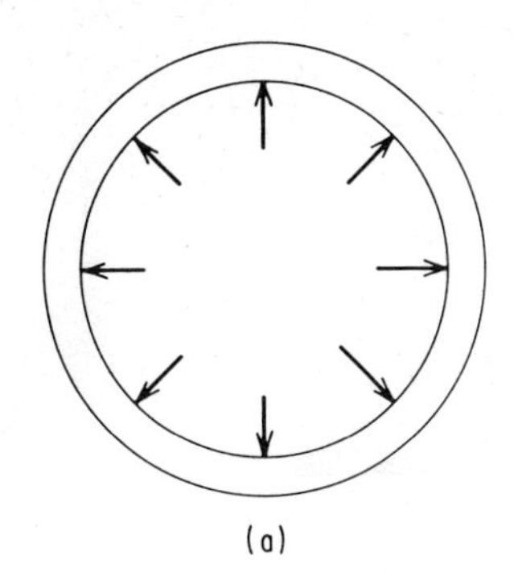

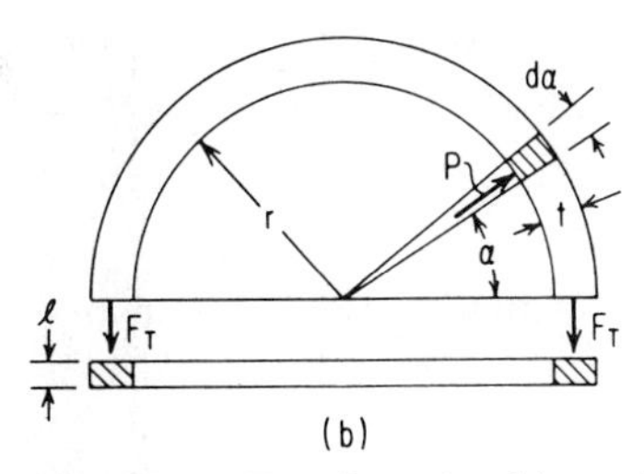

FIG. 12-8 Tensions in thin-walled reactor under internal pressure.

thin-walled reactors to calculate stresses and strains in a thick-walled reactor and obtained the following formulas (see Fig. 12-9):

$$\frac{(\sigma_t)_r}{p_1} = \frac{(r_2/r_1)^2 + 1}{(r_2/r_1)^2 - 1} \tag{12-8}$$

$$(\sigma_r)_r = p_1 \tag{12-9}$$

where $(\sigma_t)_r$ = tangential stress at inside radius
$(\sigma_r)_r$ = radial stress at inside radius
p_1 = inside pressure
r_1 = inside radius
r_2 = outside radius

Equation (12-9) represents the maximum radial tensile stress at the inner surface of the pressure vessel and that stress is equal to the reaction pressure.

The longitudinal stress σ_z is given by:

$$\sigma_z = \frac{p_1}{(r_2/r_1)^2 - 1} \tag{12-10}$$

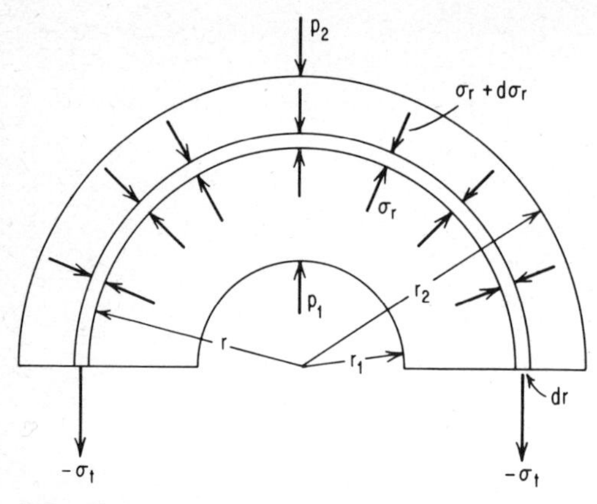

FIG. 12-9 Force balance on section of thick-walled cylinder. (*From Comings,*[10] *by permission.*)

Comings[10] has demonstrated that a thick-walled cylindrical reactor subjected to internal pressure alone is considerably more stressed near its inner surface than near its outer surface. Thus it is perfectly possible to have the inner layers stressed to near or above the elastic limit while the outer layers still are under relatively low stresses. It can be concluded that limiting the reactor design only to elastic strains would not use the strength of the steel effectively.

Several ways have been devised to use the strength of the steel more effectively. These methods will be discussed further below. The general idea is to build up the wall in layers, which are prestressed by the proper amount. When internal pressure is applied, the initial stress is overcome and reversed. Such reactors can be designed and fabricated for operation under stresses that are uniformly distributed throughout the thick wall at a specified operating pressure. Under these conditions and at this one operating pressure, the thin-walled formula of Eq. (12-5) applies.

Design procedures for multilayer thick-walled pressure vessels have been presented by Comings.[10]

The ASME code recommends designing unlayered thick-walled reactors according to the formulas:

$$t = r(Z^{0.5} - 1) \tag{12-11}$$

where $Z = (SE + P)/(SE - P)$

and

$$P = SE(Z' - 1)/(Z' + 1) \tag{12-12}$$

where $Z' = ((r + t)/r)^2$.

These formulas are valid when the thickness exceeds 0.5 r_1 or when P

exceeds 0.385 *SE*. The ASME code provides for other formulas for thick spherical shells and thick hemispherical heads.[1,12]

When designing thick-walled reactors that are built of several layers, the stresses and strains have to be calculated as accurately as possible. Designers usually check whether several safety criteria are met. These criteria are formulated as theories, e.g., the shear-with-friction theory or the distortion-energy theory. Not only the present properties of the shell are considered, but also changes of these properties with time, such as possible creep of the steel. Some reactor shapes can be assumed to be composed of several simple geometric rings and shells and the stresses and strains for each of these simple forms can be analyzed and calculated separately. When all the calculations are combined, a detailed analysis for the entire pressure vessel is obtained. A technique which does just that is called *interaction analysis*.[13] A computer program entitled CALSOR has been developed to do routinely all the complex calculations for every reactor vessel designed.

The above information on pressure design of reactors is being presented with the purpose of giving sufficient understanding to permit the catalytic reactor designer to talk intelligently to the expert mechanical designer. Actually the subject is considerably more complex and sophisticated. Besides the design of the cylindrical reactor walls, it includes the design of the heads, the closures, and other details that would be well outside the competency of the catalytic reactor designer, who normally is a chemical engineer. For such detailed mechanical design, the reader is referred to the ASME Code,[1] the *Chemical Engineers' Handbook,*[12] and a recent book by Henry H. Bednar.[14]

In this section we discussed how we can calculate the wall thickness of a reactor required to contain a reaction at a given temperature and pressure. Now we will discuss how reactors are built mechanically.

12.2
VARIOUS METHODS OF REACTOR CONSTRUCTION

The methods of construction of catalytic reactors depend mainly on meeting three conditions:

1. Temperature
2. Pressure
3. Corrosion resistance

Some reactors have to meet two sets of conditions, one for steady-state operation and the other for in situ catalyst regeneration. Normally, catalyst regeneration conditions are low pressure and high temperature.

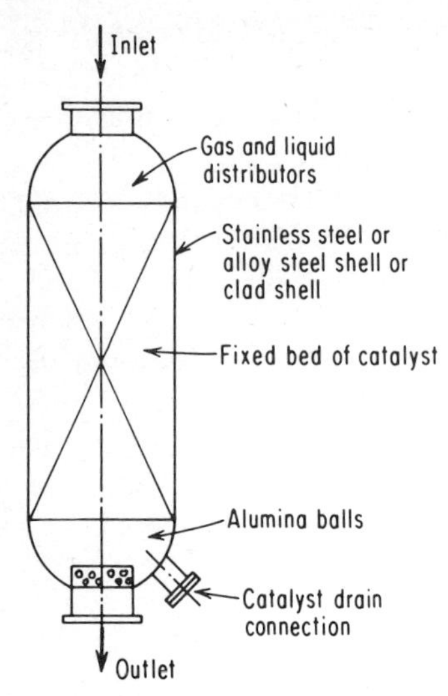

FIG. 12-10 Typical mechanical construction of fixed-bed reactor for low-severity reaction.

Low-Severity Reactors

For low-severity catalytic reactions, such as the carbon monoxide shift reaction or carbon monoxide methanation, one uses low-alloy steels and manages to contain the pressure directly in the steel shell, as shown in Fig. 12-10. If corrosion resistance is an important requirement, one uses steels that resist the particular corrosion, or if this is too costly, one uses *clad steel plates*. A clad steel is a high-strength, low-alloy steel which has been rolled together with a thin sheet of stainless steel or other corrosion-resistant metal. Titanium-clad steel plate can also be manufactured by the so-called explosion cladding process.[15,16] The lining is just thick enough to meet the corrosion allowance. The welding of clad plates must be done by highly skilled welders, and even then it must be done extremely carefully. It is advisable to closely and totally inspect these welds.

An alternative to cladding is the use of corrosion-resistant *shrouds*. A shroud is a lining that is installed in the field by introducing pieces of it in long slices through the inlet or outlet opening of the reactor and welding it together inside the pressure vessel. Of course, the shroud transmits the inside pressure to the wall without itself resisting the pressure.

High-Severity Reactors

As the temperature-pressure severity increases, any available and reasonably costly steel can no longer contain the reaction in a thin-walled reactor. In case of high-temperature, moderate-pressure reactions such as the Litol process[17] for the hydro-refining of coke-oven aromatics, one can still use a thin-walled design by installing a thick layer of impervious refractory insulation inside the steel shell.[18] The shell is maintained at a low temperature, where it can keep its high tensile strength. Such a reactor is shown in Fig. 12-11. In order to prevent the penetration of the reaction mixture into the insulation and further to the steel shell, it is customary to install a shroud inside the insulation. The catalyst charge is then filled into the pocket formed by the shroud. The shell skin temperature of such reactors must be continuously monitored in order to detect any hot spot due to crack formation in the inner insulation. This method of reactor construction can handle reactions that typically operate at 600 to 650°C and 50 to 70 bars.

For reactions that are run at temperatures below 450°C but at high pressures of several hundred bars, thick-walled reactors must be designed.

The first thick-walled reactors were fabricated by casting huge low-alloy steel ingots and forging these oversize ingots in special large forges. The machining required huge lathes. The smallest flaw in the steel casting or arising during forging could cause the vessel to fail during the final hydraulic proof test. Thus this type of reactor fabrication turned out to be extremely costly. Costs could be somewhat reduced by designing

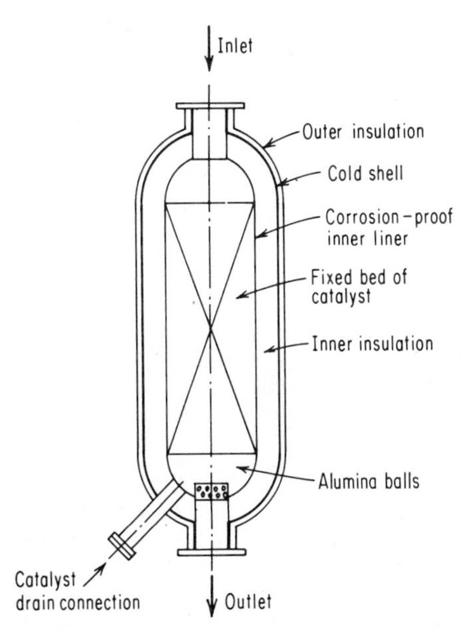

FIG. 12-11 Typical mechanical construction of fixed-bed reactor for high-severity reaction.

the reactor wall in two layers. Both were separately cast, forged, and machined. Then the outer layer was expanded by heating and was fitted over the inner layer. Upon cooling the outer layer exerted a compression on the inner layer. However, when put into operation at the operating temperature and pressure, both layers were under about the same tension.

The cost of thick-walled reactors could be further reduced by designing and fabricating them as multilayer vessels. One method is to use several steel plates that are welded at a longitudinal seam. Welds apparently weaken this type of vessel construction, as was later found. This idea was improved upon by wrapping a steel plate around a relatively thicker reactor core. The best results were obtained by wrapping profiled steel strips with grooves and tongues around a core without welding them together. This is the old German *Wickel process.* Figure 12-12 shows a preferred steel profile and its use in the Wickel process.[19] The subject is extremely interesting but too broad to be discussed here. For further information the reader is referred to four good papers[19–22] and two books.[10,14]

Meeting of Corrosion Resistance Requirements

When designing a reactor for a well-known catalytic process, the designer will know the corrosion requirements and have no trouble specifying the composition and thickness of the *corrosion allowance* of the reactor wall, lining, or shroud that will be used. The corrosion resistance of the particular wall material is usually expressed in inches per year in the United States and meters per year elsewhere. This figure is multiplied by the life expectancy of the process to obtain the thickness of the corrosion allowance.

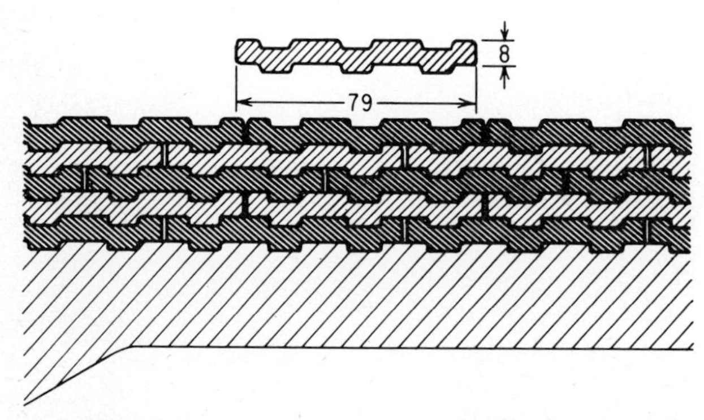

FIG. 12-12 Cross section of strip winding in the German Wickel process. (*From E. Karl,[19] by permission from the American Institute of Chemical Engineers.*)

In new processes, the search for the proper corrosion-resisting material starts immediately after the completion of bench-scale process development studies. Very extensive corrosion studies are periodically published for a large number of chemicals and construction materials by the National Association of Corrosion Engineers (NACE).[23] It is quite likely that a solution to any particular corrosion problem at hand can be found in these publications. If no satisfactory solution can be found, samples of various materials are tested over periods of several months in small automatic bench-scale reactors. One way of exposing a particular metal or alloy to reaction conditions is to construct a dead man (see Fig. 10-7) of it and use it in the automatically operated corrosion test reactor.

Finding adequate materials to resist corrosion in hydrodesulfurization reactors for petroleum-derived or coal-derived hydrocarbons is particularly challenging. Hot hydrogen under pressure makes some alloys brittle; thus austenitic stainless steels of particular composition are called for. When the effect of H_2S partial pressure is added to the hydrogen embrittlement problem, the challenge becomes even more difficult to meet. The *Nelson curves*[23] are quite helpful in this respect. For a discussion of new reactor steels, the reader is referred to articles by Estefan,[24] Clarke,[25] Lancaster,[26] Gulya and Marshall,[27] and an anonymous author.[28] Corrosion data for a petroleum hydrodesulfurization reactor have been discussed by McCoy and Hamel[29–30] and the development of the engineering design of petroleum oil hydrodesulfurizers at a British Petroleum Company plant has been reviewed in detail by Lister.[31]

NOMENCLATURE

E	Lowest efficiency of any joint in reactor wall, dimensionless [Eqs. (12-6), (12-7), (12-11), and (12-12)]
E	Modulus of elasticity, Pa
F_T	Tensile force, N
l	Longitudinal thickness, m
n	Safety factor
r, r_1	Inside radius of reactor, m
r_2	Outside radius of reactor, m
P	Pressure, bars
P_1	Inside pressure in reactor, bars
S	Maximum allowable stress, Pa
t	Reactor wall thickness, m

α	Central angle
ϵ	Strain, dimensionless
μ	Poisson's ratio
σ	Stress, Pa
σ_u	Ultimate stress
σ_w	Working stress
σ_y	Yield stress
σ_z	Longitudinal stress
$(\sigma_t)_r$	Tangential stress at inside radius
$(\sigma_r)_r$	Radial stress at inside radius

REFERENCES

1. *ASME Boiler and Pressure Vessel Code, sec. VIII: Unfired Pressure Vessels* and amendments, The American Society of Mechanical Engineers, 1962.
2. F. L. Evans, "Recent Development in ASME Pressure Vessel Code," *Hydrocarbon Process.* **54**(12):53–55 (1975).
3. I. Berglund, "Guide to Swedish Pressure Vessel Code," *Hydrocarbon Process.* **54**(12):64 (1975).
4. F. Dall'Ora, "European Pressure Vessel Codes," *Hydrocarbon Process.* **50**(6):93–96 (1971).
5. M. Koike, "Guide to Japanese Pressure Vessel Code," *Hydrocarbon Process.* **54**(12):65 (1975); "Guide to Japanese Standard Pressure Vessel Construction," *Ibid.* **54**(12):66 (1975); "Guide to Japanese High-Pressure Gas Control Law," *Ibid.* **54**(12):67 (1975).
6. R. Mazzoncini, "Guide to Italian Pressure Vessel Code," *Hydrocarbon Process.* **54**(12):63 (1975).
7. H. Steffen, "Guide to German Pressure Vessel Code," *Hydrocarbon Process.* **54**(12):62 (1975).
8. P. van Rossen, "Guide to Dutch Pressure Vessel Code," *Hydrocarbon Process.* **54**(12):61 (1975).
9. R. Hooke, *De Potentia Restitutiva,* London, 1678.
10. E. W. Comings, *High Pressure Technology,* McGraw-Hill, New York, 1956.
11. S. Timoshenko, *Strength of Materials,* part I: *Elementary Theory and Problems,* 3d ed. Van Nostrand, New York, 1958.
12. J. H. Perry, *Chemical Engineering Handbook,* 4th ed., 1963, pp. 24–7 to 24–33; 5th ed., 1973, pp. 6–91 to 6–105.
13. D. E. Witkin, *Use of Interaction Analysis to the Design of High Pressure Vessels,* Monograph by National Forge Company.

14. Henry H. Bednar, *Pressure Vessel Design Handbook,* Van Nostrand Reinhold, New York, 1981.

15. C. P. Williams, "Explosion Clad Titanium/Steel Plate," *Chem. Eng. Progr.* **66**(10):48–52 (1970).

16. G. R. Cowan et al., Explosive Bonding, U.S. Patent 3,137,937, 1964 (to E. I. du Pont de Nemours & Co.)

17. M. Orhan Tarhan and Louis H. Windsor, "Coke Ovens Yield High Quality Benzene," *Chem. Eng. Progr.* **62**(2):67–72 (1966).

18. D. W. McDowell, Jr., J. D. Milligan, and A. D. Korin, "Cold vs. Hot Wall Pressure Vessels," *Hydrocarbon Process.* **45**(3):157–160 (1966).

19. E. Karl, "Strip-Wound Pressure Vessels," *Chem. Eng. Progr.* **68**(11):56–60 (1972).

20. T. McLean Jasper, "Multilayer Vessels for High Pressure and Temperature," *Chem. Eng. Progr.* **52**(12):521–526 (1956).

21. J. Schierenbeck, "Kritische Betrachtungen zur Herstellung von Hochdruckhohlkörpern in Mehrteil-Bauart für Hochdrucksynthesen," *Brennstoff-Chem.* **36:**239–244 (1955).

22. S. Strelzoff and L. C. Pan, "Designing Pressure Vessels," *Chem. Eng.* **39,** Nov. 4, 1968, pp. 191–198.

23. George A. Nelson, *Corrosion Data Survey,* Shell Development Company, San Francisco, 1950. These data have been updated and surveyed by the National Association of Corrosion Engineers (NACE): N. E. Hamner, *Corrosion Data Survey—Metals Section* 5th ed., 2d printing, 1979.

24. S. L. Estefan, "Design Guide to Metallurgy and Corrosion in Hydrogen Processes," *Hydrocarbon Process.* **49**(12):85–92 (1970).

25. J. S. Clarke, "Why Not Just Build Reactors to the Code?" *Hydrocarbon Process.* **49**(6):79–83 (1970).

26. J. F. Lancaster, "U.S. vs. European Reactor Steels," *Hydrocarbon Process.* **49**(6):84–90 (1970).

27. J. A. Gulya and E. G. Marshall, "New Property Data for Hydrocracker Steels," *Hydrocarbon Process.* **49**(6):91–96 (1970).

28. "Which Steel for Hydrodealkylation Units?" *Hydrocarbon Process.* **48**(6):131–132 (1969).

29. J. D. McCoy and F. B. Hamel, "New Corrosion Rate Data for Hydrodesulfurization Units," *Hydrocarbon Process.* **49**(6):116–120 (1970).

30. J. D. McCoy and F. B. Hamel, "Effect of Hydrodesulfurization Process Variables on Corrosion Rates," *Mater. Protec. Performance* **10**(4):17–22 (1971).

31. A. Lister, "Engineering Design and Development of Desulfurizer Reactors," *Proceedings of the Third European Symposium on Chemical Reaction Engineering,* Amsterdam, Sept. 15–17 1964; *Chem. Eng. Sci.* (suppl.) 225–235 (1964).

Appendix A ITERATION TECHNIQUES

Iteration aims at computing x by repeated calculations of

$$x = f(x) \tag{A-1}$$

It is desired to find x for which $x = f(x)$ by assigning values to x such as $x_0, x_1, x_2, \ldots, x_n$. The first value is x_0. Then:

$$\begin{aligned} x_1 &= f(x_0) \\ x_2 &= f(x_1) \\ x_3 &= f(x_2) \\ &\cdots\cdots \\ x_n &= f(x_{n-1}) \end{aligned}$$

until

$$\frac{(x_n) - (x_{n-1})}{x_n} < \epsilon$$

where ϵ is a very small number. For the purpose of reactor design $\epsilon = 0.001$. This method is called *Picard's iteration.*

There is another technique, called the *Newton-Raphson iteration,* which is more powerful than Picard's iteration. Here x_0 is an initial guess; then an improved solution is:

$$x_1 = \frac{f(x_0) - x_0 f'(x_0)}{1 - f'(x_0)} \tag{A-2}$$

Similarly, a still better solution is:

$$x_2 = \frac{f(x_1) - x_1 f'(x_1)}{1 - f'(x_1)}$$

and so on.

$$x_n \rightarrow x \text{ as } n \rightarrow \infty$$

In order to have an efficient iteration, nothing but x must vary in Eqs. (A-1) or (A-2); otherwise there will be pulsations. Strong pulsations usually lead to the breakdown of the computations.

NAME INDEX

SUBJECT INDEX

ABOUT THE AUTHOR

M. ORHAN TARHAN, a chemical engineering consultant, holds 16 U. S. and foreign patents. An authority on catalytic reactor design and on the design of packed-bed gas purification plants, he also has had considerable experience in R&D work on catalytic processes.

A native of Turkey, Mr. Tarhan studied at the technical universities of Darmstadt and Dresden. After emigrating to the United States in 1953, he became a research and chemical project engineer at Donner-Hanna Coke Corporation. In 1958 he joined Bethlehem Steel Corporation as a research engineer. He participated in the joint development of the Litol process (a catalytic hydro-refining process for coke-oven aromatics) that Bethlehem Steel undertook with Houdry Process Corporation (now a part of Air Products and Chemicals, Inc.). Mr. Tarhan has lectured on catalytic reactor design at Lehigh University and in continuing education courses both here and abroad. He retired from Bethlehem Steel in 1982 to become a consultant.